# Hints & Kinks

# FOR THE RADIO AMATEUR

## 17th Edition

**Editor**
Dana G. Reed, W1LC

**Composition**
Shelly Bloom, WB1ENT
Jodi Morin, KA1JPA

**Cover Design**
Sue Fagan

**ARRL** The national association for **AMATEUR RADIO**
Newington, CT 06111-1494
ARRLWeb: www.arrl.org

# Contents

# Foreword

Welcome to the 17th Edition of *Hints and Kinks for the Radio Amateur*. Here, a tradition is continued by bringing together, in one convenient place, useful items published in *QST*'s most popular column, Hints & Kinks. (This edition covers two years, 2003 through 2004.) Also included—as in recent editions—is material from *QST*'s "The Doctor is IN." Finally, and new for this edition, we've also included Ward Silver's (NØAX) "Hands-On Radio" collection for the same period.

With this collection of insight, knowledge and sheer ingenuity, you're sure to find something that will benefit your station, or that will encourage you to adapt an idea to your particular application.

If you have a tip or technique that you'd like to share with the amateur community, please send it to the Hints & Kinks Editor at ARRL Headquarters. It could wind up in an incoming column—and in the next edition of this book. You can also use the handy feedback form at the back of this book to let us know what you like or don't like about the book, or any ARRL publication.

We're looking forward to hearing from you.

73,
David Sumner, K1ZZ
Executive Vice President
December 2004

# Acknowledgments

We are grateful to all the authors represented in this book. Without your willingness to share what you've learned with the Amateur Radio community, there would be no Hints & Kinks column in *QST*, and no book.

# US Customary to Metric Conversions

## International System of Units (SI)—Metric Prefixes

| *Prefix* | *Symbol* | | | *Multiplication Factor* |
|---|---|---|---|---|
| exa | E | $10^{18}$ | = | 1 000 000 000 000 000 000 |
| peta | P | $10^{15}$ | = | 1 000 000 000 000 000 |
| tera | T | $10^{12}$ | = | 1 000 000 000 000 |
| giga | G | $10^{9}$ | = | 1 000 000 000 |
| mega | M | $10^{6}$ | = | 1 000 000 |
| kilo | k | $10^{3}$ | = | 1 000 |
| hecto | h | $10^{2}$ | = | 100 |
| deca | da | $10^{1}$ | = | 10 |
| (unit) | | $10^{0}$ | = | 1 |
| deci | d | $10^{-1}$ | = | 0.1 |
| centi | c | $10^{-2}$ | = | 0.01 |
| milli | m | $10^{-3}$ | = | 0.001 |
| micro | µ | $10^{-6}$ | = | 0.000001 |
| nano | n | $10^{-9}$ | = | 0.000000001 |
| pico | p | $10^{-12}$ | = | 0.000000000001 |
| femto | f | $10^{-15}$ | = | 0.000000000000001 |
| atto | a | $10^{-18}$ | = | 0.000000000000000001 |

### Linear
1 metre (m) = 100 centimetres (cm) = 1000 millimetres (mm)

### Area
$1 \text{ m}^2 = 1 \times 10^4 \text{ cm}^2 = 1 \times 10^6 \text{ mm}^2$

### Volume
$1 \text{ m}^3 = 1 \times 10^6 \text{ cm}^3 = 1 \times 10^9 \text{ mm}^3$
1 litre (l) = 1000 $\text{cm}^3 = 1 \times 10^6 \text{ mm}^3$

### Mass
1 kilogram (kg) = 1 000 grams (g)
  (Approximately the mass of 1 litre of water)
1 metric ton (or tonne) = 1 000 kg

## US Customary Units

### Linear Units
12 inches (in) = 1 foot (ft)
36 inches = 3 feet = 1 yard (yd)
1 rod = $5^{1}/_{2}$ yards = $16^{1}/_{2}$ feet
1 statute mile = 1 760 yards = 5 280 feet
1 nautical mile = 6 076.11549 feet

### Area
$1 \text{ ft}^2 = 144 \text{ in}^2$
$1 \text{ yd}^2 = 9 \text{ ft}^2 = 1\ 296 \text{ in}^2$
$1 \text{ rod}^2 = 30^{1}/_{4} \text{ yd}^2$
$1 \text{ acre} = 4840 \text{ yd}^2 = 43\ 560 \text{ ft}^2$
$1 \text{ acre} = 160 \text{ rod}^2$
$1 \text{ mile}^2 = 640 \text{ acres}$

### Volume
$1 \text{ ft}^3 = 1\ 728 \text{ in}^3$
$1 \text{ yd}^3 = 27 \text{ ft}^3$

### Liquid Volume Measure
1 fluid ounce (fl oz) = 8 fluidrams = 1.804 $\text{in}^3$
1 pint (pt) = 16 fl oz
1 quart (qt) = 2 pt = 32 fl oz = $57^{3}/_{4} \text{ in}^3$
1 gallon (gal) = 4 qt = 231 $\text{in}^3$
1 barrel = $31^{1}/_{2}$ gal

### Dry Volume Measure
1 quart (qt) = 2 pints (pt) = 67.2 $\text{in}^3$
1 peck = 8 qt
1 bushel = 4 pecks = 2 150.42 $\text{in}^3$

### Avoirdupois Weight
1 dram (dr) = 27.343 grains (gr) or (gr a)
1 ounce (oz) = 437.5 gr
1 pound (lb) = 16 oz = 7 000 gr
1 short ton = 2 000 lb, 1 long ton = 2 240 lb

### Troy Weight
1 grain troy (gr t) = 1 grain avoirdupois
1 pennyweight (dwt) or (pwt) = 24 gr t
1 ounce troy (oz t) = 480 grains
1 lb t = 12 oz t = 5 760 grains

### Apothecaries' Weight
1 grain apothecaries' (gr ap) = 1 gr t = 1 gr a
1 dram ap (dr ap) = 60 gr
1 oz ap = 1 oz t = 8 dr ap = 480 fr
1 lb ap = 1 lb t = 12 oz ap = 5 760 gr

## Multiply →
Metric Unit = Conversion Factor × US Customary Unit

## ← Divide
Metric Unit ÷ Conversion Factor = US Customary Unit

| Metric Unit = | Conversion Factor | × | US Unit |
|---|---|---|---|
| (Length) | | | |
| mm | 25.4 | | inch |
| cm | 2.54 | | inch |
| cm | 30.48 | | foot |
| m | 0.3048 | | foot |
| m | 0.9144 | | yard |
| km | 1.609 | | mile |
| km | 1.852 | | nautical mile |
| (Area) | | | |
| mm$^2$ | 645.16 | | inch$^2$ |
| cm$^2$ | 6.4516 | | in$^2$ |
| cm$^2$ | 929.03 | | ft$^2$ |
| m$^2$ | 0.0929 | | ft$^2$ |
| cm$^2$ | 8361.3 | | yd$^2$ |
| m$^2$ | 0.83613 | | yd$^2$ |
| m$^2$ | 4047 | | acre |
| km$^2$ | 2.59 | | mi$^2$ |
| (Mass) | (Avoirdupois Weight) | | |
| grams | 0.0648 | | grains |
| g | 28.349 | | oz |
| g | 453.59 | | lb |
| kg | 0.45359 | | lb |
| tonne | 0.907 | | short ton |
| tonne | 1.016 | | long ton |

| Metric Unit = | Conversion Factor | × | US Unit |
|---|---|---|---|
| (Volume) | | | |
| mm$^3$ | 16387.064 | | in$^3$ |
| cm$^3$ | 16.387 | | in$^3$ |
| m$^3$ | 0.028316 | | ft$^3$ |
| m$^3$ | 0.764555 | | yd$^3$ |
| ml | 16.387 | | in$^3$ |
| ml | 29.57 | | fl oz |
| ml | 473 | | pint |
| ml | 946.333 | | quart |
| l | 28.32 | | ft$^3$ |
| l | 0.9463 | | quart |
| l | 3.785 | | gallon |
| l | 1.101 | | dry quart |
| l | 8.809 | | peck |
| l | 35.238 | | bushel |
| (Mass) | (Troy Weight) | | |
| g | 31.103 | | oz t |
| g | 373.248 | | lb t |
| (Mass) | (Apothecaries' Weight) | | |
| g | 3.387 | | dr ap |
| g | 31.103 | | oz ap |
| g | 373.248 | | lb ap |

# Schematic Symbols Used in Circuit Diagrams

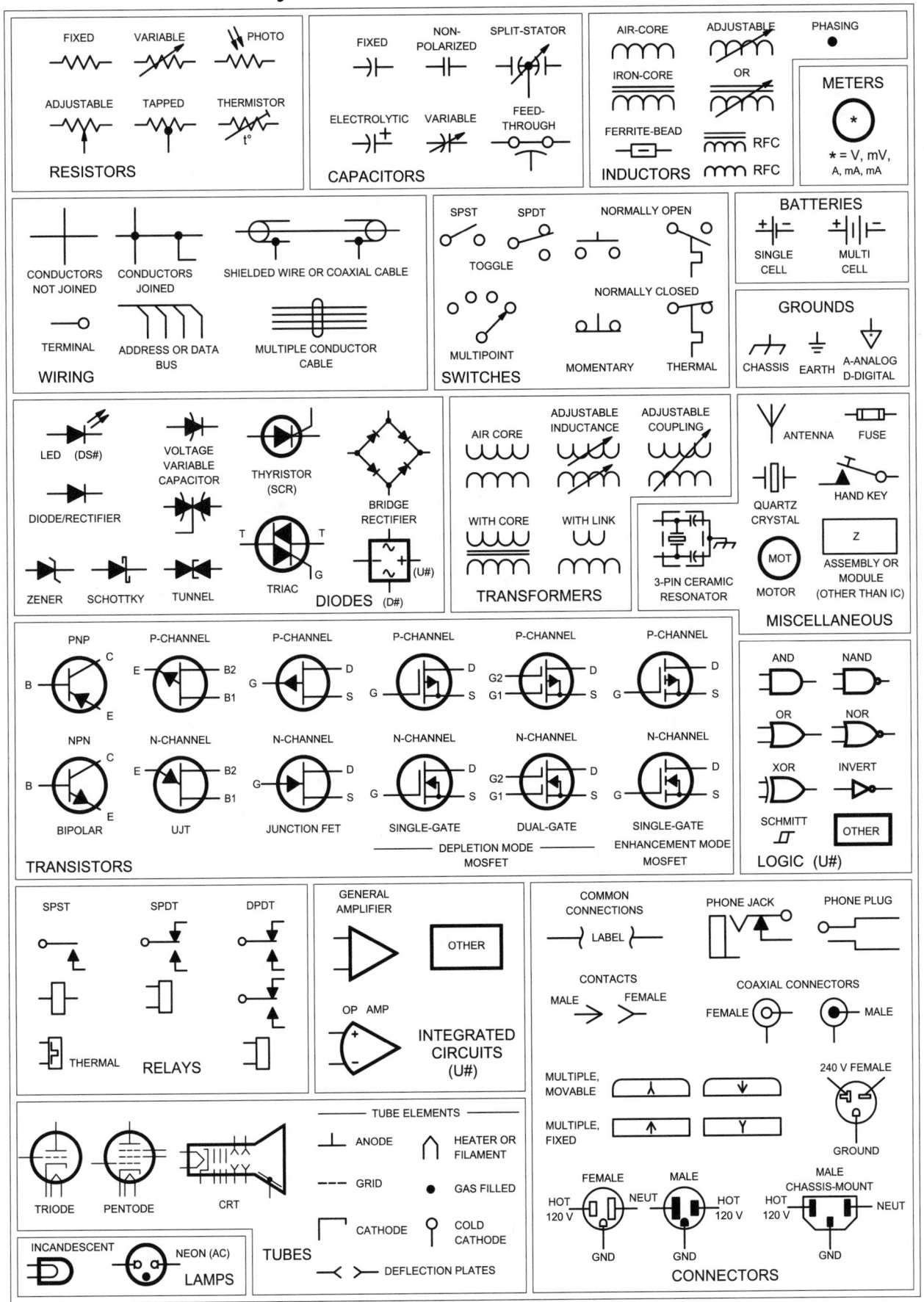

# About the ARRL

The seed for Amateur Radio was planted in the 1890s, when Guglielmo Marconi began his experiments in wireless telegraphy. Soon he was joined by dozens, then hundreds, of others who were enthusiastic about sending and receiving messages through the air—some with a commercial interest, but others solely out of a love for this new communications medium. The United States government began licensing Amateur Radio operators in 1912.

By 1914, there were thousands of Amateur Radio operators—hams—in the United States. Hiram Percy Maxim, a leading Hartford, Connecticut inventor and industrialist, saw the need for an organization to band together this fledgling group of radio experimenters. In May 1914 he founded the American Radio Relay League (ARRL) to meet that need.

Today ARRL, with approximately 170,000 members, is the largest organization of radio amateurs in the United States. The ARRL is a not-for-profit organization that:

- promotes interest in Amateur Radio communications and experimentation
- represents US radio amateurs in legislative matters, and
- maintains fraternalism and a high standard of conduct among Amateur Radio operators.

At ARRL headquarters in the Hartford suburb of Newington, the staff helps serve the needs of members. ARRL is also International Secretariat for the International Amateur Radio Union, which is made up of similar societies in 150 countries around the world.

ARRL publishes the monthly journal *QST*, as well as newsletters and many publications covering all aspects of Amateur Radio. Its headquarters station, W1AW, transmits bulletins of interest to radio amateurs and Morse code practice sessions. The ARRL also coordinates an extensive field organization, which includes volunteers who provide technical information and other support services for radio amateurs as well as communications for public-service activities. In addition, ARRL represents US amateurs with the Federal Communications Commission and other government agencies in the US and abroad.

Membership in ARRL means much more than receiving *QST* each month. In addition to the services already described, ARRL offers membership services on a personal level, such as the ARRL Volunteer Examiner Coordinator Program and a QSL bureau.

Full ARRL membership (available only to licensed radio amateurs) gives you a voice in how the affairs of the organization are governed. ARRL policy is set by a Board of Directors (one from each of 15 Divisions). Each year, one-third of the ARRL Board of Directors stands for election by the full members they represent. The day-to-day operation of ARRL HQ is managed by an Executive Vice President and his staff.

No matter what aspect of Amateur Radio attracts you, ARRL membership is relevant and important. There would be no Amateur Radio as we know it today were it not for the ARRL. We would be happy to welcome you as a member! (An Amateur Radio license is not required for Associate Membership.) For more information about ARRL and answers to any questions you may have about Amateur Radio, write or call:

ARRL—The national association for Amateur Radio
225 Main Street
Newington CT 06111-1494
Voice: 860-594-0200
Fax: 860-594-0259
E-mail: **hq@arrl.org**
Internet: **www.arrl.org/**

Prospective new amateurs call (toll-free):
**800-32-NEW HAM** (800-326-3942)

You can also contact us via e-mail at
**newham@arrl.org**
or check out *ARRLWeb* at **www.arrl.org/**

# Chapter 1

# Equipment Tips and Mods

## BATTERY-CHARGER POLARITY PLUS OR MINUS?

◊ My junk-box contains several battery chargers, or "wall warts," of various voltages and polarities. A few have only ac output. A simple bridge rectifier installed in the power-input circuit of your projects will cure polarity problems and, if the supply is ac only, will rectify the voltage so that the project always receives the correct polarity. (The input connector must float from the chassis. You may need to change the connector if one side is grounded, as are most RCA connectors.—*Zack Lau, W1VT, ARRL Lab*)

RadioShack sells several bridge rectifiers. The two pins marked "~" are the input pins. They accept any polarity: plus, minus or ac. The other two pins are marked "+" and "–." They always produce the marked polarity, even when the polarity of a connected dc source is reversed. The down side is that the bridge output voltage is 1.4 V lower than its input voltage because the current must pass through two diode junctions in the bridge.

If a "wall wart" is to be used to replace a 9-V battery, be aware that additional filtering may be necessary. I found some 3000 µF, 16 V capacitors do the trick. **Figure 1.1** shows a schematic. They are 0.65 inches in diameter, 1.05 inches high and have 0.3-inch lead spacing.—*H. M. Knickerbocker, K6SK, 7750 Highgate Ln, La Mesa, CA 91942;* **knickk6sk@aol.com**

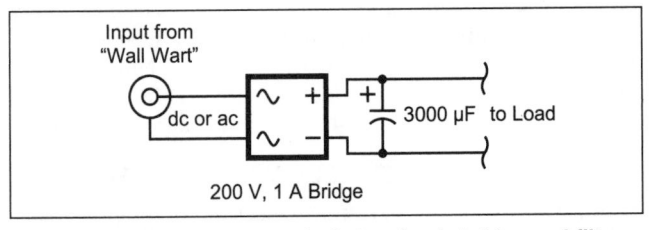

**Figure 1.1—K6SK recommends that a simple bridge and filter assembly be installed in every project with an external power supply. The practice protects projects against reversed power connections.**

## MORE PSK31 FILTER OPTIONS

◊ I just read "Use Kenwood TS-570 Optional Filters for PSK31" in the Apr 2002 column (p 64). I've another hint that also allows you to use the narrower CW filters, but without any physical modifications to the rig.

This hint allows use of the CW filters in a rig for PSK31 reception, even if the rig doesn't allow switching to them in SSB mode. One of the nice features of my older TS-690S was that it allowed selection of any filter—regardless of operating mode. Many newer rigs (like the TS-570, and my TS-870S) don't allow use of the CW filters for SSB reception.

The simple trick is to operate PSK31 in split mode: Receive in CW (using CW filters) and transmit in SSB. The trick is to adjust the receive frequency to offset the side tone. This aligns the received PSK31 signal to the transmitted SSB PSK31 signal. You can adjust the CW receive frequency through the RIT or by adjusting the receive VFO.

For example, let's consider running PSK31 at 14.070.000 MHz with a side tone at 700 Hz. Set the receive mode to CW and adjust the receive VFO to 14.070.700 MHz. (Alternatively, you might set the VFO at 14.070.000 and use the RIT to move up another 700 Hz.) Then set the transmit mode to SSB at 14.070.000 MHz. Now you're set! The CW filtering features are active for PSK31 receive, and you still transmit using SSB.

I use this trick with my TS-870, and it allows me to adjust the receive bandwidth down to 50 Hz, effectively eliminating any adjacent signals. It should work well with a TS-570 also.

It is a little trickier to set up, but allows you to keep the filters in their stock locations. On a TS-570 it allows use of the AF-DSP to narrow the receive-audio response down to 50 Hz in addition to the 500-Hz IF bandwidth. In addition, you can still use IF SHIFT to slide the filter up or down. —*Alan Wolke, W2AEW, 6 Crestwood Ave, Hillsborough, NJ 08876-4806;* **w2aew@arrl.net**

(If this doesn't work, you might try subracting 700 Hz instead, or trying the CW-reverse instead of the CW-normal mode if it's available. The CW-reverse function is often band dependent—so you might need to experiment on each band. It moves the carrier oscillator, so that the sidebands are inverted, just like going from USB to LSB.— *Zack Lau, W1VT, ARRL Lab)*

## SMALL-KNOB CURE FOR YAESU VX-150

◊ Some time ago, I purchased a Yaesu VX-150. I was quite pleased with the new rig, which is my first new hand-held in 10 years. After a short time operating, I realized that I had trouble turning the rig on and off, because the on-off knob was placed so close to the other knob and the antenna. I have large fingers and it was difficult for me to turn the small knob. One time I was finished with the rig and turned it off—except I didn't. This resulted in a dead battery the next time I wanted to use it. I began to think of how I could prevent this from happening again. After experimenting with several ideas, I decided that the knob was just too small and short given its location between the larger channel-selector knob and the antenna.

I tried several things to eliminate this problem. The one that worked was a short piece of latex tubing. I managed to slip the short piece over the existing knob. Doing so made the knob larger as well as a little longer. This solved my problem, and now I can turn the rig on and off without any trouble at all.

In working with this problem, I realized the small knob can slip off the switch shaft. I also noticed a small shim used to fit the knob to the stem of the volume control. Anyone that might try this solution should be careful not to lose that small shim. I removed the knob to install this piece of latex tubing because I thought the force required to push it down onto the knob might damage the volume control or the on-off switch. I do not recommend using any lubricant or adhesive with the tubing, because this would probably void the warranty. My fix has worked for many months of turning the rig on and off. I've never suffered a dead battery again.—*Richard Bergantzel, K6TRZ, 11134 Gaynor Ave, Granada Hills, CA 91344-3910*

## QUIETLY KEY THAT AMPLIFIER!

◊ I like operating full-QSK CW with my Kenwood TS-850. Kenwood made adding an amplifier to the TS-450 and TS-850 very easy. A simple menu setting activates an internal relay that can key most modern amplifiers. The TS-850 is usually very quiet while operating QSK, but switching on the internal amplifier-keying relay changes that! The relay is very noisy, and I found it distracting even while wearing headphones. My initial solution was to switch the relay off when not using the amplifier. While this meant digging for the appropriate menu setting each time, at least I avoided listening to that relay!

Since I like to chase DX, I wanted to find a way to key the amplifier without using the internal relay. Then I could quickly switch on the amplifier when needed. I noticed that keyed +12 V was available on the rear ACCY connector. I designed a simple circuit (**Figure 1.2**) that uses the 12 V from the ACCY connector to key the amplifier without using the noisy internal relay. The initial design was Q1 (Zetex ZTX-657-ND or equivalent) plus the two 1 kΩ $^1$/$_2$-W (RadioShack 271-1118 or equivalent) biasing resistors that I had in the parts box. I used a 1×1-inch piece of circuit board and built the circuit "ugly-style." As an afterthought, I added D1 (1N4002 or equivalent) to protect the rig from any transients generated by the amplifier. The completed breadboard was placed inside the amplifier near the jack for the keying line. It was held in place with three drops of RTV sealant. The result is a noiseless alternative to the internal relay in the TS-850. This circuit can easily be adapted to any rig with a positive keyed voltage available.

I've used this circuit for over two years without any problems. It has allowed me to operate quiet QSK running 100 W and quickly switch on the amplifier to chase that new one! —*Tom Branch, K4NR, 1910 Douglas Dr, San Angelo, TX 76904-5024;* **k4nr@arrl.net**

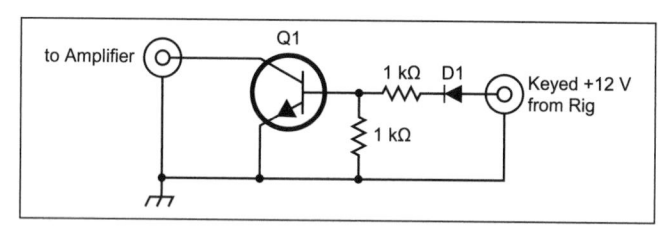

**Figure 1.2—K4NR's simple circuit uses +12 V to key amplifier. Q1 should be rated at 300 V, 0.5 A. D1 is rated at 100 V PIV, 1 A.**

## BOOSTING HF RECEIVE

◊ Whether your radio is a scanner or the new Kenwood TH-F6A, you can easily improve HF reception with one of the three methods pictured in **Figure 1.3**. With some hookup wire, just wrap about 30 turns around a small, non-metallic

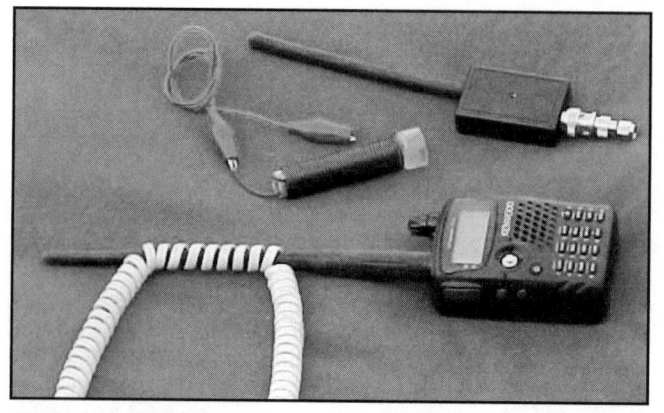

**Figure 1.3—Several ways to boost the HF reception of general-coverage handheld radios with small flexible antennas.**

tube and place it over the supplied antenna. For a more elaborate fix, you can use an active antenna in place of the supplied duck (but be careful not to transmit or you can burn it out!). Finally, "quick and dirty," wrap a few turns of a telephone receiver cord (remaining attached to the telephone) around the rubber duck. With simple devices like these, most of these radios become very satisfactory HF receivers!—*Bill Breuer, KE4SGV, 2351 Winston Ave, Louisville, KY 40205;* **ke4sgv@juno.com**

## ASTRON RS-20A POWER-SUPPLY RFI PROBLEM

◊ When working with some temporary antennas, I noticed that when my transceiver was at full power output the voltage from my Astron RS-20 power supply would fold back to about 10 V. This caused erratic operation of the transceiver unless I reduced the output power substantially.

I traced the problem to RF getting into the shack on the shield of the coax cable. I placed some ferrite beads on the cable. That reduced the problem, but did not eliminate it. I believe that the RF entering the power supply was being rectified and causing the regulator IC to reduce the output voltage.

A look at the power-supply schematic indicated that some capacitors had been added at the factory for RF filtering, but I noticed that a few sensitive areas of the circuitry still seemed susceptible to RF. I added four 0.01-μF capacitors at the following circuit points: across the voltage adjustment divider (R6, R5, R7), across the $V_{cc}$ lead to the regulator chip (IC1 pin 12 to pin 7), and across each of the dc filter capacitors (C1, C5).

I can now operate at full power and without any ferrite chokes on the coax cable. There is no indication of RF impacting power supply performance any longer.—*Harvey Mandell, WA2AAE, 18 Bishop Ln, Hicksville, NY 11801-4534*

## SWEEP-TUBE REPLACEMENTS—ANOTHER OPTION

◊ Sometimes identical tubes available use different filament voltages. Acquire the higher-heater-voltage versions of the tubes and modify the equipment to raise the heater voltage. For example, a 26JB6 (or the like) is often available for much less cost than a 6JB6.—*David M. Colburn, KD4E, 12847 Eden Ave, Hudson, FL 34667-7504;* **kd4e@arrl.net**

## A YAESU VX-5R TO KENWOOD VC-H1 INTERFACE

◊ Since SSTV is an interesting aspect of Huntington Beach RACES operations, I decided to "get into" this mode for RACES. I needed a portable SSTV system for "visual reconnaissance." My portable radio is a Yaesu VX-5R, and when it is used with the Kenwood SSTV unit, they become a "roving digital-image station" to visually report an emergency.

I could have made a simple cable to connect the two units. However, since the special 16-pin Kenwood interface cable is rather expensive, I decided to make the cable compatible with many units, rather than just my handheld. This interface box was inspired by the RS-232 breakout boxes in the computer store. You may have seen them; they are made of large back-to-back DB-25 connectors, with LEDs and a place to plug in various jumpers to go from one port to another.

**Figure 1.4** shows what the setup looks like. The interface box sticks to the bottom of the soft case with hook and loop tape. I thought of sticking the interface box directly to the radio, but found that the box would make changing the battery cumbersome.

The Yaesu adapter (CT-44) can also be eliminated if you use the special four-way plug, but I bought it with the radio, so I used it. By breaking the cables into the 2.5-mm and 3.5-mm phone-plug configuration, other radios can be interfaced into this system (see **Figure 1.5**).

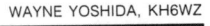

Figure 1.4—The VX-5R to VC-H1 setup. The interface box contains interconnecting jumpers that can change as equipment changes. The phone plugs increase versatility, enabling use with many transceivers.

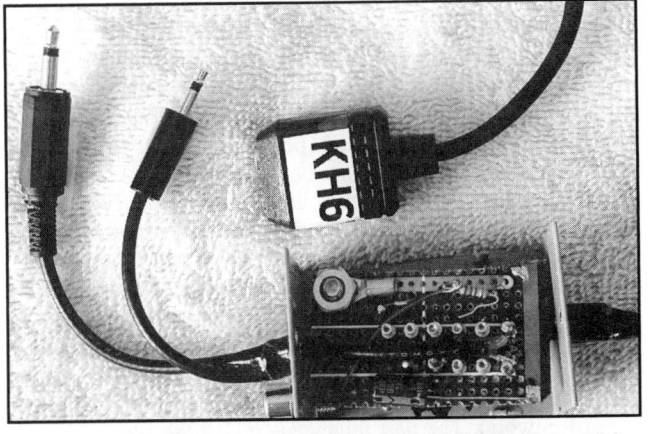

Figure 1.5—Each wire in the VC-H1 cable terminates in a gold-plated pin. The 11 pins provide versatility. I can easily reconfigure the pin connections if I change radios. The solder lug at the upper left provides a ground connection between the case and the ground bus on the perforated board.

Figure 1.6—The "flying leads" simplify construction and keep cost down. A piece of RG-8X outer jacket and some "liquid tape" provide stress relief and prevent leads from chafing on the aluminum box.

WAYNE YOSHIDA, KH6WZ

### Table 1.1
### VC-H1 Connections for SSTV and Speaker Microphone

| Wire Color | VC-H1 Pin# | Connection |
|---|---|---|
| Orange/Red | 4 | Chassis Ground |
| Shield | 16 | Chassis Ground |
| | | |
| Yellow/Black | 7 | PTT |
| Gray/Red | 11 | PTT |
| | | |
| Pink/Red | 14 | Audio Input (Mic) |
| | | |
| White/Black | 9 | Audio Output* |
| Gray/Black | 13 | Audio Output* |

*A 47-µF 16-V capacitor may be needed to avoid audio distortion.

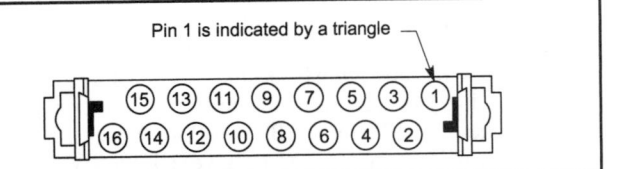

Figure 1.7—Pin numbering for the Kenwood VC-H1 optional cable connector #E30-3352-08.

## Parts List
1 Chassis box, LMB #MOO,
  1¹/₂×2¹/₄×1³/₈ inch (WDH)
1 Cable, 16-pin, Kenwood
  #E30-3352-08
1 Adapter, Yaesu CT-44
1 3.5-mm phone plug*
1 2.5-mm phone plug*
1 47-µF, 16-V electrolytic capacitor**
1 10-µF, 16-V electrolytic capacitor**
1 2 kΩ, ¹/₄ W resistor**
11 Gold-plated component pins

Miscellaneous: Shielded cable, wire, solder, etc.

*You may substitute the special Yaesu four-conductor plug. See text.
**Values not critical

## Construction

This is an easy, junk-box audio project, and not much is critical here (see the Parts List). However, to prevent hum and RFI susceptibility, leads should be kept as short and direct as possible. Use miniature coax, such as RG-174 or shielded audio cables for the speaker and mike cabling. The total cost should be around five bucks. The most expensive component is the metal chassis box!

I used some gold-plated component pins on my version (see **Figure 1.6**). However, a small piece of solderless prototyping board would be ideal, so jumpers could be easily plugged in and out, without tools. My version requires a soldering iron to reconfigure the connections.

Go to **www.kenwood.net/?do=SupportFileCategory& FileCatID=6** and download or open file CONNECTOR.PDF for information on Kenwood connectors. Scroll to page five for VC-H1 connector information. I must admit the Kenwood documentation on the VC-H1 connectors confused me a bit. Notice that one table says for "SSTV and speaker microphone" and another table says "for SSTV." Now check the discrepancy between the audio input (mic) connections. This doesn't quite make sense, however; the connections for "SSTV and speaker microphone" do enable the speaker/mic function with my Yaesu VX-5R. The connection information appears in **Table 1.1** and **Figure 1.7**.
—*Wayne Yoshida, KH6WZ, 16428 Camino Canada Ln, Huntington Beach, CA 92649-5206;* **kh6wz@arrl.net**

## AVIATION HEADSETS WITH AMATEUR RADIO EQUIPMENT

◊ Hams who fly might like to use their aviation headsets with their Amateur Radio sets. The earphones are no problem; they terminate in a $1/4$-inch plug and the ordinary ham transceiver phones or external speaker output will easily drive them. Some headsets come with a stereo plug, in which case there may be a switch on the headset to connect the two earphones for mono.

The microphone is compatible with airplane radios made for a carbon microphone. An amplifier built into the headset raises the level of the dynamic or electret microphone to a level appropriate for a carbon mic. The amplifier is powered by what would be the dc supply for the carbon mike. The output of a carbon mike is far too high for the average ham transmitter. Most are designed to use a dynamic mike with no amplifier.

A little step-down transformer accomplishes both output reduction and application of the dc supply to the headset. Some headsets may include a push-to-talk switch; others do not.

The mating jack for the small-diameter microphone plug is a Switchcraft C12B or S12B. The RadioShack #273-1380 is a suitable transformer. My transceiver has an 8-V dc supply available at the microphone connector. This proved adequate to run the microphone amplifier. If your transceiver lacks this supply, use a 9-V battery instead. The RadioShack #274-025 microphone connector fits many amateur transceivers. I have omitted pin numbers since they may vary from one make/model to another.—*Jim Haynes W6JVE, 1535 W Cleveland, Fayetteville, AR 72701;* **w6jve@arrl.net** (Also see p 1-6)

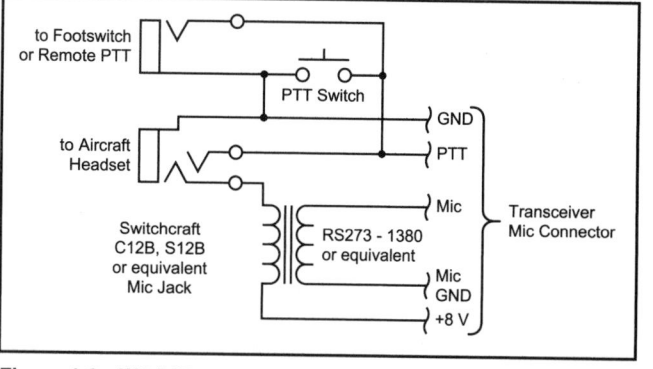

Figure 1.8—W6JVE uses this circuit to connect his aviation headset to his home transceiver. See the text for part numbers and descriptions.

## KENWOOD TS-850 AUTOMATIC ANTENNA TUNER MODIFICATION

◊ I am one of many proud owners of a Kenwood TS-850SAT. I really believe that, for the money, it's one of the best rigs available for either casual or contest use. I also use a multiband "non-resonant" antenna: a 550-foot horizontal loop fed by 450-Ω ladder line with a remote balun at its lower end, then a short length of low-loss coax. The antenna works nicely on all bands, but it requires an antenna tuner. The TS-850SAT has an internal antenna tuner that is fast and has memories that enable it to quickly retune itself when the operator changes bands. Unfortunately, as designed, the internal antenna tuner is completely bypassed when the rig is in receiving mode. For me, this was enough of a drawback for me to purchase an external, manually operated antenna tuner, which would be in-line for both transmit and receive. Anyone who has ever used a "hunk of wire" (non-resonant) antenna on a receiver knows that receiver performance is enhanced noticeably when a tuner is inserted to match the antenna. Sensitivity is increased, and front-end selectivity is improved with a tuner.

The external tuner served me well, but I soon grew tired of retuning when moving quickly up and down the bands during contests—particularly on the lower HF bands. If only the TS-850's internal autotuner worked on receive! After all, many of the newer rigs boast this seemingly simple feature.

Calls to Kenwood and Internet research unearthed no documented modifications for the TS-850's internal tuner. But one evening, while thumbing through my *QST* collection, I came upon an entry in the July 1994 "Hints and Kinks" column written by Dave DeCoons, KE2SL, which told how to perform a similar modification on the TS-850's little brother, the TS-450. Surely, given the basic design similarities between the '450 and the '850, this modification *must* be adaptable to my TS-850. After e-mail conversations with Clif Holland, KE2SL, of AVVid and Randy Starace of KK7TV Communications, and after careful examination of the TS-850's schematic and circuit boards, I came up with a relatively simple modification that puts the internal tuner in line during both transmit *and* receive.

As designed by Kenwood, the internal automatic antenna tuner sits between the output of the Filter Unit (at the transmitter output) and the input of the antenna relay. The input to the '850 receiver is cabled directly to the antenna relay. There is no path from the antenna jack through the tuner and into the receiver.

The goal of this modification is to reposition the antenna tuner in the circuitry so that it is in-line while both transmitting *and* receiving. This feat is accomplished by placing the tuner between the antenna jack (the SO-239 on the back of the rig) and the antenna relay. Once you move the tuner from its original position, the connection from the output of the filter unit to the input of the antenna relay must be reestablished by replacing the jumper that makes this connection in the absence of the tuner.

A few cautions: First, do not perform this modification if you intend to work cross-band split with the antenna tuner in-line. The antenna is tuned based on transmit frequency. Working cross-band, the antenna would not be correctly tuned on the receive frequency. Second, use a low-wattage soldering iron and exercise great care around sensitive components. Third, find or obtain the short coaxial jumper that is installed in the absence of the internal tuner. *Once you reposition the tuner, you cannot transmit without that jumper in place, even if you choose to bypass the tuner via the button on the front panel!* If you do not have this jumper, you can probably get it from Kenwood. The part number is E31-2088-05.

To perform this modification, first disconnect all power and other cables from the rig. Next, remove the top cover and locate the Filter Unit. There is a shield over the filter board. Remove the shield and set it aside with its screws.

Remove AT-1 and AT-2 cables from connectors CN2 and CN5 respectively. Do not unplug the cables from where they connect inside the tuner. Carefully label each so that they are connected properly in the steps below.

Replace the coaxial-cable jumper between CN2 and CN5. (This is the jumper that is installed in the absence of the automatic tuner, mentioned above. It jumpers the output of the Filter Unit to the input of the antenna-relay circuit.)

Unsolder jumper W3 that connects to the SO-239 on the back of the rig.

Cut off the small connectors on the ends of the AT-1 and AT-2 cables that you removed from CN2 and CN5. Prepare the ends of AT-1 and AT-2 so that you have about $1/4$ inch or so of center conductor and braid available for the connections mentioned in the following steps.

Solder the center conductor of AT-2 (tuner output) to center of the antenna jack (SO-239) on the back of the rig. Be very careful not to burn any of the wiring.

Solder the center conductor of AT-1 (tuner input) to the end of the W3 jumper that you unsoldered from the SO-239 (above).

Solder the braids of AT-1 and AT-2 together and ground them to ground lug of the SO-239.

Make sure your connections are mechanically and electrically solid and that the connections you made are not touching any other existing connections on the board. Replace the cover of the filter unit, and re-assemble the radio.

The automatic tuner is now between the antenna port (SO-239) and the antenna relay. The THROUGH-AUTO switch still works K1 in the autotuner and still bypasses the tuner if desired. The replacement of the jumper between CN2 and CN5 sends the output of the filter unit to the antenna-relay circuit.

The repositioning of the tuner does not affect its ability to intelligently tune. In fact, when the radio is tuned to a frequency remembered by the tuner, you can hear the receiver sensitivity peak as the tuner automatically adjusts to the proper setting. This improvement in receiver performance is alsoheard when the TUNE button is depressed.—*Steve Scheinberg, W3SY, 4209 Madonna Rd, Jarrettsville, MD 21084; w3sy@arrl.net*

### A JUNK-BOX MIC EXTENSION

◊ In my ham shack, my computer is about eight feet from my rack-mounted station. I wanted to have my mic over by the computer, so I need not keep turning around to use it. All I needed was a microphone extension cord, with a female mic plug on one end and a male mic jack on the other. The problem is there *are* no male in-line mic jacks around! My solution is what I call the "junk box mic extension cord." Yes, all the parts for the male end came from my junk box: 1 PL-259 connector, 1 chassis mount mic jack (4 or 8 pin male) and 1 mic plug (4 or 8 pin female). **Figures 1.9** through **1.11** show the parts and a finished jack. **Figure 1.12** shows the parts as they will be assembled.

The task requires few tools: a small screwdriver to remove tiny screws, two pairs of pliers (I prefer to use Channel Lock Pliers as one pair), solder, a small torch, flux and a vise. The vise is not required, but it helps keep parts aligned while soldering.

Eight-conductor mic cable is readily available. I recommend #26 AWG, seven-conductor with shield. Not all conductors will necessarily be connected for all transceivers; use your radio operator's manual or schematic diagram to determine the correct pin connections. Here's how it's done.

1. Remove the outer sleeve from the PL-259, and put the inner part (center conductor) back in the junk box.

2. Remove the phenolic (or plastic) female portion of the mic plug. It may be necessary to remove the threaded collar, too. I used my Dremel tool to saw it off. Most mic plugs do not require this step. Keep the outer case of the mic plug and discard the plastic portion (see **Figure 1.10**).

3. Check to see how well the threads of the chassis-mount mic jack (Figure 1.12, part 1) and the PL-259 outer sleeve

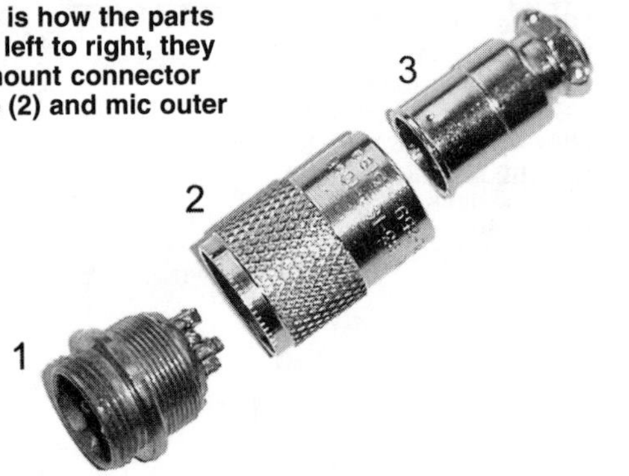

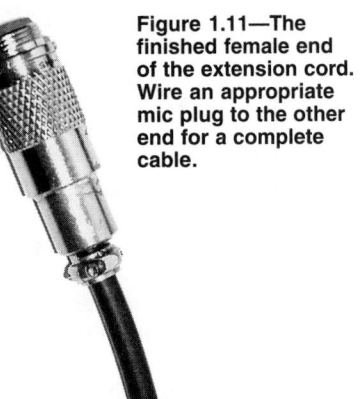

Figure 1.12—This is how the parts fit together. From left to right, they are the chassis-mount connector (1), PL-259 sleeve (2) and mic outer case (3).

(Figure 1.12, part 2) fit. Some "encouragement" may be necessary. I used two pairs of pliers to "assist" in the fitting. Now separate those two parts again.

4. Insert the outer case of the mic plug (Figure 1.12, part 3) through the "threaded" end of the PL-259 sleeve (butt end first). The outer mic plug sleeve may have a collar that bottoms out on the inside rim of the PL-259 sleeve. If not, simply insert the mic plug case into the bottom (non-threaded) end of the PL-259. Solder the "sleeve" to the mic plug outer case.

5. All that remains is to wire the chassis-mount mic jack in accordance with your transceiver's requirements (be sure to insulate the connections with tape or shrink wrap) and then thread the chassis mount mic jack into the new cable end housing you have soldered. Again some "assistance" in coupling the parts may be necessary. My rule of thumb is: Bigger pliers need less "assistance."

6. Install a standard female mike plug on the other end and you're ready to go.

I have two extensions for my ICOM SM-8 microphone. It took two hours to build them both. Good luck and have fun making a relatively cheap microphone extension cord.—*Wilbur Jones, N8KF, 3444 Airport Rd, Waterford, MI 48329-3014; n8kf@arrl.org*

### MORE EXTERNAL KEYING FOR THE IC-706

◊ I recently read the Hint for the external keying line of the ICOM IC-706MKII (July 2001, p 72). I have a '706 MKIIG and also wanted an external keying circuit. For a more robust and generic design than the one presented by KC5VDJ, I took his design as a start and added to it with an earlier design of mine from years ago. I used my original circuit to key an external amplifier with a Kenwood TS-711.

This circuit can be used for keying or controlling any external device, and it could be adapted for radios other than the '706. The KC5VDJ circuit inverts the output of the VSEND (pin 7) or HSEND (pin 3) of the IC-706. (VSEND and HSEND provide a positive voltage on receive and go to ground when

Figure 1.11—The finished female end of the extension cord. Wire an appropriate mic plug to the other end for a complete cable.

Figure 1.9—Parts used to build the female end of the mic extension cord. At left a PL-259, at center a chassis-mount microphone connector (four-pin shown, you can use eight-pin as well), at right a mic plug.

Figure 1.10—Disassemble the mic plug. Save the outer case (left) and discard the insert (center) and threaded ring (right).

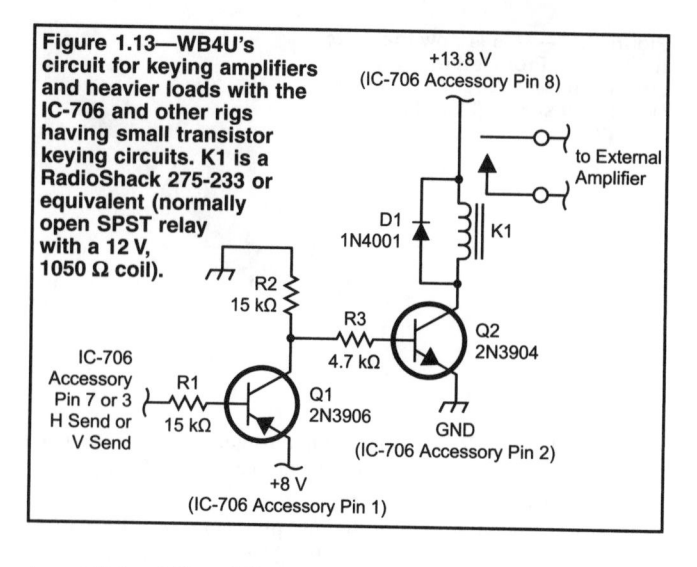

Figure 1.13—WB4U's circuit for keying amplifiers and heavier loads with the IC-706 and other rigs having small transistor keying circuits. K1 is a RadioShack 275-233 or equivalent (normally open SPST relay with a 12 V, 1050 Ω coil).

transmitting.) By adding another transistor, a relay with protection diode and one more resistor, we can achieve total isolation and control greater loads (see **Figure 1.13**).

If there's no need to invert the incoming signal, use just the added transistor circuit by deleting R1, R2 and Q1. One need only apply +8 V to the input at R3 for Q2 to turn on and complete the ground path for the relay to operate. The diode across the relay coil prevents the counter-EMF (developed in the relay coil) on deactivation from damaging Q2. A heavier relay could be used, up to about 100 mA, without circuit changes. This circuit could also be used with an HF amplifier by adding an ALC line back to pin 6 of the accessory jack on the '706 from the external amplifier.—*Johnny Knight, WB4U, 2104 Irby Rd, Monroe, NC 28112;* **wb4u@arrl.net**

## TEN-TEC PARAGON BATTERY WARNING

◊ The Ten-Tec Paragon is a wonderful transceiver, but when it's disconnected from a power supply the memories, last frequency used and clock circuits are maintained by a replaceable internal battery. The manual incorrectly states that a 9 V alkaline or NiCd battery may be used. The system has a charging circuit to maintain a NiCd battery, that will cause an alkaline battery to leak. Acids from the leaking battery drip onto the logic board directly below it. Ten-Tec replacement logic boards are no longer available.

Fortunately, Ten-Tec uses an open architecture that makes it easy to service the radio. I was able to remove the logic board and rebuild the circuits using jumpers to bypass the destroyed copper traces. The radio now works like new again.

However, the *internal* hidden battery concerned me. There is a rear-panel opening and cover plate meant for an optional EIA-232 module. I don't have that module, so I drilled a small hole in the plate. A rubber grommet allows the two wires to be brought out to an *external* 9 V NiCd in a battery holder mounted on the plate. I can now monitor the battery and replace it easily.—*Harold Keenan, KB1US, 85 Topstone Dr, Danbury, CT 06810-7037;* **kb1us@arrl.net**

## MORE ON AVIATION HEADSETS

◊ I received my July 2003 *QST* this afternoon and quickly noticed, with much interest, the "Hints and Kinks" article regarding the use of aviation headsets with Amateur Radio equipment.

I was appalled that W6JVE would mistreat his headset as he described and encourage others to do likewise! Many aircraft headsets can cost $1000, and even the less-expensive ones are priced at over $300.

The aviation industry has a standard and all of these expensive headsets are designed for a bias of 4 V at 15 mA of

current! While headsets may not be perfect and are probably somewhat forgiving of improper use, why do so? Mr. Haynes is feeding his headset with approximately twice the normal bias. If that isn't enough, he suggests "Just use a 9 V battery" if nothing else is available. Wow! To operate properly with 9 V bias, R1 (see **Figure 1.14**) would be 333 Ω, ¹/₂ W.

I am a licensed pilot with commercial and instrument ratings. I've owned two airplanes and have 40 years experience. I'm also a licensed ham operator (K5ALQ, approaching 44 years), a licensed commercial technician (40+ years) and currently an FAA Navigational/Communications Technician (15+ years). I have been very active in the proper design, modification and application of aircraft microphones and headsets—as well as owning my own headset (which I would never plug into the circuit shown in July *QST*!).

A corrected circuit, shown in Figure 1.14, provides proper bias to an aviation headset, removes dc from the primary of the transformer, matches the impedance of the headset output and shows appropriate attenuation to provide the necessary match of level and impedance to an amateur transceiver. (I disagree with simply mismatching impedances as seems indicated by the "step-down" explanation in the article. It may yield a usable output level, but it must certainly ruin any chance of getting the desired audio response from the headset. This when it is so easy to attenuate the 30-40 dB of excess output and retain all the quality!) I think his circuit only gave the desired output because the mic was probably so saturated that it had little headroom to operate in the first place and probably had little frequency response as a secondary result. I hope that Jim hasn't ruined his headset.—*Ken Blevins, K5ALQ, 11983 Rivercrest Dr, Little Rock, AR 72212*

*Example:*

An amateur transceiver manual specifies the mic input impedance at 200-10 kΩ, 600 Ω nominal. The Digi-Key on-line catalog page 1098 (**dkc3.digikey.com/pdf/T033/1098.pdf**) shows a #237-1122ND with 600 Ω/150 Ω split primary and secondary windings. We can use the 150 Ω tap to match the headset and the 600 Ω secondary to match the radio. A Google search led me to a page with T-network attenuator values for 600 Ω systems (**www.mindspring.com/~crosstec/ctdes600.**

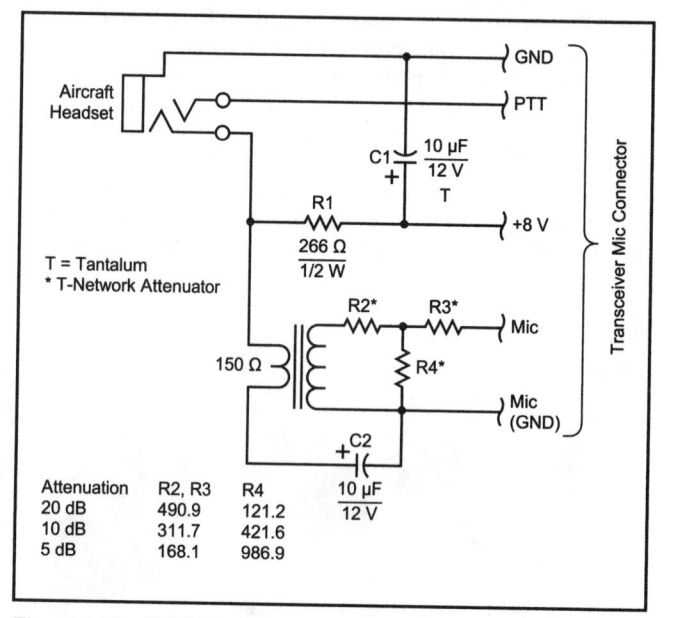

| Attenuation | R2, R3 | R4 |
|---|---|---|
| 20 dB | 490.9 | 121.2 |
| 10 dB | 311.7 | 421.6 |
| 5 dB | 168.1 | 986.9 |

Figure 1.14—K5ALQ's aviation-headset interface circuit. C1 is "optional," but its use is "best practice." The headset requires a 150 Ω primary; the secondary must match the "load" of radio and use appropriate attenuation.

html). For 20 dB of attenuation, R2 and R3 are 490.9 Ω each, and R4 is 121.1 Ω. Since these are not standard values, use resistors with close tolerances, handpick the resistors, combine parallel resistors to achieve these values or accept the attenuation yielded by standard-value resistors.—*Bob, KU7G*

## MIC GAIN ON THE RADIOSHACK HTX-100

◊ A while back, I was discussing low mic-gain problems with my HTX-100 on the air and relating the fix I discovered. Several hams listening requested more information, with one sending me a letter on the subject. So, here is my fix.

It is only necessary to replace one resistor another value. If you can follow the tiny RadioShack schematic, you will find there is a 1 kΩ resistor connected from the mic input lead to ground. (The mic lead enters the main board schematic near the center of the right side.) I changed this resistor to 4.7 kΩ. It is convenient to do this by clipping the 1 kΩ resistor leads to remove it and soldering the new resistor across the mic element.

The new resistor can be any value from 1 kΩ to 5 kΩ, depending on how loudly you speak. I originally used a 5 kΩ pot.

The 1 kΩ resistor is on the board under the top cover, up and about 1/2 inch to the right of the crystal, "xtal" in **Figure 1.15**. Before the modification, RF power was about 4-5 W. Afterward, low power is 6 W and high power is 26 W, with no on-the-air distortion complaints.—*Jerry Turner, KØLSJ, 16298 Florida Way, Rosemount, MN 55068-1877*

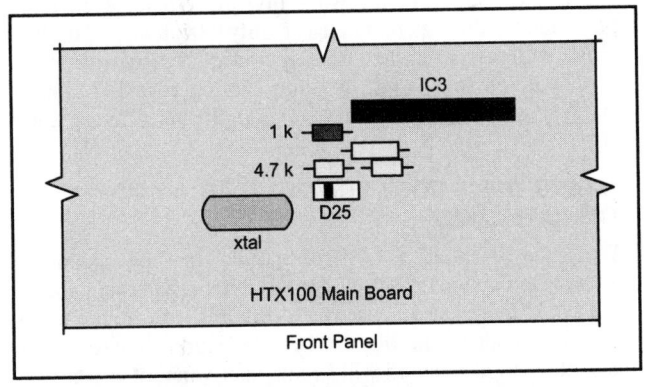

**Figure 1.15—A partial PC board diagram of the HTX-100 showing the location of the 1 kΩ (brown-black-red) resistor to be removed. Only a few parts are shown to indicate the proper resistor. The actual board contains many more parts than shown here.**

## ICOM IC-910H AMPLIFIER KEYING

◊ I recently retired my FT-736 and bought an IC-910H. This turned out to be somewhat of a challenge to say the least.

First, I found that there was no PTT jack on the rig, so I had no way to key my amplifiers for 2432 or 1296 MHz. (*QST* pointed this out in the Product Review a month after my purchase.) I figured that there is a way to do it by using a PTT voltage that switches from +3.8 to 0 V on the accessory jack, so I built the circuit in **Figure 1.16** to use this feature.

Q1 and Q2 are small power-amplifier transistors from my junk box, but general-purpose switching transistors should work. Q1 needs moderate gain. It functions to conduct enough when the input from pin 3 on ACC(1) is high to stop Q2 from conducting (the relay contacts are normally open). When the pin 3 of ACC(1) goes low, Q1 stops conducting so the base of Q2 goes high and allows Q2 to activate the relay.

Q2 must handle the current required to reliably close the relay, and it should have a voltage rating consistent with the supply voltage. Choose the value of R1 as high as possible, while still allowing Q2 to cut off when the input to Q1 is high.

A typical value might be 80 kΩ. Choose R2 so that the current through Q2 in conduction activates K1. A typical value might be 15 kΩ for a 50 mA relay.

I realize that it would be nice to state that Q1 and Q2 are certain specific parts. Yet, I think it is important to be able to build up something with the parts you have on hand and know how to figure out the value of the components to make it work.

The relay and D1 could be omitted and the collector of Q2 connected to the normal PTT terminals of outboard equipment, but then you would have no electrical isolation. R2 would then remain connected to the power source; in some cases, its current may be very high.

A second problem showed up when I tried driving the 1296 amplifier preamplifier combination via a sequencer. The antenna relays I use short the unused connection to increase isolation to the preamplifier. The IC-910H did not like this at all, because it was looking at a shorted coax and a reflected high SWR until the sequencer got around to opening the path to the antenna. The rig took a *long* time to decide that it was okay to start putting out power again.

The most obvious solution would be to key the sequencer with an external switch and have the sequencer, in turn, key the IC-910H when it was time. This would mean more wires and "stuff," so I gave up on that idea. The solution is to trick the IC-910 by using a stub in the line to reflect back and make it think it was not looking into a shorted coax. The stub, actually a cavity that was tuned, was inserted between the rig and input relay. This cavity was adjusted so the rig would not trip out and yet to provide reasonable impedance to the input of the amplifier once the switchover took place.—*Wally Lamb, WØPHD, 803 Second St N, Warren, MN 56762-1257; w0phd@arrl.net*

## ALTERNATIVE PARTS FOR THE TWO TUBE TUNA TIN TRANSMITTER (T5)

◊ I enjoyed reading the January (2003) *QST* article about a vacuum-tube version of Doug DeMaw's Tuna Tin transmitter.[1] Steve Johnston, WD8DAS, was lucky enough to come across a "lifetime" supply of 5763 tubes at a reasonable price. For others interested in building the transmitter, there are readily available substitutes for the 5763. In the mid-1960s, transmitter construction projects in *QST* and *The ARRL Handbook* started using the 6GK6 as a low-power driver stage for a

[1]S. Johnston, WD8DAS, "The Two Tube Tuna Tin Transmitter (T5)," *QST*, Jan 2003, pp 39-42.

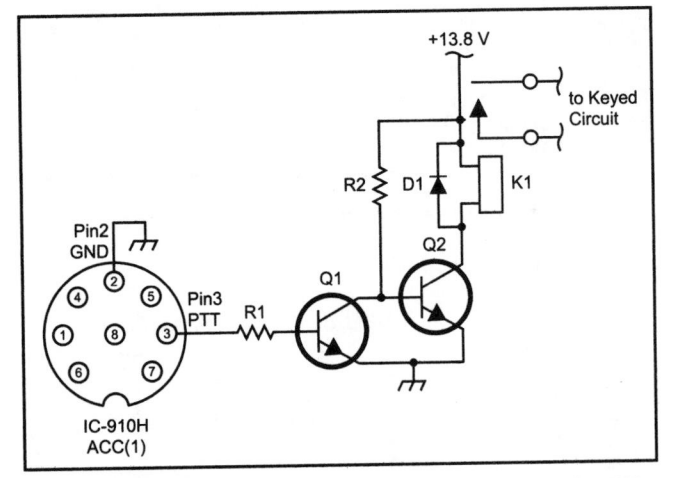

**Figure 1.16—WØPHD's amplifier-keying circuit for the IC-910H. Component choices are explained in the text. The IC-910H ACC(1) socket pins are labeled as seen from the rear of a matching plug.**

pair of 6146 amplifier tubes. **Table 1.2** compares characteristics of the 5763 and 6GK6.

Other possible substitutes are the 12BY7A and the 6CL6. These two substitutes have lesser maximum plate dissipations and will have less output power than the 5763 or the 6GK6. Don't forget that the substitutes all have different pin arrangements. See **Table 1.3**.

If the T5 is to be used on frequencies above 80 meters, the values of the two RF chokes in the plate circuits (L2 and L3) should be reduced. A 1 mH choke has a self-resonant frequency of around 6 MHz, which is suitable for 80 meters, but may have series resonances on the higher amateur bands. For operation from 80 meters to 20 meters, choke values of 120 µH would keep self-resonance above 14 MHz. The only change needed is to increase the inductance of the π-network coil slightly to account for the parallel inductance of the plate choke. If single-band operation is planned, the values of the two plate chokes can be selected for the specific band. Good values to avoid self-resonance problems are: 40 meters, 220-270 µH; 30 meters, 150-220 µH; 20 meters, 100-120 µH. —*Mal Crawford, K1MC, 19 Ellison Rd, Lexington, MA 02421; Malcolm_Crawford@Raytheon.com*

## SLOW-SPEED EXTERNAL FAN COOLS TRANSCEIVER

◊ I always objected to the high noise level from the cooling fan inside my Kenwood TS-570. I decided to position a small, external 12 V dc fan, pointed at the heatsink on the back panel of the transceiver. When connected to 12 V, however, the little fan "screamed" at a level almost as obnoxious as the internal fan.

In my junk box, I found an old wall wart dc power supply originally intended for a Black & Decker electric drill. It is rated to deliver 7.5 V dc at 400 mA with a supply voltage of 120 V ac.

The 7.5 V drives the little 12 V fan at a slower RPM than does 12 V, but it still moves a lot of air. The wall-wart case runs cool to the touch, and the fan provides enough cooling air on the transceiver heatsink so that the internal fan never comes on. I power the wall wart from the same power strip that supplies ac to my transceiver power supply, so there is no need for another switch to control the external fan.—*Steve Swaim, W5LXG, 219 La Costa Dr, Montgomery, TX 77356; w5lxg@arrl.net*

## INCREASE LAMP LIFE

◊ I found the article on solid-state pilot lamps interesting.[2] I didn't know that LEDtronics and Lumex had complete assemblies available.

If the purpose of creating the LED assemblies was to reduce lamp burnout, why not simply put a small resistor in series with the lamp? Lamp life is an exponential function of voltage, so a very small change in voltage will produce a very large increase in lamp life.

I was burning out many lamps in my Heathkit AR-29 stereo receiver, until I put a 1.2 Ω 1/8 W resistor in series with each lamp. The light output is reduced slightly, but I have not burned out a single lamp in 27 years. I've had similar results with my old tube Drake equipment. This is certainly a lot less work than creating the LED assemblies.—*Steve Lund, K6UM, 10180 Mill Station Rd, Sebastopol, CA 95472-9655*

### AD5X Responds

Actually, I used LEDs to reduce the power of the lamps (as well as stop burnout). My lamps are enclosed in very old meters and dials with no air circulation at all. The incandescent lamps were generating over a watt each, so I worried that they might damage the housings.—*Phil Salas, AD5X*

### Different Lamps may Help, Too

With the dealer charging $150 to open the instrument panel, I waited years to replace several burned out dial lamps in my Subaru, and then I did the work myself. When I found the replacements, they were rated for only 500 hours. That's a *terrible* engineering choice for something so expensive to replace. A quick review of the lamp catalog revealed similar lamps using slightly less current (less light) but offering 2500 hours of life.—*Bob Schetgen, KU7G*

## STORING THE "LOOSE SCREW" IN AN ICOM IC-706MKIIG

◊ When the ICOM IC-706MKIIG mobile transceiver is being used with the optional OPC-581 front-panel separation cable, a small (2×5.5mm) screw is used to secure this cable to the transceiver. This leads to a problem: Where do I store this screw when this cable is removed, and will I remember where it is when required, possibly for use by other ham members of my family?

There is a perfect solution! On the backside of the front panel, just above the factory applied "caution" sticker there is a 6 mm diameter, 7 mm deep recess with a small screw beneath it. This recess is just the right size for storing the "loose" screw! To be completely below this surface, however, this screw needs to be

[2]P. Salas, AD5X, "Solid-State Those Pilot Lamps," *QST*, Sep 2003, pp 38-39.

**Figure 1.17—KO8S stores the cable retaining screw for his ICOM's remote front panel kit in a recess on the back of the panel.**

## Table 1.2
## Tube Characteristics

| Tube | 5763 | 6GK6 | 12BY7A | 6CL6 |
|---|---|---|---|---|
| Maximum Plate Voltage (V) | 350 | 330 | 330 | 300 |
| Maximum Screen Voltage (V) | 250 | 330 | 190 | 300 |
| Filament Current (A) | 0.76 | 0.76 | 0.60 | 0.65 |
| Grid Capacitance (pF) | 9.5 | 10.0 | 10.2 | 11.0 |
| Plate Capacitance (pF) | 4.5 | 7.0 | 3.5 | 5.5 |
| Grid-Plate Capacitance (pF) | 0.3 | 0.14 | 0.063 | 0.12 |
| Plate Dissipation (W) | 13.5 | 13.2 | 6.5 | 7.5 |
| Transconductance (mS) | — | 11.3 | 11.0 | 11.0 |

## Table 1.3
## Tube Base Connections

| | Pin Number | | | |
|---|---|---|---|---|
| Tube | 5763 | 6GK6 | 12BY7A | 6CL6 |
| EIA Base Code | 9K | 9GK | 9BF | 9BV |
| cathode | 7 | 1 | 1 | 1 |
| control grid | 8, 9 | 2 | 2 | 2, 9 |
| screen grid | 6 | 8 | 8 | 3, 8 |
| suppressor grid | 3 | 3, 9 | 3, 9 | 7 |
| plate | 1 | 7 | 7 | 6 |
| heater 1 | 4 | 4 | 4 | 4 |
| heater 2 | 5 | 5 | 5 | 5 |
| heater center tap | — | — | 6 | — |

placed in this recess with the head facing out.

To ensure that this screw is not lost when the front panel is removed, place a small piece of transparent tape over this hole to retain the screw. A small label identifies and points to this "loose screw" as a reminder! I printed the label on plain paper, and then glued it over the factory "caution" label with a small amount of rubber cement. I did not want to use a permanent self-adhesive label, in case I may want to remove it at some point. Rubber cement does not attack the plastic or the printing on the factory label. The new label does not interfere with the attachment of the front panel to the radio because the label area is recessed below the surface of the front panel. **Figure 1.17** shows transparent tape over the screw in the "storage" area and my new reminder label.—*Karl T. Schwab, KO8S, 30752 Ridgefield Ave, Warren, MI 48088-3174;* **ko8s@arrl.net**

## DATAPORT CABLE FOR YAESU FT-920

◊ I discovered something that may be of interest to some Yaesu owners. My FT-920, and other models, use a five-pin DIN connector on the rear panel for the data port. A nice source for a five-pin DIN cable with a molded connector is an old AT/XT keyboard. These old keyboards are usually free for the taking wherever you can find them, because they are obsolete. Where I work, we had a storeroom of old junk computer parts with a stack of these keyboards. It does not matter whether the keyboard works or not; all you need is the cable. It is easy to open the keyboard and release the cable from its header connector. If you like, the header is also easy to remove from the circuit board to be used in your project, such as a homebrew sound card interface. The DIN pin out is easy to determine using an ohmmeter to check for continuity. —*James Matis, K2TL, 11 Moss Haven Way, Howell, NJ 07731;* **k2tl@arrl.net**

## NEW KNOBS FOR YOUR YAESU FT-50 HANDHELD

◊ I have big hands and it's hard for me to get a grip on the small volume and channel knobs atop the Yaesu FT-50 radio, especially when I have the slip-on rubber grip on the radio. Yaesu builds the VXA-100 air-band transceiver on the same frame, and it uses much bigger knobs (although their functions are reversed from what they are on the FT-50). The part numbers are:

RA012580B VXA-100 Channel knob (the volume knob on a FT-50); cost: 61¢.

RA0125700 VXA-100 Knob (vol) (the channel knob on a FT-50); cost $1.01.

Carefully pull off the old knobs, and after lining up the two cutouts with the plastic bosses on the outer knob and the flat section on the shaft and the inner knob, press them onto the shafts.

You might want to order several sets of knobs with your local club; there is a $4 minimum shipping charge.—*Ron LaPedis, N6QGK, 2115 Sea Cliff Way, San Bruno, CA 94066-1040;* **n6qgk@arrl.net**

## KEY PADDLE HOLD-DOWN

◊ I've struggled for years trying to keep my keyer paddle from moving around on the desk, especially under my heavy-handed usage. I've tried double-back tape, small dabs of rubber cement and other glues. The list goes on and on. All those methods had one disadvantage or another.

I've now discovered the perfect method of eliminating that problem. Con-Tact brand (**www.contactbrand.com**) shelf paper makes a material they call "Grip Liner." It's relatively inexpensive and is easily cut with ordinary scissors. One roll could probably last a lifetime and find many uses in the ham shack.

I cut out a rectangular piece and laid it on the desk where I wanted the paddle located. This simple stuff keeps the paddle right where I want it to be; no matter how hard I bang on it. When I want to move it, I can quickly do so without having to go through the difficulties I had with things I tried before. The material can be located in any kitchen supply store and the cost is about $4. What a difference!—*Larry Winslow, W0NFU, 4500 Whitman Ave N, Seattle, WA 98103;* **larry_w@comcast.net**

## EASY POWER SWITCH GUARD

◊ I have owned a number of MFJ antenna analyzers such as the model 249, 259 and now a model 269B. These are very useful instruments, but they use a large number of batteries. So, when the batteries need replacement, cost can be a factor. That's not so bad if you've used the unit and have run the batteries down, but it's no fun grabbing your analyzer and finding it completely dead without having been used.

With their exposed push-on/push-off power switches, the analyzers are very prone to accidental power on. I remember a visit I made to a power plant control room some years back. I noticed that critical switches there often had a guard around them to prevent accidental switch or button closure.

Thinking about this and looking around the shack, I found a simple solution. I had several plastic protector caps (**www.caplugs.com**) from some N connectors I had. To create a similar switch protector, I simply cut the bottom of the cap out with a hole large enough to pass the existing switch shaft. I then used a hot glue gun (a silicone adhesive can also be used for a no-mar attachment) to affix the cap switch protector in place over the power button. Now, simply pushing something against the analyzer (like the carrying case) will not cause an accidental power up. You have to insert a finger into the cap intentionally to access and turn on the switch. **Figure 1.18** shows a completed installation. Switch guards can also be made from plastic bottle caps or even large nuts and washers.—*E. Kirk Ellis, KI4RK, 203 Edgebrook Dr, Pikeville, NC 27863;* **e.kirkellis@netzero.com**

## A QUIET FAN

◊ I always objected to the high noise level from the cooling fan inside my Kenwood TS-570. I decided to position a small, external 12 V dc fan, pointed at the heat sink on the back panel of the transceiver. When connected to 12 V dc, however, the little fan screamed at a level nearly as obnoxious as the internal fan.

In my junk box, I found an old "wall wart," a dc power supply originally intended to be a battery charger for a Black & Decker electric drill. It is rated to deliver 7.5 V dc at 400 mA with a supply voltage of 120 V ac. The 7.5 V drives the little

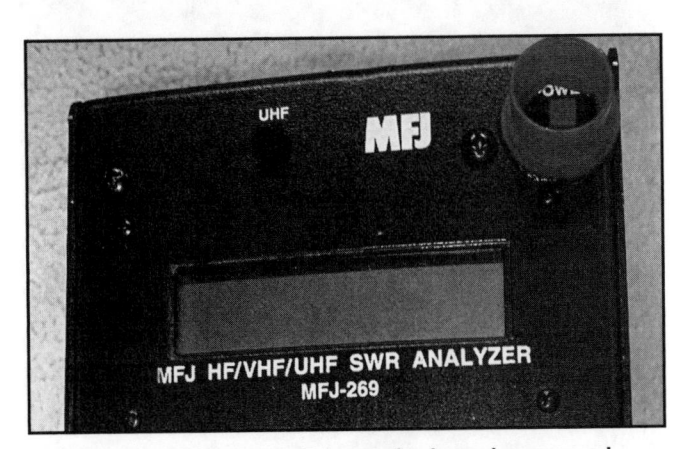

Figure 1.18—The power switch guards shown here are red plastic "caplugs" that are commonly used to cover RF connectors. Others can be made from plastic bottle caps.

fan at a lesser RPM than it would run on 12 V, but it still puts out lots of air.

The wall wart case runs cool to the touch and provides enough cooling air on the transceiver heat sink that the internal fan never comes on. I power the wall wart from the same power strip that supplies ac to my transceiver power supply, so the fan runs whenever the rig has power.—*Steve Swaim, W5LXG, 219 La Costa Dr, Montgomery, TX 77356*

## A MICROPHONE A-B SWITCH

◊ When I first connected my new headset with its boom microphone to my ICOM 706 MKIIG, I had to disconnect my ICOM SM-20 desk mic. Both microphones have 8 pin round connectors, so I have an ICOM OPC-589 adapter cable to interface them with the modular connector on the radio. I purchased the headset for DX work and continue to use the desk microphone for ragchewing and casual contacts. I did not want to spend $35 for another adapter, or play with cables and connectors when I wanted to switch from one mic to the other.

What I really wanted was a microphone A-B switch. A search for one made it clear that I would have to build it myself. I determined that I would need an 8 pole, double throw switch, a couple of 8 pin mic connectors, a cable with a modular RJ45 connector and an enclosure. I looked around the shack to see what I already had and what I needed to buy.

I found an old 2 position computer serial port data switch with two 9 pin D-type connectors on it taking up space on a shelf. That provided me with the switch and the enclosure. I also found half of a computer network jumper cable with an RJ45 connector still on it, left over from another project. I even came across an 8 pin round microphone connector. So, all I needed to buy was another mic connector.

There is plenty of real estate on the back flange of the data port switch box to accommodate a couple of microphone connectors. Indeed, enough room, so that when I punched holes slightly too big for the connectors, I had plenty of extra room to try again!

The switch already had perfectly cut, stripped and tinned wires that I reused. I did remove the leads that went to the input/output connector and replaced them with the open end of the network cable. I also removed the A and B D-connectors and reused the wires on the microphone connectors. The result of my efforts is shown in **Figures 1.19** and **1.20**.

I learned by trial and error that mapping of the round and modular connector pins was necessary. I could not find the

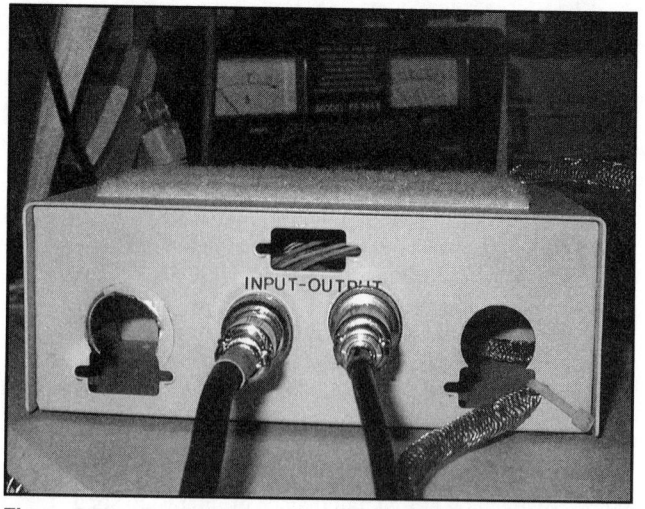

Figure 1.20—The rear of the data port switch. Both microphone inputs and an output cable can be seen.

pinout on the Internet, which forced me to look at my radio and microphone instructions. Each provided me with their respective pinouts, which I mapped to each other.

This was a simple, low cost project that makes switching microphones very convenient.—*Howard S. Robins, W1HSR, 380 Hitchcock Rd, Waterbury, CT 06705*

## BE CAREFUL AROUND TV RECEIVER SCREENS

◊ We have an entertainment center cabinet in our family room that holds assorted equipment, including a VCR and a TV receiver. Our VCR has both rear and front panel video/audio connectors and is located directly above the TV receiver. We take home movies with our video camera that we eventually transfer over to standard VHS tapes by using a patch cable between the video camera and the VCR. I previously used the front panel input to the VCR, leaving the cable plugged into the VCR all the time. I stored the rest of the cable beside the VCR when not in use.

One time, the cable end that plugs into the camera fell down and touched the TV screen cathode ray tube (CRT). Apparently the HV static discharge on the CRT faceplate was enough to destroy the input stage of the VCR. It no longer worked! Luckily we had a rear input to use. I still leave the cable plugged into the rear of the VCR but it exits out the rear of the entertainment center and is short enough that it cannot possibly touch the TV screen. A word to the wise: Don't let any of your equipment cables touch the front of an operating TV CRT screen as that CRT HV charge could damage the sensitive input circuitry of a handheld transceiver, microphone or data port.—*Jim Kocsis, WA9PYH, 53180 Flicker Ln, South Bend, IN 46637*

## KENWOOD TS-850(S) BATTERY REPLACEMENT

◊ After purchasing a used Kenwood TS-850SAT and reading on-line comments about the rig, I decided to replace the rig's memory back-up battery.[3] The battery hadn't leaked (as it had for some '850 owners), but I wasn't going to wait until something went awry and I wound up with more than a battery replacement on my hands—such as damaged PC-board traces.

At first I thought I was lucky: It appeared that the battery in my TS-850 was in a coin-cell holder and I'd be able to simply slip it out of the holder. To my dismay, I discovered that the holder is spot-welded to the battery, so the battery/

Figure 1.19—The data port switch configured as an A-B microphone switch. A front view.

[3]mailman.qth.net/mailman/listinfo/kenwood. Another good site to search for information on Kenwood and many other rigs: **www. w9wze.org/ReflectorSearch/SearchReflectorForm.php**.

holder combination must be unsoldered from the Digital PC board (X46-3080). This requires removal of the top and bottom covers, the front panel and at least partial removal of the Digital PC board to gain access to the board bottom.

Although you can purchase direct-replacement batteries with welded-on holders, when it comes time to replace the battery again, you must resort to the same procedure described earlier.[4] Considering the difficulty, doing that once in a lifetime is enough for me! I wanted to simply be able to snap out the old battery and insert a new one without the unsoldering/soldering hassle. Standard CR-2430 coin cells (without the welded-on tabs) are available from several distributors (see Note 2) and RadioShack.[5]

At **www.jzap.com/n6tr/850repair.html**, I found some information provided by Bill Smith, KO4NR, on his approach to the problem: Remove the existing battery/holder and substitute a separate battery/holder combination located off the Digital PC board. Unfortunately, RadioShack no longer stocks coin-cell holders and I couldn't locate them anywhere locally. Although Newark and Allied Electronics stock CR-2430 holders and batteries, I didn't want to pay $5 for not meeting the minimum order requirement ($25). Besides, from what little I could see from the pictures of the Keystone holders, I wasn't sure the CR-2430 holder would exactly match the holes in the Digital PC board.

A call to Fred Reimers at FAR Circuits provided a quick solution.[6] Fred offers a small PC board with a CR-2430 holder and adhesive-backed mounting tape (you can get the battery from RadioShack). During disassembly of the front panel and digital PC board, I was able to access the bottom of the board after removing only three cables: one above the battery and two near the upper-left of the board. Positioning the rig on its left side gives easy access to the solder pads. Use a wrist strap and a low-wattage soldering iron with a fine tip. After removing the original battery/holder from the Digital PC board, I attached a pair of color-coded wires (cut from a length of ribbon cable) to the vacated holes. Use color-coded wires to ensure you wind up with the correct polarity: The battery's negative pin is at the top of the board; the two positive pins are near the middle of the board. Both positive-pin holes are connected by a PC-board trace so you need to connect the wire to one hole only.

I attached the other ends of the wire to the FAR Circuits board, again ensuring proper polarity. Using the supplied double-stick tape, I secured the board to the left-hand face of the left wall separating the fan/final assembly and RF unit (X44-3120), placing the board within the RF-unit compartment. In this position there's easy access to the battery-holder clip and it's simple to pop out the old battery and insert a new one. In this location should the battery ever leak, there are no PC-board traces to damage.

After I reattached the board and front panel, some of the front-panel key functions didn't work. I discovered the problem to be a disconnected cable near the bottom of the front panel. This short, flat multiconductor cable interconnects the front panel and the digital PC board and is located (as viewed from the top of the transceiver) below and to the left of the VFO knob. So be careful when moving/positioning the front panel. Having another inch or two of cable there would've been nice—as would an easily removable memory back-up battery.—*Paul Pagel, N1FB, 4 Roberts Rd, Enfield, CT 06082-6127;* **ppagel@erols.com**.

---

[4]Direct-replacement batteries with welded-on tabs can be found at Allied Electronics, 7410 Pebble Dr, Fort Worth, TX 76118, tel 800-433-5700; **www.alliedelec.com/**, Allied stock number 774-0087, Dantona CR2430-FT1; Pacific Coast Parts Distributors, 153 E. Compton Blvd, Gardena, CA 90248; tel 310-515-0207, 800-421-5080; fax 800-782-5747; **www.pacparts.com/**, part number W09-0514-05; East Coast Transistor, 2 Marlborough Rd, West Hempstead, NY 11552; tel 800-645-3516; **www.kenwoodparts.com/**, Sanyo CR2430 FT.

[5]RadioShack, tel 800-843-7422; **www.radioshack.com/**.

[6]FAR Circuits, 18N640 Field Court, Dundee, IL 60118; 847-836-9148 voice/fax; **www.farcircuits.net/**. Price: $4 plus $1.50 shipping and handling.

# The Doctor is IN

**Q** Rob, KA1NHM, in New Hampshire asks: I am hitting a hamfest this weekend with the express purpose of finding a desk mike for my ICOM IC-718. I understand there is an impedance issue with ICOM rigs, and that only certain desk mikes will work properly without adjustment. Can you enlighten me a little on this? Will I be able to use a D-104, for instance? Or should I stick to trying to find a good, used ICOM mike?

**A** An amplified D-104 will work fine, but a non-amplified one will not. Most modern rigs have the same nominal mic impedance (600 Ω), but if you pick up a mic intended for another brand, you will have to rewire it. A mic designed for a Kenwood transceiver will also need some attenuation to work with an ICOM radio (Heil sells an adapter for this purpose).[7]

**Q** Wally Veal, N4ZNH, writes: I have a Kenwood TS-570D and recently purchased an Ameritron AL-811H amplifier. What I'm looking for is a wiring diagram for the remote connector from the rig to the amplifier. The amplifier relay jack calls for a shielded audio cable with a standard male phono plug to connect to the rig's normally open amplifier keying circuit. The keying circuit in the amp has positive 12 V dc open circuit and provides 100 mA of current when pulled to ground. The amp also has an internal snubber diode across the relay coil. The ALC circuit also uses a shielded audio cable with a standard male phono plug to connect the ALC jack on the amp to the negative-going ALC input jack on the rig. Any help in configuring the cable or...if you know of a source for such a cable, that would be greatly appreciated.

**A** According to page 61 of the Instruction Manual (you can download it from **www.kenwood.net/indexKenwood.cfm?do=SupportFileCategory**), you'll see that pin 2 of the remote connector goes to the ground/shield, pin 4 of that connector goes to amplifier relay and pin 6 goes to the amplifier ALC circuit. There is also a collection of connector diagrams available on the same Web site, including the microphone, remote and accessory connectors. That should get you going!

**Q** Chuck, KT6P, has a speaker question: I have a Motorola TSN6000A speaker that I want to use with my Kenwood TM-V7 VHF/UHF transceiver. The speaker is 3 Ω and the radio asks for an 8 Ω speaker. Will I damage the radio by connecting the speaker as is? Or can I just put a 5 Ω, 5 W resistor in series with the speaker?

**A** It is usually best to use a speaker that properly loads an audio output amplifier. A proper load ensures maximum power transfer plus minimum distortion. Too low a speaker load impedance could severely tax the output characteristics of the audio amplifier. While adding a resistor in series with a speaker will increase the impedance seen by the amplifier, it will also mean that power will be wasted (driving a resistor!). You'll need more volume than normal—and this may increase distortion quite a bit.

All this being said, most audio amplifiers will work satisfactorily over a fairly wide range of impedances. The design latitudes are generally wide enough to accept reasonable load impedances. Whether a 3 Ω load is "reasonable" for this par-

ticular amplifier is difficult to say without extensive investigation. You might want to check with the manufacturer. My suspicion is, however, that he would tell you to avoid putting a lower impedance on the output line, because of his liability for failure of the output circuit. Accordingly, I would suggest that you get a low power audio output transformer having a 250-500 Ω primary and a 3.2 Ω secondary; it should be rated for about 2-3 W. The transformer will not load the output circuit and your output level should be more than adequate. A suitable part would be a 500-3.2 Ω transformer (45-709) from Ocean State Electronics[8] or a 250-3.2 Ω transformer (P-TK17) from Antique Electronic Supply.[9] Both are rated at about 2 W. You could try adding the resistor to see what effect that has on the audio output level and distortion, but almost half your power will be wasted as heat! A 2 W resistor should be adequate.

[Several readers commented on the Doctor's solution ["The Doctor is IN," Dec 2003, p 52] to feed a 3.2 Ω speaker from an 8 Ω source with a 250 or 500 Ω transformer. A better way to do this is to use a multi-tapped line to voice coil transformer as an autotransformer. Connect the 8 Ω secondary tap and the common across the audio output line and the 3.2 Ω tap and the common to the speaker. Let the primary "float" unconnected. A 70 V PA line to voice coil transformer works (RadioShack 32-1031).

At the risk of a malpractice suit, the Doctor needs to clarify the question of speaker impedance raised in his December column ("The Doctor is IN," Dec 2003, p 52) and the related Feedback item (Feb 2004, p 54). The original proposition of using a 5 Ω, 2 W series resistor between the speaker and the transceiver is actually a much better solution than a 250 Ω to 3.2 Ω transformer, which is wrong. The peak power delivered from a transformer of that impedance ratio would only be about 150 mW, while the series resistor would deliver about 1 W to the speaker. Still, nearly half the total power output would be dissipated by the resistor. The best solution, and one the Doctor stands by (presented in February's Feedback) is to use an autotransformer, made from a common 70 V line to voice coil transformer (RadioShack 32-1031) with an open primary. Thanks to all who wrote in, but especially to Hans Glista, WA1LWS.]

**Q** Merrill, KFØWL, writes: I bought a new Kenwood TS-450 transceiver in 1992. The memory battery is original and is still working okay. My question is how much longer can I expect this battery to last and how difficult would it be for me to replace it when the need arises? I do have the service manual but it doesn't give much detail on the replacement procedure. Thanks.

**A** According to one of the Internet equipment forum users groups, it takes about half an hour and some soldering ability to replace the battery in the TS-450, as it is soldered in with tabs. Some folks replace it with a different type of battery that has wire leads. It may be a good idea to replace it in spite of the fact that it's still functional. One suggestion is to put in a new replacement cell every 7 years, before the battery starts leaking. Leaking memory batteries can be a big problem with older electronics and they can do considerable damage. Some of the major battery manufacturers talk about storage lifetimes of 5 to 10 years for lithium cells, so 7 years appears to be a good compromise. NiCd batteries would need replacement more frequently, although lithium is usually the cell of choice for most equipment.

[8]Ocean State Electronics, PO Box 1458, 6 Industrial Dr, Westerly, RI 02891; tel 800-866-6626; **www.oselectronics.com**.
[9]Antique Electronic Supply, 6221 S Maple Ave, Tempe, AZ 85283; tel 480-820-5411; **www.tubesandmore.com**.

[7]**www.heilsound.com/**

**Q** John, WA8FNJ, writes: I recently acquired a Collins R-390A receiver and I've seen references to a "diode load." I understand that it can be used as a source for audio output, but where does it come from, what is its purpose, and do all receivers have this?

**A** The R-390A receiver "diode load" is a pickoff point for audio. The jumper is electrically located directly after the R-390A receiver's detector. The audio frequency response is thus limited only by the selected IF filter and the detector circuit and not shaped by the audio amplifiers or the audio passband of the receiver. Hence, it's an ideal tap point for wideband audio. The term originally came from the location of the AVC load resistor, which is often fed from the detector, and that was frequently a diode. Not all receivers have a so-called "diode load," but most receivers have a spot, following the detector, where audio can be sampled.

**Q** From Ed, N5QVQ, comes this: I have a satellite XM portable radio receiver that I am trying to adapt for use in my airplane. The only inconvenience is that it needs the audio output amplified with a volume control. When used in an auto or a similar installation, it uses a cassette adapter that plugs into an existing stereo system for amplification and control of volume. I am currently using a portable cassette (9 V dc battery power) player for this purpose and then connecting its output into the audio panel of my plane.

Do you have any ideas for a homebrew adapter using an IC and voltage regulator I can build and power with the existing 12 V dc cigarette lighter source, thereby eliminating the cumbersome cassette player?

**A** You might consider the amplified speakers that come with computers. These are popular with homebrewers of QRP gear; they are effective as an inexpensive solution to the audio question. They are frequently powered at the 12 V dc level or have a built-in diode rectifier to convert ac from a "wall-wart" supply. As such, they'd be easy to power from a dc source. You might also consider an amplified extension speaker available from RadioShack (**www.radioshack.com**; catalog no. 21-541).

Page 19.25 of *The 2005 ARRL Handbook* has a headphone mixer using an LM386—its approximately 400 mW output is probably similar to that of your cassette player and you'd be able to mix the input with other feeds to your headset. That completed mixer is shown in **Figure 1.21**. If you need more output, use an LM380 IC. The LM386-4 has a maximum voltage rating of 18 V dc and the LM380 has a maximum voltage rating of 22 V dc, so there's no need for a voltage regulator with either device. The data sheet for the LM386 device can be found at: **www.national.com/ds/LM/LM386.pdf**. The data sheet for the LM380 can be likewise found at **www.national.com/ds/LM/LM380.pdf**.

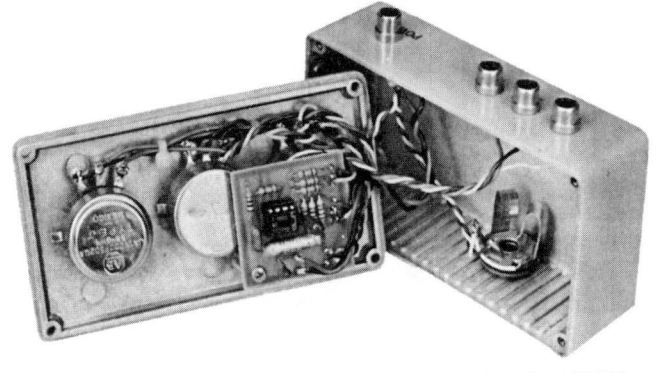

Figure 1.21—A simple audio mixer/amplifier using the LM386. It appears in the new 82nd edition of *The ARRL Handbook*, page 19.25.

**Q** From Sergio R. Rubio, KP4L, comes the following: I have had an Amp Supply LK-500ZB amplifier for over 15 years. It has a big ammeter to read plate current and it has slowly been collecting condensation behind the front glass, to the point that it is impossible to use. The meter is in the left side of the front panel; at the right side there is another meter that reads grid current and plate voltage, where condensation is not present. For your information, the power supply (3 kV, 1 A) is located at the left side of the amplifier, where the condensation is present, while at the right side is a pair of 3-500Z tubes, where the temperature is higher, but there is no meter condensation.

What can be done to eliminate the condensation, short of taking out the meter and cleaning it periodically? I have tried several remedies with no result, including the use of a hair dryer.

**A** The relative humidty of the air within the meter is apparently high and the temperature of that air is reaching the dew point. The air is then condensing on the cooler surface of the meter glass. It is probably condensing on the interior of the meter case, as well. The condensation is the result of warm, moist air coming into contact with a cooler surface.

The problem can be attacked two ways. Keep the glass surface warmer than the air it contacts, or lower the relative humidity of the internal air by ventilation or by the use of a dessicant (silica gel) within the meter. To keep the surface warmer than the air it contacts, you could put a heat source inside the meter, such as a resistor or a light bulb, and keep it on continuously. A light bulb could be powered from a separate wall supply or transformer, but run at a lower voltage for increased life. A 12 V bulb powered from a 6.3 V transformer would probably furnish sufficient heat to the meter interior. That would prevent the meter surface from getting cooler than the air within it and thus keep that air from condensing. A heat source near the meter should also help—but may not be as effective. That could account for the fact that the meter nearer the tubes is not condensing.

Condensation, such as you describe, may also suggest a ventilation problem. Once a significant amount moisture gets into the meter (as vapor), that moisture-laden air can condense on the inside meter surface if it reaches the dew point. Because natural ventilation of the meter seems inadequate to get the moisture out of the meter, I would suggest that you remove the meter glass, or open up the meter so that it can dry out (in an air-conditioned room).

Try placing a small dessicant bag within the meter housing and then re-close the meter. A semi-sealed container will often draw cooler air inside as it cools down. This moisture-laden air will then be trapped inside the meter case without an easy exit path. It may also be advisable to carefully drill a small ventilation hole in the meter case. This will require disassembly of the meter—something you'll have to do in any case.

The object is either to rid the interior of the meter of moisture-laden air by ventilation or the use of a dessicant within the meter or prevent that air from reaching the dew point by warming the interior meter surface. I hope some of these remedies help and, good luck!

**Q** Doug Poppa, KD7LFS, asks: I would like to monitor the modulation output from my linear amplifier on an oscilloscope while I am transmitting. What do I connect to the amplifier output line to get into the input of the oscilloscope? Are there any commercially made units available or do I have to build one?

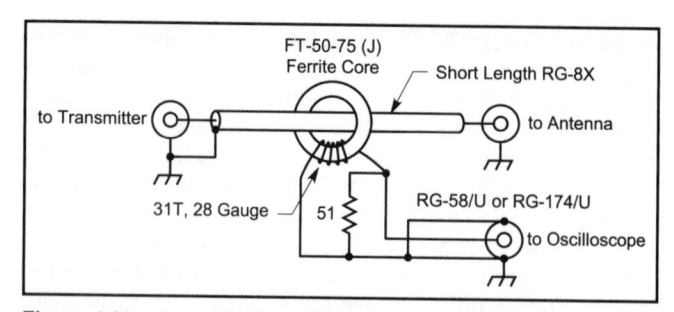

Figure 1.22—A coaxial line sampler for oscilloscope monitoring of a transmitted signal. The transformer is an FT-37-75 ferrite core wound with 28 gauge enamel wire. The primary is a short section of RG-8X coaxial cable passed directly through the core. This wide-band RF line sampler has a ratio of 30 dB. Thin 50 Ω coaxial line can be run directly to the monitoring oscilloscope. The line should be terminated in its characteristic impedance, either at the coupler or at the oscilloscope.

**A** Perhaps the most convenient monitoring method is to build a line sampler or a line coupler with a fixed wide-band coupling ratio. Page 25.27 of the 2005 *ARRL Handbook*[10] describes a simple version—31 turns of 28 gauge wire wound on an FT-50-75(J) ferrite core for the connection to the scope and RG-8X passed through the core for the transmitter connection. This coupler has a fixed ratio of 30 dB and is flat from 0.5-100 MHz. It is shown in **Figure 1.22**.

Bear in mind that the oscilloscope will have to have a vertical amplifier bandwidth wide enough to view the sampled signal. If the cable run to the 'scope is short, place a terminating resistor (51 Ω) directly at the coupler, as shown, and do not terminate at the 'scope. If the run to the 'scope is long, place the terminating resistor directly at the oscilloscope input and don't terminate at the coupler. In any case, do not double-terminate the sample line.

There are commercial units available (Bird, et al), but be careful. Many of these are frequency sensitive and will produce an output level that is dependent on the input frequency. These would have to be adjusted for operation on different bands to give equal response at all frequencies.

**Q** From Don, KG4NLP, comes the following: I found the article in the Aug 2004 "The Doctor is IN" (p 54), which talked about oscilloscope monitoring of a transmitted signal, interesting. I would like to know where to get the FT-50-75 ferrite core for this project.

**A** The FT-50-75 core number refers to both the OD of the core and the ferrite mix used. The first number, "50," specifies a core with an OD of 0.5 inches and an ID of about 0.30 inches, large enough to pass the RG-8X coaxial cable, which is used as the line section. The second number, "75," specifies a ferrite mix of 75, which signifies a permeability (μ) of 5000. Note that the number specified in the Figure 1.22 caption refers to a core size only large enough to pass thinner coax (thanks to Phil, KE3FL, for pointing this out). To use the RG-8X cable specified, the FT-50-75 ferrite core specified should be used.

You can get these from a number of different sources, including the following: Palomar Engineers, as a size F-50, type 75 (**www.palomar-engineers.com/Ferrite_Cores/ferrite_cores. html**); CWS ByteMark, as a type F-50-J (**www.cwsbytemark. com/prices/toroidal.php**); Ocean State Electronics, as a type FT50-75 (**www.oselectronics.com/ose_p88.htm**) and Amidon Corporation, as an FT-50-75 (**www.amidoncorp.com**).

---

[10]Available from your local dealer or the ARRL Bookstore. Order no. 9280. Telephone toll-free in the US 888-277-5289, or 860-594-0355, fax 860-594-0303; **www.arrl.org/shop/; pubsales@arrl.org**.

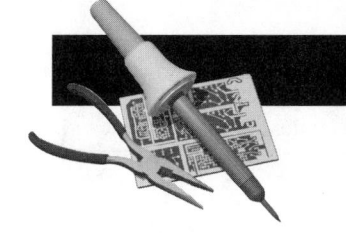

# Chapter 2

# Batteries and Other Power Sources

## ANOTHER TWO-BATTERY SOLUTION FOR MOBILES

◊ I write this in response to Steve Sparks, WK5S, his problem with the battery isolator and his solution.[1] I have the similar battery set up in my '94 Chevy van, in which I run a dual-band radio in cross-band mode that is left on most of the time. I also have a HF rig, scanner and a CB radio along with various amplifiers for RF and stereo (not the CB).

As a member of a Fire Department, I have experienced firsthand the problems with running an isolator for dual batteries. The newer trucks that I've seen now have the batteries wired parallel, no isolator. Understanding how these work, I've realized that there is at least a 0.7-V drop measured (depending on the manufacturer) from a diode on each battery—not good.

A slight modification is needed to the wiring on WK5S's dual battery setup by adding an on/off/on switch between the ignition switch and the continuous-duty relay coil (see **Figure 2.1**). The center terminal is connected to the relay, the up-position to the ignition switch (as in Steve's original schematic) and the down-position terminal wired to the second battery. This will activate the relay with the engine off. This allows me to eventually self jump-start my van when I leave my lights or dome light on all night. The center-off position works well for copying weak HF signals by eliminating wiper and turn signal noise. It also works well for shutting down the second battery if it shorts from all my deep cycling.

This setup does work great, and it would be good for campers, trucks with winches, trailer lights and so on.—*Chuck Blum, N9XUG, Machesney Park, IL 61115-2809;* **Smoke896@yahoo.com**

[1]S. Sparks, WK5S, "A Two-Battery Solution for Mobiles," *QST*, Jun 2001, p 71.

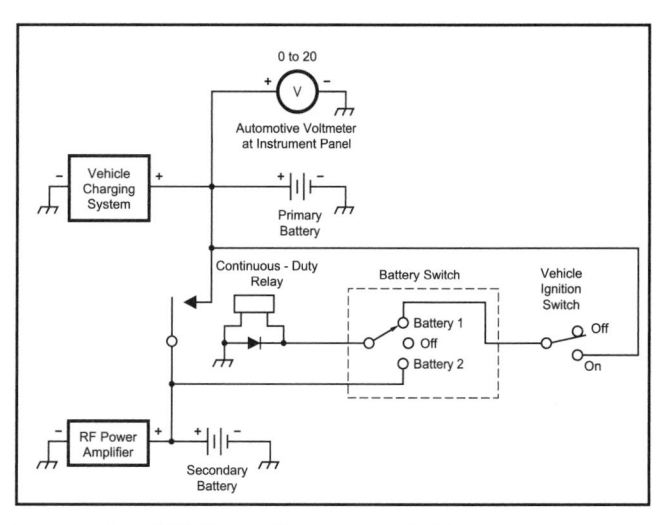

**Figure 2.1—N9XUG's modification to WK5S's two-battery mobile installation.**

## BATTERY CHARGING SUPPLIES

◊ A hint of mine about 14-V battery systems was printed in the June 2001 column. I have more comments about the article that followed mine on 14-V batteries, which discussed ways of selectively paralleling batteries (in parallel for charging, separate for discharge). This is a situation I have dealt with on my boat (as have many other maritime mobiles). I've tried diode isolators, and although there weren't any diode failures, there were several problems.

The first problem had to do with heat—with a 120-A alternator, they get *hot*! None of them ever failed, but I did burn myself once—and I never like having things run that hot. I even put a fan on them!

The second, more serious problem was that diodes are not "perfect" with regard to their junction drop. At very small currents (typical 1-A to 2-A maintenance-charge rates on a fully charged battery), the voltage drop across them would decrease to 0.2 to 0.3 V. Yet a diode passing the majority of the current would have more than 0.6-V drop (typically 0.9 to 1.1 V). This results in overcharging of the already-full batteries in the system. In my boat, I have three batteries, one for keeping house, one for the navigation radios and one for starting. I was "boiling out" the start battery every year!

So I converted to West Marine "Battery Combiners." Each of these has a 100% duty-cycle relay or contactor and a small voltage sensor to drive it. In use, you attach the charging device(s) to one battery. When it begins to charge and the voltage rises, the relay closes, connecting the batteries in parallel. After the charger is switched off, the battery voltage drops and the connections open. Obviously, a good ham could build such a thing, but for those who don't want to do so, West Marine sells the package! They have two models: a 50-A model (#143268, $69.99) and a 150-A model (#128293, $179.99). They are rated at that amperage for continuous duty, with a closing-current rating of 200 A and 400 A, respectively, and a "five minute" rating of 100 A and 200 A. They both are rated as drawing 250 mA when on, and only microamperes when off. There is a terminal that allows you to force them on (or off), and they have a small LED indicator. West Marine also has a continuous-duty 12-V dc solenoid rated at 80 A continuous (750 A make, 100 A break, #289407, $22.99).

West Marine (**www.westmarine.com**; 1-800-262-8464) has a nice big catalog ($5, refundable on first purchase), with lots of goodies that may be of interest to hams, even those who are landlocked!

Those who deal with dc wiring, particularly at high amperages, may also want to acquire a catalog from Spectro Wire & Cable (2208 Pole Rd, Moore, OK 73153; 1-800-255-6371; **wire@aol.com**; **www.spectrowireandcable.com/**). They are a great source for heavy-duty wire, lugs, fittings and tools—I've used them for more than 10 years, and they are a very high-quality supplier. They have a Battery Terminal Anti-Corrosion Protection chemical (4 oz #50095, $4) that is the best I've ever seen for preventing corrosion on battery terminals! They do have a $25 minimum order.—*Hartley Gardner, W1OQ, 3602 N 31st St, Phoenix, AZ 85016-7009;* **w1oq@arrl.net**

## ALKALINE VERSUS HEAVY DUTY BATTERIES IN HAM AND TEST EQUIPMENT

◊ I use only so-called "heavy duty" batteries in most of my portable test equipment and ham gear, since that equipment may sit on the shelf for weeks or months between uses. Alkaline battery chemistry can produce corrosive liquids as the batteries age and discharge. That can damage the battery compartment and sometimes the circuitry of the gear.

Heavy duty battery chemistry works the opposite way. Those chemicals tend to dry up as the batteries age and discharge. Hence, the likelihood of chemical leakage is significantly less than in the alkaline cells. In my 15 years as a ham, I've seen lots of radio gear ruined from leaking alkaline batteries, but I've yet to see any leakage from heavy duty batteries. Although alkaline batteries may give longer run times, it's a cheaper (heavy duty batteries are often half the price of alkaline cells) and safer solution to use heavy duty batteries in any equipment that has infrequent use. I now use alkaline batteries only if they are to be used in equipment that is very power hungry (a digital camera or a handheld transceiver that will see short-term use) or in equipment that sees frequent use and will be operated short-term until the batteries are exhausted. Keep this in mind the next time you plan to install batteries in that expensive piece of gear.—*E. Kirk Ellis, KI4RK, 203 Edgebrook Dr, Pikeville, NC 27863;* **e.kirkellis@netzero.com**

## FLOAT CHARGING AND BATTERY BACKUP WITH A RIGRUNNER

◊ I recently discovered that powering my home station through a RIGrunner makes adding a large gelcel battery for automatic back-up power very easy. [Most other commercially available dc distribution panels will work as well.—*Ed.*] Both the RIGrunner and MFJ versions of these dc distribution panels are shown in **Figure 2.2**.

In his series of articles on standby battery power (*QST,* March through May 1990; available on the ARRL Web site under the TIS/Emergency Power section), W4MLE shows that a gel cell battery can be safely floated across a regulated 13.8 V dc power supply for battery back up. Since all of the outputs on a RIGrunner are individually fused and can also be used as inputs, it's easy to have a regulated power supply and a gel cell connected to the power bus simultaneously. This not only allows operation when ac power disrupted, it also allows the battery to provide power for peak loads, assist in surge protection, and filter any residual ripple from the power supply.

To do this, I simply plugged my Astron RS-35 35 A, 13.8 V

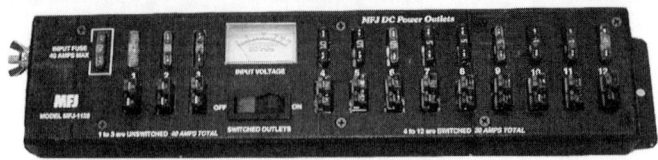

Figure 2.2—A couple of commercially available dc distribution panels. The RIGrunner (top) and the MFJ products are shown. They are both suitable for the application described.

dc power supply into the RIGrunner input position using a 35 A fuse. I then connected my 85 Ah gel cel to position 2 of the RIGrunner using a 40 A fuse in that position.

As W4MLE mentions in his sidebar in the April 1990 *QST,* your power supply might need to be protected from reverse current flow when ac power is lost. Installing a hefty diode in the line from the power supply is one way to do this. [Be aware that the diode will dissipate about 18 W at 35 A (assuming a 0.5 V forward junction drop) and will need to handle the full load current of the supply, so you will need a suitable heat sink. A Schottky high-current rectifier having low forward drop would be the choice here. Also, make sure that the float supply is turned on before connecting it across the battery. This will avoid the inrush current through the dc supply filter capacitors and possible regulator damage.—*Ed.*]

If you use the popular Astron line of linear power supplies, it's even easier. They use a 723 IC for regulation. Adding a 10 kΩ, ½ W resistor between pin 4 of the IC and the wiper of the voltage-adjust potentiometer restricts the current flow to protect the IC. To do this, merely disconnect the power supply from everything, open the case and locate the "L" shaped trace between pin 4 of the IC and the wiper of R5. Cut the trace on the circuit board with a Dremel tool or Xacto knife and bridge the gap with the 10 kΩ resistor.

As is mentioned, a fuse is also needed between the power supply and the battery to protect the crowbar SCR if the over voltage crowbar circuit ever fires. The fuses on the RIGrunner automatically perform this function for you!

So I now have automatic standby power, improved surge protection, peak load supply and better filtering...all for the cost of 10 kΩ resistor! Thanks to Michael Tracy, KC1SX, at ARRL HQ, for his help with this.—*Gary Wilson, K2GW, Section Emergency Coordinator, Southern New Jersey Section;* **k2gw@arrl.net**

# The Doctor is IN

**Q** Hugo, VE7HVA, asks, "I want to charge some batteries. Could you tell me what percentage of a full charge is considered a trickle charge?"

**A** First, let's clarify the question a bit. *Full charge* refers to a state-of-charge. *Trickle charge* on the other hand refers to a slow charging rate. Unfortunately, the term trickle charge is not always well defined. The basic idea however is easy to understand. Trickle charge is a charge rate sufficiently small so as not to overcharge or damage a battery even after an extended or indefinite charge period.

While the exact rate can vary, a trickle charge rate is considered to be well below the maximum charging rate, usually around a few percent of C. Rechargeable NiCd batteries will typically lose about 20% of their charge per month, so a small "trickle" current is often used to maintain a battery's full charge if stored in a charger. Some chargers sense when a battery has reached full charge and will switch to a "trickle" mode to maintain the battery.

If C is the charge capacity of a battery in ampere hours, typically, 0.05 to 0.1 C is generally accepted

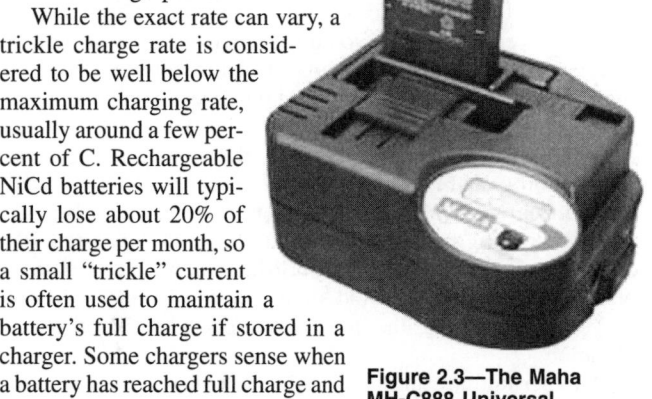

Figure 2.3—The Maha MH-C888 Universal Drop-in Charger and Conditioner is an example of a device that can help prolong the life of your batteries.

as being the appropriate amount of current to charge most NiCd batteries. This would typically charge a battery in about 10 to 20 hours. Internal evolved gas recombination structures in each cell grab oxygen as it is produced at the cell plate, which prevents the cell from outgassing. This evolution/recombination process continues indefinitely with no detrimental effect to the cell except for internal heating (which is why cell temperature is often monitored by high-rate charger). At low charge rates, this heating is negligible, and can be ignored.

Let's now consider a charge rate example for a 1000 mAh battery. The 0.1C rate would be 100 mA. While most NiCd batteries will do quite well on that rate to charge the battery from a discharged state, it is not a good idea to continue to push significant current through a battery once it is fully charged. Once a battery reaches full charge, if a charger continues to try to charge it, the current is simply passing through the battery, to be dissipated as heat, in the battery, in the charger or both. Permanent battery damage can occur and its longevity compromised.

Overcharging can also result in a phenomenon known as voltage depression. The telltale symptom is a reduced battery voltage resulting from secondary chemical reactions. Voltage depression is often mistaken for the virtually non-existent but much feared memory effect.

By the way, the NiCd charging aspects of this discussion also apply to nickel metal hydride (NiMH) cells. Lead-acid batteries however have significantly different "trickle charge" requirements. A "float voltage" is introduced when the battery is fully charged. This essentially means that the output of the charger should be at the same voltage as a charged battery—almost no current flows.

A lead-acid charger of this type typically pushes the cells into fully-charged states and then into mild overcharge in order to equalize the level of charge throughout the cells, and then drop down to the maintenance, or *float*, voltage-limited state. Since the battery voltage is equal to the charger's voltage, there is no current flow. As this is analogous to a float level control in a tank of liquid, hence the name. Unfortunately, the ideal charging voltage is sensitive to temperature—the better designs have temperature compensation of the charging voltage.

It is important to note that constant-voltage charging "float voltage" techniques do not apply to NiCds. The nickel-cadmium cell has a much flatter charge/discharge curve of cell voltage versus state of charge, so voltage sensing is not a good indicator of charging progress. Top-of-the-line NiCd chargers rely upon several factors to determine the fully charged state, such as negative-slope region at full charge, cell temperature, terminal overvoltage, and time limiting. After reaching this point, the charger will switch to a constant-current (not constant voltage) mode.

My general recommendation is to charge batteries and battery packs as slowly as you have the patience for—lower charge (and discharge) rates lead to longer life. Of course, there is probably something to be said for finding the best personal tradeoff between the cost of waiting around vs. the cost of buying new battery packs. NiCds can be stored at either full or no charge. The bottom line is that the best source of information for a *particular* battery is the battery manufacturer. Consult their Web page or data sheet.

More information on batteries and charging is found on the ARRL Technical Information Service "Batteries" information page. See **www.arrl.org/tis** and follow the links to the page.

**Q** Here's a question about power supplies: I've been contemplating the purchase of a new 12 V dc power supply for my station. I'm a bit confused about the difference between switching power supplies and linear power supplies. Specifically, what's all this talk about "hash" and "low noise"? What should I buy…a switching power supply or a linear one?

**A** The power supply you buy should really depend on your application. First, let's talk a bit about the differences between switching and linear supplies. All ac-dc power supplies do several important things and, among others, they must carry out the following functions: voltage conversion, rectification, filtering and regulation.

Consider that, in order to generate the 13.8 V dc appearing at its output, the station low-voltage dc power supply needs to convert the 115 $V_{rms}$ ac wall voltage to a low voltage. It can use a step-down transformer as a voltage converter or, in the case of a switching supply, it can do the conversion by using switches and energy storage components (inductors and capacitors). In operation, the switches are either ON or OFF and control inductors and capacitors to both *source* (provide) and *sink* (absorb) current in a repetitive or cyclic fashion to a load.

The cyclic nature of this switching is referred to as the power supply's *switching frequency*. While in the ON or OFF state, the switches dissipate very little power and so this conversion technique exhibits greater efficiency compared to a linear power supply. In other words, the switching supply requires less input power to produce a given output power. Additionally, because there's no heavy high-current power transformer required, the weight and size of the supply is but a fraction of that of the linear power supply. A 13.8 V dc, 25 A switcher can weigh as little as 3 pounds, while an equivalent linear supply will weigh in at a hefty 25 or 30 pounds…quite a difference! The weight and size differences become even more dramatic as the power output increases.

The rectification process is generally similar in both supplies; that is, they both use solid-state diodes to convert ac to dc. The smoothing or filtering components can be lower in value in a switching supply because the switch frequency is so much higher (70-500 kHz, compared to 60 or 120 Hz). The filtering requirements of a switcher are complex and demanding, however, because the rise-time of the switching waveform creates spurious pulses (transients or spikes) that are harder to filter. Capacitors become more critical because, at the high switching frequencies the capacitor's ESR (equivalent series resistance) becomes a substantial part of its reactance. A linear supply, on the other hand, has only the fundamental 60 or 120 Hz sine wave to deal with and that is relatively easy to filter and smooth with high orders of capacitance.

The regulation processes are a bit different, in that the switcher generally doesn't need a high current linear pass transistor and can accomplish its regulation task by appropriate modulation of its switching waveform and by altering the duty cycle of its conversion circuits. The load and line regulation specifications of both supplies are similar, with the linear supply having a slight, but not significant, edge.

So, with all the weight and size and efficiency advantages, why don't we always use switching power supplies? Well, the switching supply can have one serious disadvantage. The switcher's converter or switching frequency is generally in the range of 70 kHz to 500 kHz. And, that switching waveform is generally a square wave or a repetitive pulse train with lots of transients and spikes, so the very action of switching produces lots of electrical noise and harmonics. That noise is generally located right in the middle of the HF radio spectrum. **Figures 2.4A** and **B** show an oscilloscope trace and spectrum display of the noise output of one switching supply built for amateur use. The switching noise is obvious.

Switching power supplies designed for communications use, therefore, usually require extensive filtering and waveform shaping to limit their RF noise output. That noise can be both *radiated* (broadcast) and *conducted* (transmitted over wire). The power supply will have to be carefully shielded to limit its radiated noise and carefully filtered to reduce its conducted noise. Even with extensive shielding and filtering, these supplies can have ripple, noise and hash figures in the 30 to 50 mV$_{rms}$ range, with their ripple and noise usually dependent upon, and directly related to, load current (a higher load current bringing higher noise). By comparison, a linear power supply's ripple and noise figures are at least an order of magnitude better, generally around 1 to 2 mV$_{rms}$, with some com-

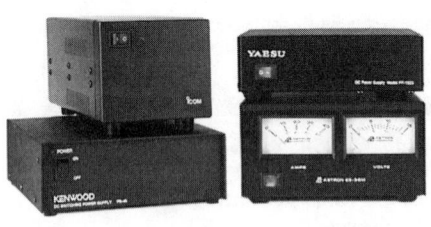

Figure 2.5—Some of the switching power supplies reviewed in the January 2000 issue of *QST*. Two additional supplies were reviewed in the September 2000 issue.

ing in at half these values. *QST* reviewed several switching power supplies in the January and September 2000 issues and, while some were better than others, all were found "acceptable." Some of the supplies tested can be seen in **Figure 2.5**.

So, what does all this mean? It means that you should choose the right supply for the right application. For the quietest of RF environments, you'd probably be better off with a linear power supply. For example, I would not use a switching power supply for critical, low-level, weak-signal receiver use in the VHF-UHF range. On the other hand, if your primary operation is on the HF bands and you have a clear need for portability and low weight and your requirements demand high current capability at the same time, then you'd be fine with a switching supply. Many HF high-power solid-state RF amplifiers usually come with built-in switching power supplies—a linear supply would simply be too large, too heavy and too expensive for the high current demanded for this application.

Another option can, and should, be considered, however. All of the station 12 V dc power can come from batteries. That's right—batteries! Sealed lead-acid batteries can now be used to supply all of an amateur station's power requirements and these can be float-charged on a suitable battery charger. Not only is the power pure (it's as dc as you can get!) and clean, but the batteries can be counted on to provide emergency power, as well. It's a worthy option to the 12 V dc station ac-driven power supply and the Doctor urges its consideration. Watch for an article on full-time station battery operation in an upcoming issue of *QST*.

**Q** Brian, KA7KUZ, writes: I have a question regarding batteries. I have 4 AA 1.2 V 1600 mAh nickel metal hydride batteries. I suspect that one of the batteries is not holding a charge. Using a simple volt-ohm-milliameter (VOM), what do I check for to determine if the battery is holding a charge? Thanks!

**A** The VOM would certainly be useful, but you would need to measure the terminal voltage of the cells under load. Charge the batteries for the recommended charge time and place a 5 Ω, 1 W resistor across the terminals. This will draw about 250 mA from the cell. If the measured voltage drops significantly under this load, that cell is not holding a charge. On a good battery the terminal voltage will drop slightly under load, but it will stabilize fairly quickly. On a bad cell the voltage will drop significantly and will keep decreasing rapidly. Good luck!

**Q** Usher Thomason, NN4EE, writes: Do you know a manufacturer that sells a switching circuit device that would switch a repeater from the 120 V ac power grid to a 12 V battery that is serving as a backup power supply upon power failure? We want to install emergency power backup on our repeater.

**A** The Doctor referred this question to Joe Carcia, NJ1Q, the W1AW station manager. W1AW uses a mains trans-

**(A)**

**(B)**

Figure 2.4—A shows an oscilloscope of the switching noise on the dc output line of a switching power supply made for amateur service. B shows the spectral characteristics of that noise.

fer system to activate our emergency power generator in case of an ac systems outage. Joe replied: "We use a Kohler switch here. The automatic transfer switch is used to take us off the mains and onto the emergency generator. Here's a link to the Kohler residential site: **www.kohlerpowersystems.com/residential.html**."

The Doctor advises that you also check with your local power company. Some utilities have stringent requirements for emergency power backup systems and changeover switches. They are rightly concerned about safety issues and protection for their power line technicians, because of the danger of putting ac voltage back on the distribution system. If the transfer isn't done properly, it's possible to put 120-240 $V_{rms}$ ac on the local distribution transformer secondary, which then gets transformed to high-voltage on the input side of the pole transformer and out to the lines. An unsuspecting power company technician, working on a supposed "dead" line, could find it not so dead after all, with dire consequences.

**Q** Here's a question from Paul, W5PDA: Recently, I tried to charge a deep-cycle marine battery as my primary power supply had failed. The battery had been sitting for about five months without being charged. When I last charged it, all went well. But when I tried to charge it this time, my battery charger's "reverse polarity" light came on. I've charged many batteries with this charger, but never encountered this problem, as I'm careful about observing polarity. Do you have any ideas?

**A** The first thing I would try is a dc voltmeter on both the charger and the battery to make sure that the polarities are what you think they are. A reverse hookup should be readily apparent when you check for polarity on both the battery and charger. Assuming there are no discrepancies between your attempted hookup and what the meter tells you, the charger may be improperly recognizing something like a shorted cell or a very low terminal voltage as a reversed polarity condition. Alternately, the battery may just be very depleted and drawing a larger than expected charge current, which the charger isn't able to furnish.

You said the battery had been last charged 5 months ago. Lead-acid batteries don't do well when left for extended periods without a "float" charge and your 5 month interval definitely qualifies as an "extended period." That's a long time for a lead-acid storage battery to be idle, especially at warmer room temperatures. A warmer temperature will tend to accelerate the formation of lead sulphate crystals in the electrolyte and on the plates, and that can permanently damage the battery. I would bet that your battery terminal voltage has now dropped below 12 V, or even lower. Generally speaking, lead-acid storage batteries don't like their terminal voltage to drop below 10 V (about 1.7 V/cell) or irreversible battery damage can occur.

A float charger should be placed across the battery (a dc power

Figure 2.6—A modern design AGM lead-acid battery. Battery technology has come a long way!

OPTIMA BATTERIES

supply that can be accurately adjusted to 2.23-2.25 V dc/cell or 13.4-13.5 V dc, in the case of a 12 V battery) and left on the battery while it is in long-term storage. A station dc power supply will provide a suitable float charge if the output voltage can be measured accurately with a digital voltmeter and set to 13.4-13.5 V dc. Don't rely on a power supply without measuring and setting the voltage first. Some station dc power supplies put out in excess of 13.8 V dc—this is too much voltage to use as a float charger for an extended period. The float voltage should be below the voltage that causes significant battery gassing, and most battery manufacturers recommend 2.20 to 2.25 V per cell. Incidentally, excessive float voltage may account for some premature standby battery failures at repeater locations.

Make sure the float-charged battery is in a well-vented area. Charging all lead-acid batteries (even float charging) produces hydrogen and oxygen, which vents (except for special sealed *AGM [absorbed glass mat]* or *VRLA [valve-regulated lead-acid]* batteries) and the combination can be highly explosive. Modern battery types are clearly the best way to go. These produce almost no external gassing and recombine most of the hydrogen with oxygen within the battery. **Figure 2.6** shows a new design AGM lead-acid battery.

I would try your charger on another known good battery and see how it reacts. Also, accurately measure the open-circuit terminal voltage of the battery. If the terminal voltage is low (less than 12.5 V), try charging the battery at an elevated voltage (about 14.8 V dc) and monitor the voltage and charge current carefully. If the charge current doesn't drop after 2 hours (deep cycle marine batteries may need even more time) of charging at that elevated voltage, the battery may be beyond saving. The battery will be venting hydrogen and oxygen during this time, so be sure to provide adequate ventilation. If the charge current has dropped, lower the charge voltage to about 14.2 V dc. Continue to charge, while monitoring the charge current (the charge current should level to below 1 A) or until the terminal voltage of the battery reaches about 13.2 V dc open-circuit with the charger disconnected. Keep the terminal voltage in float at 13.4-13.5 V dc when the battery is idle for an extended period of time (longer than 3 weeks).

IOTA ENGINEERING, LLC

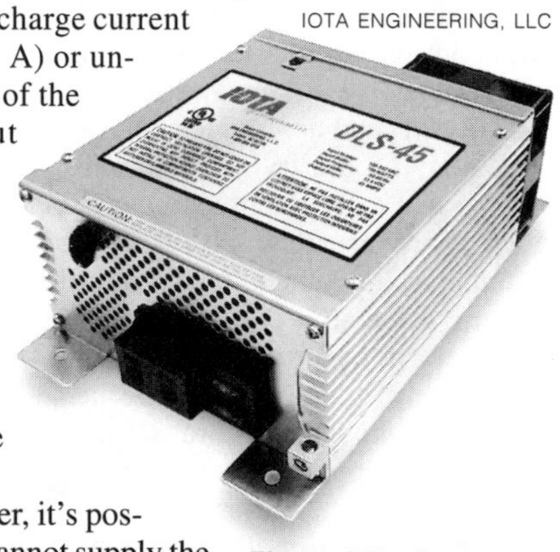

Figure 2.7—A newer tri-state lead-acid battery charger. These are completely automatic and will maintain the battery in a safe, "float" charge condition.

As I mentioned earlier, it's possible that your charger cannot supply the initial current that the battery is demanding because of the battery's discharged state—the charger may be clamped at its maximum voltage with the battery still demanding more current. As such, the charger could be shutting down—falsely indicating a "reverse polarity" condition. Modern 3-state chargers provide an initial "bulk" voltage to bring a discharged battery back to about 75% capacity, a so-called "absorption" voltage to bring the battery to full charge and finally, a maintenance or "float" voltage to maintain the battery at its designed terminal voltage. These modern chargers automatically set the charge levels by monitoring battery terminal voltage and charge current. Some older "trickle" type chargers can damage a battery, as their float voltage levels are either too high or, if they shut down completely, there's no float voltage at all. Few, if any, maintain a proper float voltage. A modern 3-state charger is shown in **Figure 2.7**.

By the way, an old trick for "reviving" a badly sulphated lead-acid battery is to hit the battery with a rubber mallet several times. This will sometimes dislodge and break up the lead sulphate crystals. It's only a temporary fix, however, as unless the electrolyte is thoroughly replaced, the lead sulphate will remain in solution. Even electrolyte replacement is a marginal fix for a badly sulphated battery. So don't rely on this. Make sure that battery is properly maintained to begin with and you won't have to worry about sulphation and battery damage.

**Q** Dick, KF4NS, asks: Why are the tabs on rechargeable batteries welded instead of soldered? I am preparing to rebuild a 12 V rechargeable battery pack with 10 cells of the same rating, with tabs already connected on top and bottom. The only problem I see is one concerning the orientation of the tabs. In order to rebuild the pack using the original case, I have to connect the battery tabs at angles other than their pre-welded direction. I have soldered tabs to rechargeable batteries in the past, using whatever conductive material I can find, but what is the proper material to use and of what width and thickness?

**A** The tabs on battery packs of multiple cells are typically spot-welded. Automatic spot-welding offers a way to make the electrical connections to the cells quickly with robotic assembly equipment and with minimal heat conduction to the cell interior. The heat generated in spot-welding is for a very brief interval and is highly localized.

Battery manufacturers try to build packs that are rugged and, of course, as cost effective as possible. A welded terminal connection is far stronger and easier to implement than a soldered one. Furthermore, the welded connection can conduct peak currents better (it's better suited to thermal loading and it has lower resistivity) compared to a soldered joint. The makers generally use alloy or stainless cases, which would require special flux and solder for a good connection. That connection *can* be made with conventional tin/lead solder and standard rosin flux, but I wouldn't advise it. You'd need lots of heat (not particularly good for the cell) and a very clean surface.

When you are trying to fit cells into an original case, it's best to use a flat conductor, as wires will often intrude and prevent proper cell fit. It's why the manufacturers use strap-like material. Copper strap would probably be easiest to use, but you can also use other flat conductors. The thickness and width are not critical, as the run is short enough so that the resistance of the bonding material will be low.

If you do reuse the tabs from an old battery and solder them, you'll preferably need to use an acid-based solder. A good source for stainless and alloy soldering can be found at **www.ccis.com/home/hn/index.htm**. Make sure you clean the joint thoroughly and completely after soldering to remove all the residual flux (it should be easy to do this on a flat bat-

tery). And, of course, keep that acid-based solder *away* from electronic gear, as its corrosive properties will wreak havoc with electronic connections. It does so primarily because there is always some residual acid flux remaining, as it's almost impossible to thoroughly clean a complex shaped soldered joint. The remaining acid will eventually corrode the joint.

**Q** Jon, KC5LVW, writes: I need high current capability (90 A) for my solid state HF amplifier. I want to use regulated power supplies and not batteries so the question is: Can I parallel two regulated power supplies to give me the current capacity I need? If I can, what should I be aware of or what factors should I look out for?

**A** It is possible to do this, although I generally don't recommend this approach, except in a laboratory situation. The technique is generally known as *load sharing* and it involves careful voltage matching of power supplies. There are a couple of things to look out for:

1) If the voltage of one supply is marginally less than the other, that supply can act as a load, rather than a source. Conversely, the supply with the marginally higher terminal voltage will be supplying most of the current. Make sure there are steering diodes present to protect against reverse current flow in each supply. Those diodes will account for a voltage drop equal to the diode's forward voltage drop (generally 0.6-0.7 V for silicon-based semiconductors). That diode will have to be a high current device that can handle the full output current of one supply (45 A), along with proper heat sinking for it. In order that one supply doesn't handle most of the current, the supplies will have to be voltage matched within at least 100 mV (0.1 V) and preferably 50 mV (0.05 V). This should be done at the output side of the steering diodes.

2) If there is an imbalance in the voltage between the two supplies, the supply providing the bulk of the current will likely go into *foldback current limiting*. The second supply now must handle the entire load. It, too, will then go into a current limit state and shut down, with the result that there will be no output. There are techniques for ensuring that the two supplies voltage track. Some of these are discussed in a useful application note from Texas Instruments and Unitrode (**focus.ti.com/lit/ml/slup094/slup094.pdf**). One technique involves making one supply a master and the other a slave. The master supply receives voltage sense from the load and it supplies a control voltage to the slave supply.

Because of the difficulty in balancing the supplies and the loss of voltage (and consequent power) from a steering diode, I would avoid this approach if I had other options. If you do decide to go this route, make sure the power supplies you choose have good long-term voltage stability, good voltage-setting resolution, and are capable of accepting a remote voltage sense input.

# Chapter 3

# Mobile and Portable Stations

## A PORTABLE SHACK

◊ For years I have enjoyed operating portable, mostly from my motor home, where I had a rather decent station setup that could be used while underway. My Hustler mobile antennas performed wonderfully as I worked the world. I thought it couldn't get any better. Then I discovered QRP—I was immediately drawn to the vision of taking a QRP station almost anywhere and operating from places I'd not considered before.

After selling off all my QRO equipment, I recycled the money into QRP kits and equipment. The smaller, lighter and simpler rigs all fit into easy-to-carry cases and can be set up using lightweight battery power. Many companies produce cases or packs made for particular radios that enable the operator to carry a complete station in one small package. I tried to devise my own compact carrying case using shoulder bags, briefcases and camera bags, but none of these fully satisfied my needs.

I wanted a case to carry the equipment that I need not unpack to operate. My friend Walt, WB8E, had the answer: a station in a portable cooler. After operating portable with Walt a few times, I could see the advantage of his system. His station consists of a Kenwood TS-50 running 5 W through the AT-50 tuner. The audio is filtered through a RadioShack DSP-40. The station is powered by a couple of hefty outboard batteries.

I liked his idea, but I wanted a smaller cooler to fit my somewhat smaller station. I went to the local Kroger store and found several coolers—some too small, some too big and one just the right size.

I bought the Coleman 16 Quart Excursion Cooler. This was the perfect size for my K1, RS DSP-40 and my 6.4 Ah gel cell. I like having the battery in the same container to reduce the baggage to handle in the field. There's no mount for a tuner in my cooler; my K1 has a built-in auto tuner that I disable when using the MP-1 Super Antenna—a wonderful compact radiator.

After some thought about mounting equipment in the cooler, I decided that sheet-metal screws may not hold in the plastic walls of the cooler, so I decided to through-bolt the brackets and clamps. This keeps the equipment secure during a possibly bumpy ride to the operating location. The DSP unit bracket mounts to the side (which becomes the top in the operating position) using two $1/4 \times 20$ bolts and nuts.

I didn't want to bolt the K1 down with a homebrew bracket, so I made a couple of hold-down clamps from a piece of scrap nylon block (see **Figure 3.1**). I drilled holes in the blocks for the bolts to pass through. To protect the finish on the K1, I lined the contact surfaces with thin rubber sheet. This setup clamps the K1 securely to the cooler and yet makes it easily removable.

The RS DSP-40 needs power to operate so I made up a Y power cable to supply the DSP and the K1 with one cable from the battery. [Remember to fuse the lines.—*Ed.*] The audio cables have $1/8$ inch plugs to fit both the K1 and DSP unit. A $1/4$ inch mono to $1/8$ inch stereo adapter is used for stereo headphones plugged into the DSP unit. The paddle is a Palm Mini

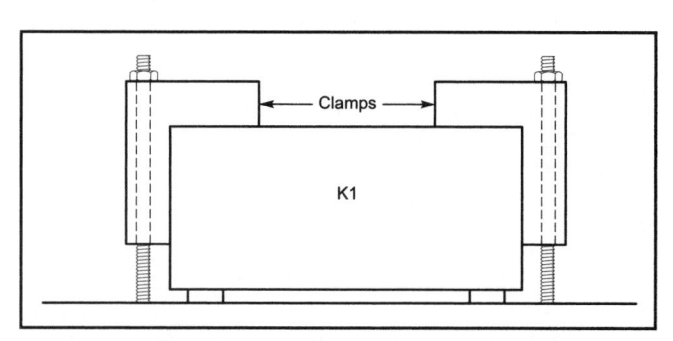

Figure 3.1—A diagram of the nylon clamps that hold the transceiver in the cooler.

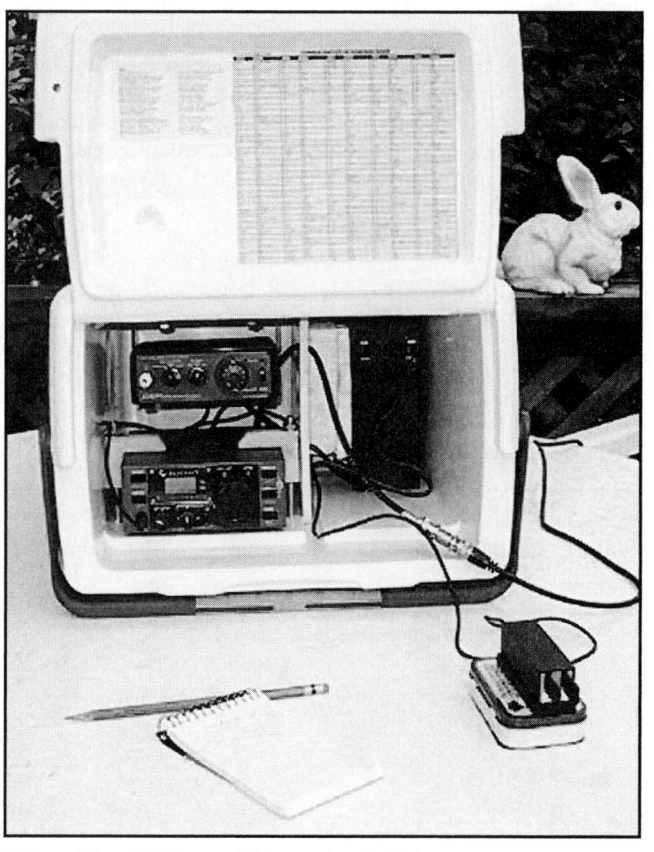

Figure 3.2—AF8X's portable station built into a portable cooler. The lid holds operating aids: a DXCC list and list of menus for the transceiver.

Paddle from Germany. The magnetic base of this paddle needs some heavy ferrous-metal to hold it securely while sending. I use an Altoids tin filled with about $8 in quarters for weight. This has the added advantage that some emergency money is handy in case you get hungry or thirsty and can find a snack bar.

The lid of the cooler is hinged and when open is a handy place to keep information needed while operating, such as a list of DX prefixes and in my case, a menu list for the K1 (see **Figure 3.2**). I'm looking forward to operating portable with this setup, or as Walt calls it, "A Lark in the Park."—*Dick Arnold, AF8X, 22901 E Schafer St, Clinton Township, MI 48035-1875;* **af8x@arrl.net**

## MOBILE AND PORTABLE LOGGING HINTS

### A Custom Log

◊ I recently acquired one of those new MF/HF/VHF/UHF all-mode boxes. As a result, I have been doing a lot more portable and mobile operating lately. I have the rig, mic, key, tuner, antenna, battery and other accessories organized into a couple of packages so that everything is easy to grab when I suddenly decide that I want to get on the road or out in the field. The one shortcoming that I encountered was my station log. I was not willing to risk taking my *ARRL Log Book* with me, as it represents an irreplaceable record of station activity, QSLs sent and received, DXCC countries worked, Maidenhead grids contacted and so on. I usually ended up keeping mobile and portable log data on scraps of paper and transferring it to my permanent log later. This was a haphazard approach at best, and sometimes resulted in my forgetting to note one or more important pieces of information such as frequency or time.

In response to this problem, I decided to make up a convenient paper log form on my computer. I used Microsoft Works to do this, but any spreadsheet and/or word processing program should do the job.[1] I started by using the spreadsheet function to make up a log form that duplicates the data fields in the *ARRL Log Book*. The only difference is that the QSL Sent and Received columns are replaced by a column labeled "M/P" to indicate mobile or portable and another labeled "X," which I use to flag when the entry has been transferred to my permanent station log. I designed the form to exactly fill one standard page in landscape format, and formatted the spreadsheet cells with a solid line border. Next, I used my printer's "two-up" and two-sided printing functions to print several sheets of paper with four such log pages per sheet (two per side). The two opposite sides are printed "head to tail" instead of the usual "head to head" format. Finally, I printed one sheet with two log pages on one side and a blank page on the other side. This sheet is run through the printer one more time, with "KR8L MOBILE/PORTABLE LOG" printed in 36-point type on the bottom half of the blank page using the word processor.

When the sheets are stacked in the proper order and folded

Figure 3.3—The *ARRL Mini Log Book* (Order #7539, $4.95) is convenient for records of mobile/portable contacts.

in half, the result is a 5$^{1}/_{2}$×8$^{1}/_{2}$-inch booklet. Three staples along the folded top edge keep everything together. There is a title page on the front and a blank page on the back, and all of the log pages are oriented the same way as you page through the booklet. I now have a handy, neat, and good looking log booklet that I can keep in a side pocket of the camera bag that I use to carry the rig and accessories. Because the format duplicates that of my *ARRL Log Book*, it is a simple matter to transfer data to my permanent station log when I return home. —*William A. Parmley, KR8L, 4540 S Ammon Rd, Idaho Falls, ID 83406;* **kr8l@arrl.net**

[This is a fine idea for a customized radio log. You may prefer the smaller, more finished *ARRL Mini Log Book* published for just this purpose. See **Figure 3.3**.—*Ed.*]

### An Audio Log

◊ An easy method of logging those oh-so-sweet DX mobile contacts is to use one of the many digital voice recorders available at business and electronics stores. Without fumbling for paper and pencil, you can keep your eyes safely on the road.

The cost of these miniature units has dropped significantly in the past few years. I purchased the model DR-32 from RadioShack on sale for $39.95. It contains two folders of 15 minutes recording time each. This allows me to keep personal notes and QSOs in one folder and work-related memos in the other. This arrangement has proven very convenient.

The features and prices vary considerably. Key-chain models with less than a minute of recording time can be had for under $10. Professional units capable of downloading two hours of recording to a PC and taking digital photos can cost $200. Serviceable units with multiple folders and 30 minutes of recording time cost $40 to $50.

This method has allowed me to safely log many great mobile QSOs that would have been otherwise forgotten or lost. A great side benefit is retaining all items on the grocery list that the spouse just relayed on your way home from work! —*Robert G. Hunt, KY7C, 926 Copper Basin Rd, Prescott, AZ 86303;* **robthunt@hotmail.com**

---

[1]You can download *Works* and *Excel* worksheets from the ARRLWeb at **www.arrl.org/files/qst-binaries/**. Look for 03HK09.ZIP.

# The Doctor is IN

**Q** From Bill, KD5WCT, comes the following: I am preparing to install a mobile rig in my car. I'm trying to find a way to route the power cables through the firewall into the engine compartment. I've searched the Web, but I don't find much information specific to my car. I'd like to avoid drilling a hole through the firewall, but I've inspected the car a couple of times and don't see any obvious exit hole.

**A** I don't have any specific experience with your vehicle, but I have installed wires through firewalls in several vehicles without drilling holes. Typically, I look for places where the existing wires and cables already pass through the firewall. There is usually a wire harness passing through a rubber boot/grommet at some point. There may be, additionally, a plugged hole in the firewall used for a harness your vehicle doesn't use. It may take some looking to find it, as these are sometimes well hidden.

The pass-through bushings on modern vehicles are well integrated with their harnesses and form a very tight fit—it may take a bit of work to get an additional cable through. I push the wires or cable through the hole in the grommet. If necessary, a lubricant (like petroleum jelly) on the wire can help. If things are very tight, a stiff wire—such as a coat hanger—can be pushed through initially, but be careful; it's easy to damage cables with that sharp end. Tie a string to one end of the hanger and pull the string through the grommet. The string is then used to pull the wires through the firewall. If there are in-line fuses on the wire, the wires can be cut in order to make the pass-through easier. The cable then spliced after routing and everything can be tied down with nylon cable ties. **Figure 3.3** shows an example of a dc power cable coming through a firewall grommet. Note the high current connector. This will make it easier to route the remaining cable to the battery. The cable should be routed away from and around any heat-producing areas in the engine compartment.

Some mobile operators find that shielding the dc power leads helps to reduce electro-magnetic interference (EMI) from electrical/electronic components within the engine compartment (engine management electronics, fuel injectors, ignition distribution). A good choice for this cable would be RG-8/U type coaxial cable with the shield grounded; its center conductor is amply sized for any reasonable current demand. Just make sure the shield is sufficiently tied back along the center conductor—loose shield strands can short to the "hot" lead. Use a separate cable for hot and ground; don't rely on the shield for the ground conductor.

If you're totally stumped as to finding a suitable firewall exit point, go to a neighborhood auto audio equipment installer. They usually know the layout of many vehicles (they've lots of practice!) and, if you give them a prepared cable, they will usually be able to install it for you at nominal cost.

**Q** Mike Perry, N7MP, writes: I have a Hustler 6 band vertical mounted on my travel trailer. I would like to adapt it to the 160 meter band if I could just figure out how. I may have a solution but need some verification. I think I can remove the existing 80/75 meter coil, mount a sloping aluminum plate on top of the tubing at that location, then remount the 80/75 meter coil on one side of the plate and a 160 meter coil on the other side. Will the new L/C/F and single-layer coil-winding calculator define the size coil I'd need for 160 meters?

**A** No, the LCF calculator merely calculates the inductance of a coil, or the resonant frequency of a coil/capacitor combination. You'll need to make use of a much more complex calculation—the size of a loading coil needed to resonate a shorter antenna. The equation to do that appears on page 6-31 of the 20th edition of *The ARRL Antenna Book*[2]—and it is pretty complicated to deal with. Fortunately, a graph, which makes the calculation easy, is provided in Figure 55 on that page. Using a *Dimension B* of zero and an antenna length of 6% (for an 8 foot whip at 160 meters) gives a coil reactance of about 4000 Ω. This translates to an inductance of about 350 µH for a base loaded coil at 1.8 MHz.

That value agrees well with that presented in Table 1 on page 16-5 of *The ARRL Antenna Book* (345 µH). The inductance will increase as the coil is moved higher and it will be about double that figure for a center-loaded antenna. The specifics for a coil of that inductance (700 µH) are 190 turns of 22 gauge wire, 3 inches in diameter, 10 inches long. That's a pretty large inductor, especially to mount at the antenna center. Considering the wind loading and motional dynamics of a mobile installation, you'd probably be better off with a base mounted coil of 345 µH (135 turns of 18 gauge wire on the same size form). I would urge you to read chapter 16 of the current (20th edition) of *The ARRL Antenna Book*. It pertains particularly to mobile antennas and loading coil design.

Your particular situation is complicated by the fact that there are multiple loading coils involved. While there are techniques to model that situation, the most practical solution may be to measure the antenna with an antenna analyzer and calculate the inductance required to resonate the antenna. Or, you could just add more inductance until the antenna resonates on 160 meters,

Figure 3.4—An example of a dc power cable firewall grommet installation. Note the high current connectors. These will make it easier to route the remainder of the line to the battery terminals.

[2]Available from your local dealer or the ARRL Bookstore. Order no. 9043. Telephone toll-free in the US 888-277-5289, or 860-594-0355, fax 860-594-0303; **www.arrl.org/shop/**; **pubsales@arrl.org**.

while carefully observing the antenna analyzer. Remember though, that the coil Q will probably be pretty high (the reactance will be necessarily high in order to resonate a short whip on 160 meters) and this will result in a very narrow bandwidth (about 6 kHz with a coil Q of 300). Don't expect to cover all of 160 meters with low SWR with that combination! Operating 160 meters efficiently from a mobile station represents a challenge that few hams have tackled. Good luck!

**Q** Robert, WA2AXZ, asks: The manual for my Jeep Wrangler Sahara warns against the installation of transmitting equipment. I know that all new cars today are almost 100% computer controlled and operated, from the engine spark to the dash gauges. I want to install a HF and 2 meter mobile in the beast but I fear the worst, a fried Jeep control computer! How can I install a rig and antenna safely (as I have done for over 30 years in other vehicles) without needing to key the mic for help when the car dies?

**A** I'm afraid there's no easy answer here, but there are solutions. I would try a moderate power level HF transceiver first and increase the power output incrementally and see if that has any effect on the control computer. If you increment the power in small steps from a low level and carefully observe the effects at each level, I don't believe you'll have to worry about permanently damaging the digital control equipment within the vehicle. As always, use the minimum power necessary to get the job done.

There may be a manufacturer's service note that the dealer is aware of (or not—you may have to do some research) that addresses that issue. Rely on the manufacturer for assistance. If the vehicle is sold for any law enforcement application, it will certainly be modifiable to accept VHF/UHF radio equipment and you should be able to get that data. Ferrite toroid and/or bead filters placed on input and output control lines of the computer could also be an answer. Look at the ARRL Web page dedicated to RFI suppression; it speaks to automotive RFI issues: **www.arrl.og/tis/info/rfigen.html**.

Make sure your mobile installation is based on sound engineering principles. Keep the input dc power leads large enough to handle the current (you may have to go to shielded dc input lines—easily done when RG-8/U type coax is used for the dc) and make sure that the SWR is low, keeping the feed line as short as possible. Also, keep the RF where it belongs—within the coax and not on the shield braid. A choke balun at the antenna may help ensure that. Another tip: Keep the antenna as far as possible from the engine compartment. For help with automotive RFI problems see *The ARRL RFI Book*.[3] Good luck—mobile operation is usually possible from any vehicle with the proper precautions.

**Q** Paul, KI4CBT, asks: I use an ICOM IC-W32A handheld transceiver, mounted on a dashboard bracket with RG-58/U, going to an NMO antenna mount through a hole in the metal roof of my old friend, a beat-up station wagon. Since the coax shield is bonded to the roof metal of the car through the antenna mount, it results in a ground plane. On my newer car, I would like to use a magnet mount, to avoid the drilling. The magnet mount would make no direct electrical contact with the roof metal. Will I lose the ground plane benefits? Should I ground the antenna coax to the car so the coax shield is grounded? I believe I can do that at the dashboard.

**A** Even though the antenna isn't dc coupled to the roof of the car, there is still an RF connection and an effective counterpoise via capacitive coupling to the roof. The magnet mount and the car body provide enough capacitance, especially at VHF/UHF, to ensure a good RF ground. I don't see any benefit to grounding the coax to the dashboard. Such an antenna, however, could result in increased danger with respect to lightning, as it will provide a path inside the car (grounding to the dash won't help, as the lightning would already be inside the vehicle).

The lightning vulnerability depends a lot upon the design of the magnet mount used. Some mounts provide a relatively porous (electrically) membrane between the mount and the car body. This could offer a relatively easy path to ground for a high enough charge. Coax grounded to the metal chassis via a negative car battery terminal is generally ineffective for lightning—the path is too long and tortuous. On the other hand, with a properly installed NMO socket, lightning can arc from the center conductor to the ground rim—a relatively short distance. The object with lightning control is to bleed off an electrostatic charge *before* it results in the catastrophic discharge of a direct strike. The membrane between the mount and the car body would need to be able to pass that energy. A good idea would be to punch several holes (with a paper hole punch) in the plastic or vinyl membrane under the magnet mount. The idea is to make it easier for an arc to occur to the car body when that voltage reaches a flashover point and bypass the more dangerous path through the transmission line.

I suggest you look at some material on lightning protection at the ARRL TIS Web site: **www.arrl.org/tis/info/lightning.html**.

[3]Available from your local dealer or the ARRL Bookstore. Order no. 6834. Telephone toll-free in the US 888-277-5289, or 860-594-0355, fax 860-594-0303; **www.arrl.org/shop/**; **pubsales@arrl.org**.

## A PIC PROGRAMMER FOR ALL COMPUTERS

◊ I have an old autopatch and I wanted to add a CW IDer to it. The natural choice of methods for building this IDer is a PIC processor. *The 2001 ARRL Radio Amateur's Handbook* had just the ticket on pages 22.59 through 22.65. When I built the PIC programmer shown there and plugged it into the back of my laptop computer, it didn't work. Some research showed that the problem lay in the voltages on the RS-232 port. The specification for RS-232 communication ports includes 12-V minimum levels, and the PIC requires 12-14 V on the pin 4 ($\overline{MCLR}$) to assert the programming mode. Many computers do not meet the standard (my laptop only hit a little over 8 V). So, I needed a programmer that would be compatible with the original found in the *Handbook*, but work with any computer, including my laptop. So I set out to redesign the PIC programmer with these goals:
- Work with any computer.
- Work at the end of a serial cable.
- Support in circuit programming.
- Be easy to build (and cheap).

The downside of the new programmer is that it requires an external dc power supply of 15-25 V (+15 V is the +13-V regulator's minimum input requirement; +25 V is the +5-V regulator's maximum input rating). A couple of series connected 9-V batteries do the trick; the programmer consumes little current, so they should last a while. Remember to disconnect them when you're not using the programmer.

I have provided two methods of setting the program voltage. R10 and R9 provide about +12.7 V, sufficient to put the PIC in program mode, but 240-Ω resistors are rare. As an alternative, make R10 220 Ω with R11 1.5 kΩ and V1 a 1-kΩ trim pot available at RadioShack. This lets you use all standard part values and gives the added benefit of being able to precisely set the output voltage to +13 V.

Be careful with the +5-V supply. The TO-220 packaged 7805 has the input on pin 1, output on pin 3 with ground in the middle. The TO-92 is just the opposite: input on pin 3, output on pin 1. The pin numbers on the schematic are correct for the TO-92 package.

This programmer maintains computer control of the programming mode on the PIC as in the original design; this is the purpose of Q1-Q4. When TXD (P1-3) goes low the PIC is taken out of program mode and held in reset. When TXD goes high $\overline{MCLR}$ rises to +13 V. C1 and C2 make sure that RB6 and RB7 are held low while $\overline{MCLR}$ rises to its programming level.

I used a wire-wrap socket to hold the 16F84 for programming. This socket is above the level of the board, making it easier to remove PIC.

P3 supports in-circuit programming. For its use, the target project must include a similarly wired connector. The download package includes a diagram of my IDer project, which includes such a connector.

While hand wiring this project is quite acceptable, there is a PC-board pattern and parts placement diagram in the download package.[1]

You need two pieces of software to program PIC projects: a compiler translates your source code into machine code that the PIC understands. I use *MPLAB IDE*, which is available from the Microchip Technologies Web site (**www.microchip.com**). Follow the link to "Development Tools" and then look for the latest version of *MPLAB IDE*. You'll need a broadband Web connection: The current version is 6.20 and the complete system download is over 25 MB.

Next, you need a programmer. This uploads the machine language file to the PIC via the programmer. The one specified in the *Handbook* is called *PIX*, and I've included it in the download package. There are other choices and I tried some of them, but they didn't work on my laptop. *PIX* works great.

Now, you will also want a manual (125 pages) for the PIC so you can know what it all means and figure out how to make the PIC do what you want. You will find this at: **www.microchip.com/download/lit/pline/picmicro/families/16f8x/30430c.pdf**.

You may find this a bit daunting if you are not familiar with microprocessors and assembly language. There are countless tutorials available on the Internet, some right on the Microchip Technologies site. *The ARRL Handbook* gives some good places to go and books to buy too. Don't let the idea of programming scare you away from trying it.

By this time you have built your programmer, downloaded the software, and now you are ready to dive into it. I just want to give a couple of suggestions that will help you get started. First, how do you get *MPLAB* to work? I had the same question. I found the answer by looking in the help files of the program, of all places. Start up *MPLAB* and click on [HELP] [MPLAB IDE Help] [MPLAB IDE Project Tutorial] [How do I create and build an MPLAB IDE project?].

Carefully follow the instructions given there and you will be set. Remember the IDE environment that is *MPLAB* is quite robust and includes a great deal of wonderful tools to help you develop PIC programs. I do not pretend to have it all figured out. I just want to encourage you to keep playing, searching the help and stepping through the tutorials provided with the program. Microchip also has a downloadable reference guide that may help.

The next step is programming the PIC. I use the *PIX* program, as I stated before. It is a pretty straightforward program. To use it you first need to know what your serial port is: COM1, COM2, etc. You can find this by clicking [Start] [Settings] [Control Panel] [System] [Device Manager] [Ports].

You should see something labeled COM_. Once you know this, then you are ready to edit the configuration file for the programmer. Go to the directory where *PIX* is installed and find the PIX.CFG file. Open it using *Notepad*. Find the line "Port=LPT1" and put a semicolon right at the beginning of the line. Then, add a line that says, "Port=COM_", filling in the blank with the number from the device manager. Next, find the line that says, "Programmer=Shaer" and put a semicolon

[1]You can download this package from the ARRLWeb at **www.arrl.org/files/qst-binaries/**. Look for 03HK08.ZIP.

right at the beginning of that line. Now look for the line that says, ";Programmer=Ludi" and remove the semicolon at the beginning of the line. Save the file and start up *PIX*.

When the program starts, a dialogue box will come up that says something like, "No/Bad Hardware. Not True Continue." Select "Yes." The only thing that bothered me about this program when I started using it was the terminology. I see choices like "BLOW PIC" and "BLOW EEPROM." I had heard of and used terminology like "burning an EPROM," but never this. It turns out that this terminology is equivalent to the more ami-

able "Program PIC" and "Program EEPROM." So, don't let the terminology scare you. When you press F9 to "BLOW" the PIC, the processor is not going to blow up or fry.

Consider what sort of projects you may have around the shack or at home and look at the wide variety of PICs available. Above all, be adventurous and wade into the wonderful world of processor-based solutions. You will be amazed at how easy it can be once you get past the initial hurdle of learning something new.—*Ralph J. Gable, WA2PUX, 658 French Glen, Oregon, WI 53575-2723;* **wa2pux@arrl.net**

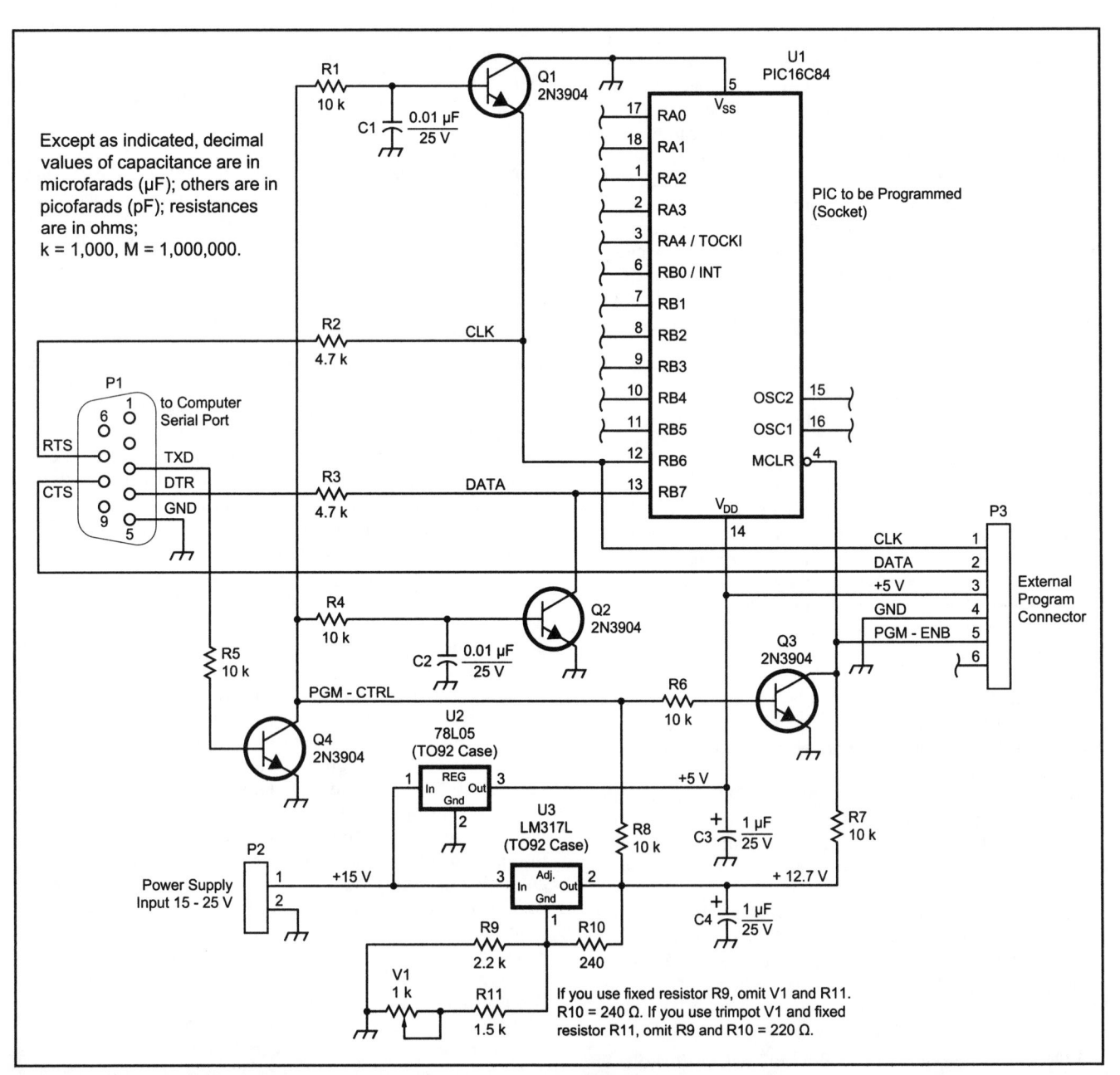

**Figure 4.1—A schematic of WA2PUX's PIC programmer. Unless otherwise specified, use ¹/₄ W, 5%-tolerance carbon-composition or film resistors.**

C1, C2—0.01 µF ceramic.
C3, C4—1.0 µF 25 V radial-lead electrolytic.
P1—DB9, female (right angle).
P2—2-pin header.
P3—6 pin header.
Q1-Q4—2N3904 or equivalent (NPN bipolar).
R1, R4-R8—10 kΩ resistors.
R2, R3—4.7 kΩ resistors.

R9—2.2 kΩ (see text).
R10—220 Ω or 240 Ω (see text).
U1—18-pin DIP wire-wrap socket (see text).
U2—78L05, 5-V, regulator (TO-92 case).
U3—LM317L variable-voltage, three-terminal regulator (TO-92 case).
V1—1 kΩ 15-turn trimpot.

## PSK-31 COM-PORT SOFTWARE PROBLEM

◊ I had been frustrated trying to run PSK-31 using my computer with the *Windows XP* operating system. I had installed a PSK-31 program that could use the RTS line of the COM1 port to key the PTT on my transceiver. My problem was that the RTS line was constantly held high. I feared that there was some exotic problem with *Windows XP*.

It turns out that the solution was very simple, but it eluded me (and maybe other hams) for several days.

I had simply unplugged the cradle for my Palm Pilot and plugged in my PSK-31 interface into the COM1 port, but I had not realized that the Palm Pilot *HotSync Manager* program in my computer was still controlling the COM port. Once I disabled *HotSync Manager* the PSK-31 program was able to key my transceiver properly. What a relief!—*David Powell, NM5U, 1732 Ponderosa St, Los Alamos, NM 87544-3034;* **nm5u@arrl.net**

## USB, EIA-232 AND AMATEUR RADIO

◊ Many computers now come with no EIA-232 ports, and I've seen a few letters from folks seeking USB-to-EIA-232 converters. There are several on the market, but apparently not all of them implement EIA-232 completely enough to work with transceiver-control software.

Therefore, I would like readers who have working systems to send me information about that system: manufacturer's name, model number and Web site for the converter and transceiver-control software, a dealer where the converter may be purchased and the make/model of transceiver with which the system operates. In a few months, I'll gather the responses and publish them here.

This problem highlights another: It's time for Amateur Radio operators and manufacturers to begin supporting the USB standard. If you're planning or building an accessory, watch for the May/June issue of *QEX*. There, Dick Lichtel, KD4JP, tells how to implement a slow USB interface using the Microchip 16C745 PIC. **Figure 4.2** shows the completed interface controlling a VFO. The parts cost for the interface is only about $20. I've placed the article on the *QEX* Web page as a sample at **arrl.org/qex/qx5lichtel.pdf.**—*Bob Schetgen, KU7G, ARRL Senior Technical Editor;* **ku7g@ arrl.org**

## QUICK ANSWER TO A QUESTION ABOUT USB, EIA-232 AND AMATEUR RADIO

◊ I recommend products from **www.ionetworks.com,** specifically, **www.ionetworks.com/products/usbtoserialconverters/.** These converters work every time, all the time.

The key to their success is software that keeps the specific physical COM port on the device pointed at the operating system (OS) COM-port assignment. The problem with many adapters is that the COM-port number changes when starting the OS. *Windows XP* is particularly bad about it.

I do "a bit" of this stuff in the marine field, and this product is the only one that works for folks who have no technical knowledge. Once it is set up and running for them, it keeps working.

On my boat, I connect to a "four-porter": I run PACTOR on one, an NMEA autopilot on another and a GPS NMEA on another. They are always in the correct "place." The unit seems to be "RF proof," as it runs near marine radios and never flinches. —*Craig Owings, HP2XBA;* **craigo@pancall.com**

### Another USB Story

◊ I saw your request for help with USB/EIA-232 devices. I can share my experience with such a device. I first needed a multiport board to implement a small RAS modem pool for our e-mail server. I found a company called Quatech that sells such a board (Quatech, 662 Wolf Ledgers Pkwy, Akron, OH 44311; tel 800-553-1170; **www.quatech.com**; **sales@ quatech.com**). Their PCI multiport 232/485 board supports all modem lines. It has been in place now for four years.

I later had a need for a true EIA-232 port to expand a test set. I had written many *Visual Basic* programs that read torque data via a 19.2-kB standard COM port. As you stated, The old boxes (computers) had two standard COM ports COM1 and COM2. I purchased a new Compaq/HP box that had only USB ports. I went to Quatech again, and found they make USB/ 232 adapters, too. My program/hardware uses all the control lines for handshaking: RTS, CTS, CD, DSR and DTR. The adapter works flawlessly. The operating system in this case is *Windows 2000 Pro*. They (Quatech) supplied a CD that installed the drivers. (That was a bit confusing at the start because it kept reporting new hardware. That happened because it was installing a new device driver for each port.) I bought the four-port model: QSU 100. They make one-port, two-port, four-port and

DICK LICHTEL, KD4JP, AND DYER MATLOCK, N4PZM

Figure 4.2—The photo shows the 3.75 MHz output of a AD9854-based VFO that is controlled by a Microchip PIC16C745 USB microcontroller (right). The USB controller requires no additional drivers to interface with a PC.

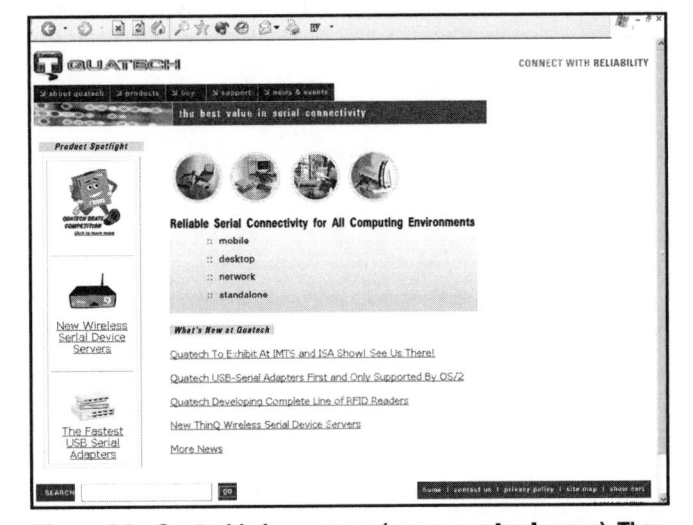

Figure 4.3—Quatech's home page (**www.quatech.com**). They supply USB/EIA-232 converters recommended by K1EHW.

16-port versions, in my case, COM3 through COM6. I set my source code to test each one, and again all lines are supported. I don't operate digital modes, but I'm sure the device will work with any rig requiring the hardware handshaking and a "STANDARD" EIA-232 interface. I hope this helps someone. **Figure 4.3** is a screen capture of Quatech's home page. —*George Peters, K1EHW, 41 Barbara Dr, Norwalk, CT 06851-5306;* **k1ehw@arrl.net**

# The Doctor is IN

**Q** Here's a question from John, KE4QK: Most previous ham radio-computer interfaces address the incompatibility of TTL (+5 V) radio serial ports with computer serial ports (–9 V) as a problem (see *The ARRL Handbook*, 1995 edition, p 22.11). I have seen several such items use the printer parallel port (LPT1) rather than the serial port for connections between the radio transceiver and the computer. Does this circumvent the problem?

**A** Yes, the printer port is TTL level compatible. A lot of software for communications, however, is written around the serial port because it gives the program more control capability (if desired, although some serial port software doesn't need it). Also, it is sometimes nice to be able to use both ports at the same time. Some contest logging software makes use of the parallel printer port for CW keying while the serial port is used for transceiver control.

**Q** Ken, WA1UMD, writes: I'm looking for a company that sells software for drawing a schematic and I couldn't find anything. I don't need design software—I already have the design. I'm looking for a way to produce a professional looking schematic without having to use drafting tools on paper. Is there anything available under $100?

**A** As you've noticed, schematic drawing software can be expensive. We use *AutoCAD* (**usa.autodesk.com**) here at *QST*, both for general drafting and schematic drawing. It offers an extensive symbol library, but it would be prohibitively expensive for an individual user and it probably offers a lot more than you'd need. Several programs that might work for a casual user are available and, best of all, two of them are free! *ExpressPCB* (**www.expresspcb.com**) is a company that offers free schematic drawing and PC board layout software.

You can download drawing software directly from their site. Another is *CircuitMaker* (**www.circuitmaker.com**). They offer circuit design, simulation and drawing software at moderate cost. A student version of their schematic software (CM 60) can be downloaded free of charge. Another source is *DeltaCad* (**www.dcad.com**). They offer general drafting software; you'll have to make your own schematic symbols, but that doesn't appear to be too difficult. Their program sells for about $40. There are more, but these should get you going.

**Q** Bob Smith, KC4WJO, asks: I am building the "Quick and Easy CW With Your PC" project, from page 22.22 of the 2004 edition of *The ARRL Handbook*.[1] I have not been able to locate the NE567CN tone decoder IC. It's not listed in the Allied, Newark or Digi-Key catalogs or at their Web sites. Can you tell me where I can find this device or if an alternate part number is available?

**A** Both the Doctor and the ARRL Technical Information Service (TIS) frequently receive questions about parts and their generic equivalents, and this is a perfect example. An IC may not be able to be found under its manufacturer specific part number, but it may be available under its generic name. In this case, the NE567CN, a phase locked loop tone decoder, is available from several sources as a different part number. It can be found at JDR Micro Devices (**www.jdr.com**) as an LM567, at Mouser Electronics (**www.mouser.com**) as a 513-NJM567D, at Ocean State Electronics (**www.oselectronics.com**) as an NE567N and at Digi-Key (**www.digikey.com**) as an LM567CN-ND.

If you're having difficulty locating a specific part, try searching for it under its generic part number. As an example, the National Semiconductor LM78M05CT TO-220 voltage regulator can be located by entering "7805" into a standard Internet search engine, then looking for the respective part data sheets.

# Chapter 5

# Troubleshooting/Test Gear

## X-RAYING A PCB WITH YOUR SCANNER

◊ Have you ever tried to draw the schematic diagram of the circuit on a medium-complexity PC board using the visual method? This is sometimes needed when you have to troubleshoot or understand a piece of equipment for which you have no schematic. The other day I was trying to do just that, and after flipping the board about 400 times, got myself thoroughly frustrated. I thought there must be a better way. A short brainstorm later, I rushed to my scanner (*not* a frequency scanner, but an HP Scanjet 6300C). Five minutes later, the problem was solved. Here's how to do it.

1. Scan *both* sides of the board, in full color and good resolution (about 120 dpi should be okay). If the board is small, you may want to enlarge the images. If the components do

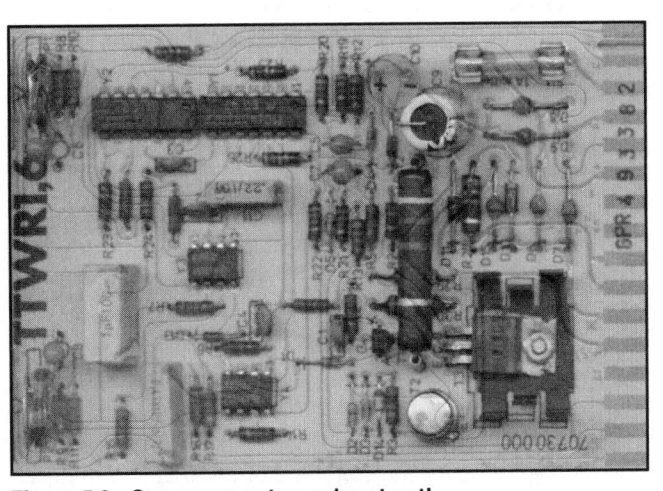

Figure 5.3—Superman, eat your heart out!

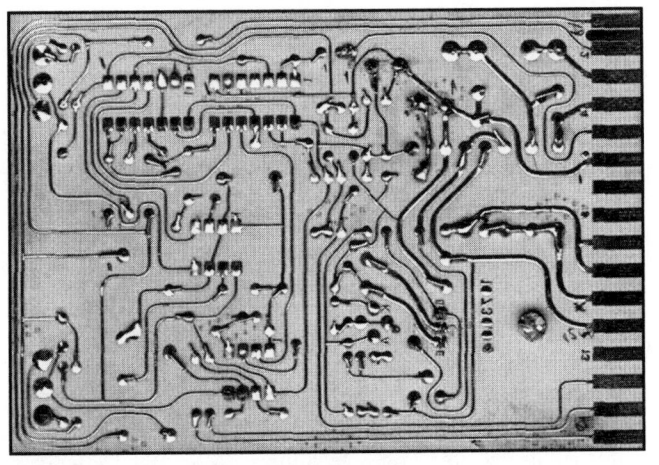

Figure 5.1—The copper side of the board.

not allow the board to lie parallel with the scanner's glass, either hold it in the right position with your hand or place something that supports the board parallel to the glass. I found that my scanner produces excellent images from 3-D objects that are not more than an inch or so deep. (I hope yours does, too!) Save the images as .TIF files. Please note that *sometimes* it helps to save the copper side as a *grayscale* (or B/W) picture, because the traces become clearer. "Experiment" is the name of the game here!

2. Now you have the images of the copper and component sides of the board (**Figures 5.1** and **5.2**, respectively). For the next step I used *CorelDRAW!* (Ver 9), although any image-processing program with the ability to apply a transparency effect to an image can be used.

Start a new file, then *import* the images into it. Position one image on top of the other, but "flip" one of them horizontally, using the MIRROR button (this has been done in Figure 5.2). Then, apply the transparency effect to both images (this is done via the GLASS button on the left). You must apply uniform (or FLAT) transparency, and vary the intensity of the effect alternately for both of the images, until you get the most satisfactory picture (**Figure 5.3**). Also, you may bring one or the other "on top" to check which order gives the best result.

3. Done! You have successfully "X-rayed" the board, and you may now instantly and effortlessly see the connections between components. You can also see the color bands of resistors and any visible values printed on the board or the other components. If you wish, print the final image and trace the connections by hand. This way, you can produce a schematic much more quickly and accurately.

Now, *why* didn't I think of this way earlier in my life? —*Tasos Thomaidis, SV8YM/2, 10, Mitr. Chrisanthou str, GR 551 32 (Kalamaria, Thessaloniki, Greece);* **sv8ym@ hotmail.com**

Figure 5.2—The component side of the board.

## BETTER FEEDLINE-LOSS MEASUREMENTS WITH ANTENNA ANALYZERS

◊ Various publications through the years have shown how the SWR measured on a shorted (or open) feed line can be used to calculate feed line attenuation. One of the claims made in the manual for my SWR analyzer is that it can be used in a similar fashion to measure feedline attenuation. While that claim is technically true, I found that those measurements are only feasible if the feed line has more than 3 dB of attenuation.

The practical concept behind the theory is simple to illustrate. We start with a transmitter feeding 1 W of incident power into a transmission line. That is, FWD = 1 in Eq 1.

If the line is shorted or open at the far end and the line attenuation is zero, 100% of the forward power becomes reflected power, making REF = 1 in Eq 1.

Since FWD = REF, the SWR calculated by the standard formula Eq 1 is infinite. (Actually any value divided by zero is undefined but in electronics, we bend the math rules to make undefined the same as infinity.)

$$SWR = \frac{1 + \sqrt{\dfrac{REF}{FWD}}}{1 - \sqrt{\dfrac{REF}{FWD}}} \qquad [Eq\ 1]$$

For similar reasons, if the feed line had infinite attenuation, all of the incident power is attenuated before it can be reflected back to the wattmeter. As a result, REF = 0 in Eq 1, and the measured SWR would be 1:1.

Zero feed line attenuation manifests itself as infinite SWR and infinite feed line attenuation shows up as 1:1 SWR. Any other attenuation values show up as SWR values between 1:1 and 8:1.

As an example, consider that a 1 W transmitter feeds a line with ¹/₂ dB attenuation. The 1 W forward power is attenuated to 891 mW by the time that it reaches the open end. The 891 mW is reflected at the open end and further reduced by the ¹/₂ dB attenuation to 794 mW as it travels back to the wattmeter. Using Eq 1, an approximate SWR of 17.4:1 is measured; that is, ¹/₂ dB correlates to an SWR of 17.4:1. **Table 5.1** shows some correlations between SWR and feed line loss.

Various charts have been created to convert SWR measurements to feed line attenuation. This was a handy method in the days when a wattmeter was a luxury and most hams only owned an SWR meter. (With a wattmeter, attenuation can be calculated directly from FWD and REF. There's no need to calculate SWR.)

Unfortunately, when I tried to use my antenna analyzer for the same measurement, I ran into a significant flaw right at the point where theory meets practice. A 3:1 SWR is the highest usable value calibrated on my antenna analyzer; an SWR of 17.4:1 is beyond the useful range of measurement.

A 3:1 SWR corresponds to a 3 dB feed line loss. Since all of my feed lines are good quality, my feed line loss is less than 1 dB. The SWR measured using my analyzer always fell somewhere between 3:1 and infinity. This made reading and estimating my feed line loss difficult to impossible using my antenna analyzer.

My solution is reasonably simple. I happened to find a 4 dB attenuator for 50 Ω line in my junk box. I connected the attenuator to the SWR analyzer and the feed line to the attenuator. If a feedline has zero attenuation, the 4 dB attenuator alone will cause the measured SWR to be approximately 2.3:1. Let's use a 1 W transmitter to prove that the reduction in SWR as measured at the transmitter is true. The 1 W FWD power is reduced

### Table 5.1
**Feed Line Loss versus SWR**

| Loss (dB) | SWR |
| --- | --- |
| 6 | 1.6:1 |
| 3 | 3.0:1 |
| 2 | 4.4:1 |
| 1 | 8.7:1 |

### Table 5.2
**SWR Equivalent to Several Attenuation Levels**

| Attenuation (dB) | Max SWR |
| --- | --- |
| 3 | 3.0:1 |
| 4 | 2.3:1 |
| 5 | 1.9:1 |
| 6 | 1.6:1 |

### Table 5.3
**Actual Line Loss and SWR fro SWR Measured with 4 dB of Attenuation**

| Line loss (dB) | SWR + 4 dB | SWR (0 dB attenuation) |
| --- | --- | --- |
| 3.0 | 1.50 | 3.0 |
| 2.0 | 1.67 | 4.4 |
| 1.0 | 1.92 | 8.7 |
| 0.75 | 2.0 | 11.6 |
| 0.50 | 2.1 | 17.4 |
| 0.25 | 2.2 | 34.8 |
| 0.10 | 2.3 | 86.9 |

by 4 dB to 398 mW when it reaches the open end. That 398 mW is reflected and then as it passes through the attenuator a second time it is reduced by an additional 4 dB to 158 mW before reaching the meter. Again using Eq 1, if FWD = 1 W and REF = 158 mW then SWR = 2.3:1. Any additional feed line loss causes the measured SWR to be reduced to less than 2.3:1 since it further reduces the REF power reaching the wattmeter.

The calculated SWR for some common attenuators and zero feed line loss is included in **Table 5.2**.

Now reconsider the original example using the 1 W transmitter connected to an open feedline with ¹/₂ dB of attenuation. Without the 4 dB attenuator, the SWR measured 17.4:1. The attenuator by itself reduces the measured SWR to 2.3:1. The 4 dB attenuator plus the additional ¹/₂ dB of feed-line loss reduces the measured SWR to approximately 2.1:1. This value falls within the usable calibration range of my antenna analyzer. **Table 5.3** provides some comparison values.

By measuring the SWR with the line connected through the attenuator, I can now get a much clearer picture of feed line attenuation. Because all of my measurements now fall within the calibrated range of my analyzer, it is now much easier to make reasonably accurate measurements of feed line attenuation.

One final point needs to be mentioned regarding the electrical length of the line being measured. Notice that an open or shorted feed line also acts as a resonant circuit. This phenomenon can affect the accuracy of your measurement. Make your measurement at a frequency where the line acts as an open circuit (maximum impedance).—*Dan Wanchic, WA8VZQ, 1209 13th St N, St Cloud, MN 56303;* **wa8vzq@arrl.net**

## SURFACE-MOUNT TEST TWEEZERS

◊ Here's a simple tool that you can easily build to quickly sort and test unmarked SMD components.

Passive surface-mount devices (SMDs) are frequently unmarked and can be difficult to test. If you use test probes and a multimeter they may flip or spin out of the probe tips when you apply pressure, which can be very frustrating.

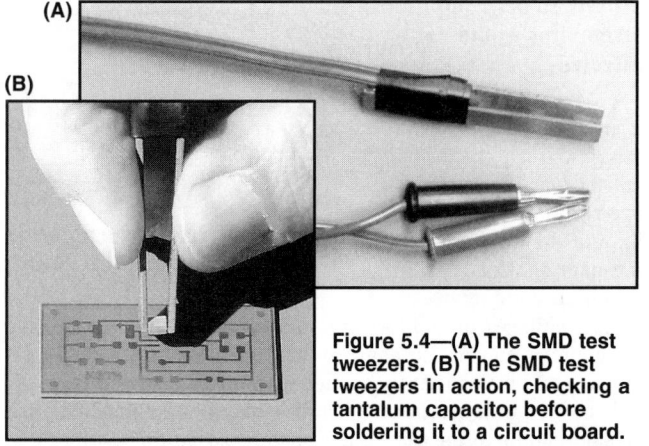

Figure 5.4—(A) The SMD test tweezers. (B) The SMD test tweezers in action, checking a tantalum capacitor before soldering it to a circuit board.

To solve that problem, build the SMD test tweezers shown in **Figure 5.4**. They grip SMD capacitors and resistors squarely, allowing for quick and easy measurements. I use these and an autoranging multimeter, such as the Craftsman model 82040 (**Figure 5.5**, about $20) to quickly double-check the value of each component before mounting it to the circuit board.

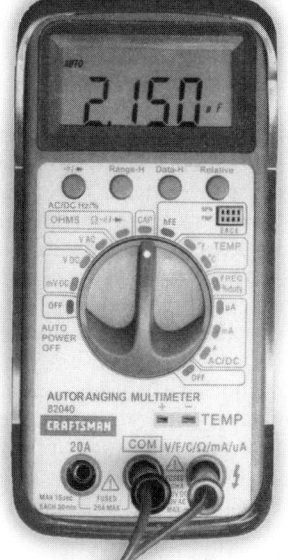

Figure 5.5—A typical autoranging DVM (Craftsman #82040) used with the SMD tweezers.

### Construction

This is an easy one-evening project. All of the parts are listed in **Table 5.4**. Cut out the parts shown in **Figures 5.6** and **5.7**. Then use a plastic abrasive pad to polish the copper side of the PC board until it is shiny. Glue the assembly (**Figure 5.8**) together with "five-minute" epoxy, making sure the foil sides face inward. After the epoxy has cured, squeeze the tweezers together and carefully sand the tips so that they are flush with each other and square. Remove

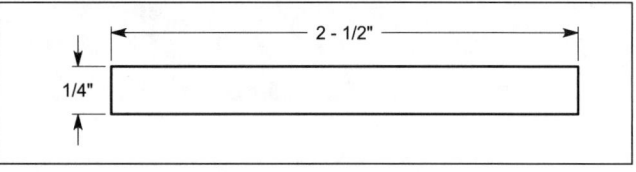

Figure 5.6— Fingers for the SMD test tweezers are made from two pieces of FR4 PC-board material.

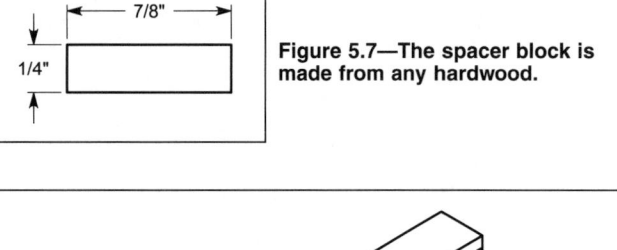

Figure 5.7—The spacer block is made from any hardwood.

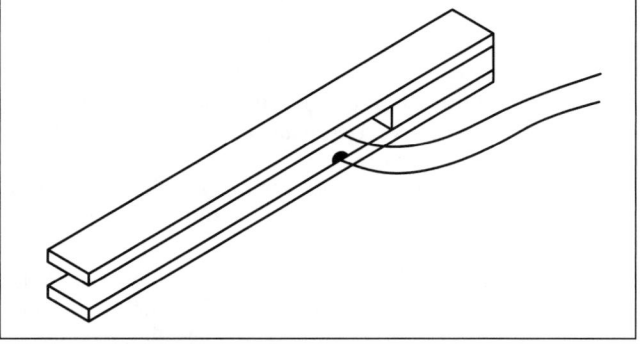

Figure 5.8—Assembly of the SMD test tweezers.

### Table 5.4
### SMD Tweezers Parts List

| Qty | Description |
|---|---|
| 2 | $2^{1}/_{2} \times ^{1}/_{4}$ inch FR4 circuit board |
| 1 | $^{1}/_{4}$-inch-square by $^{7}/_{8}$-inch-long hardwood block |
| 2 | Test leads, about 12 inches long |
| 2 | Plugs to fit your multimeter |

any sanding burrs from the ends with a small file. Next, carefully solder (don't overheat the epoxy) the test leads to the foil. Finish the tweezers with heat-shrink tubing or electrical tape arranged to dress the wires out of the way. Keep the multimeter leads short to minimize stray capacitance.

To use the tweezers, simply connect them to an autoranging meter and grip the SMD. Very rapid measurements are possible using this simple tool.—*Dean F. Poeth II, K8TM, 218 Gower Rd, Schenectady, NY 12302;* **www.Poeth.com***;* **dpoeth@worldnet.att.net**

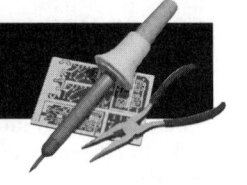

**Q** Thomas, N2YTF, has a troubleshooting question: Yesterday I bought an RF Concepts 4-32 440 20W RF amp used at my club's hamfest. At first it worked just fine, putting out 30 W with the max 5 W input. The built in GaAsFET worked well also (the GaAsFET can be switched in and out independently of the power amp section).

Within 10 minutes of light on-off use on 432, trouble developed with the preamp. Now when switched in, received signal strength drops significantly. Power output and operation without the preamp seems just fine.

I'm curious as to just what happened. Nothing looks bad inside the amp; there was no smoke or noise, as far as I could tell. Did transmit power fry the GaAsFET or is it more likely that there is a relay failure somewhere along the way? If the GaAsFET is fried what would I expect? I have a schematic for the amp. I only paid $25 for it, and although I don't have any electronic engineering experience, I would like to try diagnosing/repairing this amp or learn trying.

**A** This problem could be a stuck relay or a bad FET. On SSB, the rig's VOX circuitry or the amp's RF switching may cycle that relay on and off a lot. Transistor failure is quite common with modern RF switched preamplifiers and SSB. The output of the preamp sees a huge amount of power everytime you transmit enough power to switch the amp into transmit. If the relay doesn't switch fast enough the GaAsFET will fry. Old-fashioned JFETs are much more rugged, but don't offer the low noise performance possible with GaAsFETs. If that old amp has not been used a lot, the relay may have been a bit sluggish and may not have switched fast enough. The result may be a bad GaAsFET. The easiest way to diagnose the GaAsFET is to substitute another. Try Mouser (**www.mouser.com**) or Down East Microwave (**www.downeastmicrowave.com**).

To test the relays, you can simply measure across their contacts with an ohmmeter. You could also temporarily solder wire jumpers across them and try using the amp in receive only.

If the amp is an older unit and if the FET looks like it has been replaced before, there may be some sort of intermittent problem with the switching circuitry that caused the FET to fail—unfortunately, this can be very difficult to diagnose. I would replace the relays and all transistors and diodes associated with controlling the relay. Replacing power supply bypass capacitors might be a good idea as well.

One way to avoid this problem is to hard wire a push to talk (PTT) connection, so the amplifier switches when you press the PTT switch, before any RF is generated.

Finally, $25 for the amp was a good deal. And the Doctor is pleased to hear you're willing to tackle the repair. This is one of many "real" things you can do with ham radio!

**Q** Roy Burris, N4NYJ, writes the following: My cousin wants to have a working computer; the big problem is that something is causing the lights in her house to flicker too often. About 2½ months ago, she was using her computer when the house lights started to flicker more than she had ever seen them do before. The computer and the monitor both went dead and neither has worked since. Do you have any idea how the voltage from the wall outlet to her

outlet strip could be stabilized, so her computer or monitor would not be affected?

**A** My primary concern would be an intermittency within the house wiring. One of several failure modes can occur. Should the connection to the neutral wire be compromised at the service entrance, voltages on a 115

Figure 5.9—A simple electrical outlet tester can identify many local ac wiring problems.

V ac circuit can rise to dangerous levels, as the 230 V ac service input is intermittently applied across two load branches on either side of the neutral, which now may not be connected to ground and/or to the center tap of the service transformer. In older services, a local ground may not be present and the only ground wire is the neutral connection, which is usually grounded at the service entrance. These intermittent conditions can damage appliances such as a computer, but more importantly, they can present a potentially serious shock hazard. One telltale symptom occurs when the lights flicker—they can actually get brighter (rather than dimmer) than their normal "on-state." My suggestion would be to have the house wiring checked by a licensed electrician as soon as possible. *Do not*, unless you are qualified to do so, get into the sub-panel service entrance…those voltages can be lethal and are always "hot."

A good idea would be to purchase an electrical outlet checker and polarity tester, as shown in **Figure 5.9**. These can be obtained at most electrical or building supply houses for a few dollars. They will warn you about crossed neutral-ground connections, switched hot-grounds, open neutrals and grounds and other local service wiring problems.

As far as protection for computer gear is concerned, try an ac line transient suppressor, otherwise known as a "surge suppressor." It can protect the equipment from excessive "spike" voltages on the ac line, but will do nothing for the intermittent house wiring we spoke about. Nor will it protect against low line voltages (so-called "brownouts"). The Doctor also needs to caution you about using light-duty computer "surge suppressors" with high current amateur transmitters. These devices are frequently not robust enough to handle the ac current demands of higher power amateur gear and may be built with poorly constructed ac outlets designed for relatively low current loads. Look for one that has at least a 15 A load rating.

An excellent stabilization technique for computer equipment (and amateur equipment, for that

Figure 5.10—An Uninterruptible Power Supply (UPS) can correct for many line voltage level changes, spikes, line transients and outages. The better ones produce a sine waveform.

matter, if the rating is high enough) is an Uninterruptible Power Supply or UPS. These will produce an ac output voltage of the correct (115 $V_{rms}$ ac) level, regardless of input line level fluctuations. They are usually designed as "zero-crossing" devices, which means they switch on at the input sine wave polarity transition and there's no output voltage turn-on "glitch" (thus the term "uninterruptible"). Good ones produce a sine-wave or a near sine-wave output waveform synchronized to the ac line frequency and they generally have transient suppression built in. **Figure 5.10** shows a high quality UPS. Try to stay away from those that generate a modified square wave output and test any prospective UPS candidate for RFI susceptibility. Some of these can be affected by RF energy from nearby transmitters and antennas. Good luck!

**Q** Here's a question from David, KC2JD: I need to calibrate my VTVM (vacuum tube voltmeter). I remember that I used to use a new mercury cell as a standard because they were an accurate 1.35 V dc. Since mercury cells are long off the market, is there a good replacement?

**A** The easy route is to borrow a good digital VOM and use it as a secondary reference. Today's better DVMs sport accuracies as high as ±0.025% and this will certainly be sufficient for your VTVM. Another way to go is to measure a fresh cell (battery) with that DVM and use the known cell voltage to calibrate the VTVM. You'd actually be employing a form of *transfer metrology*, in which you transfer a known measurement to calibrate an instrument.

Additionally, precision voltage regulator ICs have gotten better and cheaper. Perhaps the National LM4041 IC would meet your requirements. This has a reference voltage of 1.225 V dc and good accuracy. Point your Web browser to **www.national.com/pf/LM/LM4041.html**. You may also be able to obtain some true metrology voltage standards on the surplus market. These occasionally surface. Good luck!

**Q** Dale, N8MI, writes: I built an older transmitter from the 1955 edition of *The ARRL Handbook*, page 158. The B+ voltage is 365 V dc. My problem is that I can't get the final (a 6L6) to draw more than 35 mA of plate current at resonance. This is into a 50 Ω resistive load. I noticed that the screen voltage was low, so I paralleled a 10 kΩ resistor with the 18 kΩ screen resistor. This brought the plate current up to 45 mA, but according to the article, the 6L6 should load to at least 75 mA. The power supply is capable of delivering 90 mA because it will draw that out of resonance. Does the Q of the PA tank circuit affect the plate current?

**A** No, the Q of the PA tank circuit does not affect the plate current, as long as the ratio of the unloaded to loaded Q is enough to effect the desired impedance transformation. However, I would carefully check the final plate coil and the output coupling coil (L1 and L2 in the original circuit). You may not be getting enough coupling between the coils, even though the number of turns is the same. You probably need to increase the number of turns on L2 until the final amplifier draws the desired plate current (75-100 mA) at resonance.

Also, I would advise that you bring the screen resistor up in value a bit. With the original screen resistor bypassed with 10 kΩ, you now have about 6.4 kΩ in the screen supply and

you may be coming close to exceeding the maximum screen dissipation rating of the 6L6 (3.5 W). The maximum rated screen voltage for a 6L6 is 300 V—measure it and the screen current to be sure. Adding turns to the output coupling coil (L2) will probably affect the point of resonance of the final plate tuning capacitor, as well as increasing the coupling. A swinging output coupling link or a capacitor in series with L2 would afford an easy way to get variable output coupling without messing with turns (that's how they did it in the "old" days). Have fun with that vintage transmitter!

**Q** From Lou, W8VU, comes the following: I've got a transmitter problem, and would like a diagnosis. I am restoring a Johnson Viking Valiant, and I have a problem. After tuning up the transmitter in CW with plate current dipped, and the output loaded to the recommended values into a dummy load, tuning the final to resonance (going past the plate current "dip"), the output power actually *increases*! I've neutralized the finals but I'm not 100% confident that it's perfect. At the dip, with plate current at the recommended value, I cannot get the nominal output power of 200 W. Tuning off the dip, however, the output jumps to the nominal value of 200 W. Can you prescribe a course of treatment to cure this ailment?

**A** The condition you describe is generally attributable to parasitic oscillation or a neutralization problem in the final amplifier. You say that you're not entirely confident that the neutralization is correct and I would suspect that it's not. Neutralization is particularly critical at the higher frequencies and even more so with multiple tube finals (which the Valiant has—with three 6146s). Try adjusting the neutralization capacitor to make maximum power coincide with minimum plate current. Make sure you turn off the plate voltage before you do this! Get it close by ensuring that there is no grid current change with variance of the plate capacitor—remove plate and screen voltage from the amplifier—but apply excitation (drive) to the final. Do this on 10 or 15 meters.

Be sure that all the final tubes are of the same type; *do not* intermix type 6146B tubes with 6146 or 6146A types. The "B" type tubes have different interelectrode capacitances and require different neutralization parameters. Also check the parasitic suppressors in all three final amplifier plate leads—make sure that the suppressor chokes are well soldered. A cold joint here could account for a parasitic in one tube.

Neutralization can be checked by connecting a low-level signal source to the transmitter output (an RF analyzer). Tune the pi-network (*tune* and *load* capacitors) for a 1:1 SWR on the analyzer, then couple a receiver (through a link or a capacitor) to the final amplifier input grid circuit and detune the neutralization capacitor. Maximize the received signal appearing at the grid circuit with the plate tune and load capacitors; then adjust the neutralization capacitor for minimum response (feedthrough) at the receiver. Do this with the plate and screen voltage *off*.

If you eliminate all parasitics and carefully neutralize the final amplifier, maximum power should coincide with minimum plate current. As an aside, you also might want to check that the three final amplifier tubes are reasonably well matched as far as grid and plate characteristics and transconductance are concerned. Good luck!

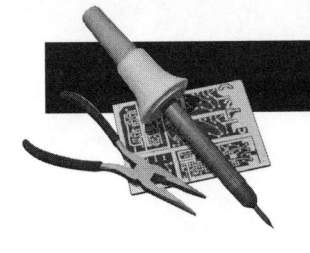

# Chapter 6

# Restoration

## BATTERY LEAKAGE REMOVER

◊ At one time or another, most of us have left batteries in a device for too long—only to open the device and find a mess. This happened to me recently and I tried a product now widely available called "CLR" (an acronym for calcium, lime and rust). It comes as a liquid and a spray foam. I sprayed CLR on the battery holder section of the equipment case and the mess went away in less than five minutes. After a quick rinse and air dry the battery compartment was clean. I then attacked the battery-negative contact spring, which was covered with battery drainage and rust. Again, in five minutes it was clean. I lightly sanded the contact point and reassembled the device. It works fine. The repair was cheap, quick and effective!
—*Dave Routzon, W5GT, 6917 Post Oak Dr, North Richland Hills, TX 76180-3418;* **w5gt@arrl.net**

## SAVING "FOGGED" PLASTIC

◊ In attempting to clean equipment, volatile and potentially harmful substances are often used—not only to your health—but also to the equipment. While cleaning some nearby gear on my bench I was not aware that a plastic cross-needle SWR meter in an MFJ Versa Tuner accidentally became "fogged." Thinking the meter worthless, I further exacerbated the problem by spraying cleaner on the plastic cover, as I tried to "buff" out the plastic, but it only made matters worse. But before tossing it in the junk box I came upon a procedure that refurbished the plastic cover, making it as clear as new and essentially rendering it "crystal clear."

I have an erasing pencil (a long soft white eraser, a Pentel "Clic" eraser). With 5 minutes of very easy labor, I was able to erase the fogged plastic cover and make it as bright and clear as it was when new. I believe the eraser material is available in other form factors as well; the pencil style is not a requirement.—*Robert Cowan, WB6DAC, 2740 Canary Dr, Costa Mesa, CA 92626;* **wb6dac@attbi.com**

**Q** Here's an interesting question from Woody, K4JWP: I'm looking for a 525 kHz quartz crystal needed for the restoration of my 1935 Single Signal Superhet receiver. I built this receiver, at the time, from its description in the May 1935 issue of *QST*. My crystal was in a Bliley holder. The crystal was cube shaped, as I recall. Unfortunately, it disappeared when I was away during WW II. Now the main obstacle to restoration of the receiver is finding a suitable crystal. I believe that a 455 kHz quartz (or ceramic) crystal might work.

**A** There are several routes to go. First, it may be relatively easy to find a 455 kHz crystal from an older receiver. These were quite popular and were used in crystal filters in receivers of the '40s and '50s. If you can find one of these, it should be possible for you to shift the IF frequency 70 kHz lower in frequency by a slight change in local oscillator frequency and then re-tune the IF amplifiers. I note that the IF transformers are 500 kHz types and are shunted by 100 pF trimmers. If a 455 kHz crystal is used in the crystal filter, try putting an additional 27 pF capacitor across the trimmers of the IF transformers and re-tune the IFs for 455 kHz. You would also have to re-tune the beat frequency oscillator (BFO), but that shouldn't be a problem.

Another possibility is to re-grind a 455 kHz crystal to 500 kHz. *QST* has published many articles on crystal grinding, and this is not as difficult to do as you might think. The ARRL Periodicals Search Web site will help (**www.arrl.org/members-only/qqnsearch.html**). The IF transformers should easily tune to 500 kHz, as they were originally designed for that frequency.

Crystals are still custom ground by manufacturers such as JAN Crystals (**www.jancrystals.com**) and International Crystal Manufacturing Co (**www.icmfg.com/crystals.html**). If you supply them with a suitable holder, they might even be able to grind a blank to fit that holder. Your original crystal or at least a holder for it may be able to be found at a hamfest or on eBay or the several reflectors and newsgroups on the Web that are devoted to antique radio and "boatanchor" equipment.

**Q** Carl, K4VVX, writes: I need an opinion/explanation on building parasitic suppressors for HF amplifiers (tube type). Carbon composition resistors are getting difficult to find. I understand the need for low inductive resistance. I am restoring an old amplifier that I built about 25 years ago and need to replace the old overheated and broken parasitic suppressors. Are carbon film and carbon composition resistors interchangeable for this application?

**A** Whether or not they are interchangeable depends on the style and manufacture of the particular resistor and its characteristics. While the low frequency measurement is a good sign, the real question is the impedance at the frequency in which parasitics are likely to occur—60 to 120 MHz. I'd suggest repeating the measurement with an RF instrument, such as an RF impedance bridge.

The resistor's time constant (t), parasitic inductance ($L_p$) and resistance (R) determines the HF limit of the resistor and $\tau = L_p/R$. For a parasitic inductance of 100 nH ($100 \times 10^{-9}$ H) and a resistance of 47 $\Omega$, the upper break frequency, $f = 1/(2\pi\tau)$, is about 75 MHz.

Another issue is the ability to handle overloads—something that carbon composition does much better than carbon film. Metal oxide resistors seem to have reasonably low inductance, excellent overload capabilities, and they do make good VHF dummy loads, but I'm not aware of anyone who has used them for parasitic suppressors. Good luck!

# Chapter 7

# Construction/Maintenance

## MORE ON SALVAGING PARTS FROM PC BOARDS

◊ With no intent to show disrespect to Steve, W7VEW, his suggestion in Hints & Kinks (Nov 2002, p 69) is a downright dangerous and environmentally bad practice.

Steve suggests we recover parts from PC boards by sanding the solder from the solder side of the PC board until the parts fall from the other side. While he cautions readers to use eye and breathing protection during the work, he neglects the fact that the sanding process generates large numbers of small, even microscopic, particles of lead-bearing solder. This presents a human and environmental hazard that extends beyond the time that the process is being conducted.

Such particles will contaminate the work area. They can be picked up on one's hands, feet and clothing later, from where they can eventually be inadvertently transferred to one's mouth and/or eyes. The particles can also be stirred up with other dust by physical activity, or even air currents, and, once airborne, are subject to inhalation at a later time by the ham, his/her family, visitors or pets. Either method of exposure can result in lead poisoning, which is cumulative over time and amount of exposure.

Even if one could be sure that one vacuumed up absolutely all of these particles, when the shop vacuum is emptied, where does the solder go? Into some landfill or other dumping site, where it will contaminate the soil and ground water supply.

While this method may seem convenient, I would caution readers to *not* use it for the reasons I've listed above. The heat-gun method is much safer, even if slightly less convenient.

Readers should also remember that PC boards and other equipment containing solder should be recycled in an appropriate fashion, rather than being discarded in landfills. Check with your local or state government for electronic-equipment recycling programs that are designed to keep lead out of the environment.

Let's not keep dumping lead into our environment to pollute the soil and our ground water supplies.—*Carl R. Stevenson, WK3C, 4991 Shimerville Rd, Emmaus, PA 18049; wk3c@fast.net*

## MORE ON HOMEBREW LABELS

◊ I've read John Bandy's suggestion in Hints and Kinks (Sep 2000, p 69) on how to prepare professional looking labels for home built equipment. I have a variation that I believe is somewhat easier.

Using a laser printer, print the desired label on a #5660 Avery clear laser label. Normally, I trim the label to fit the need, so after printing instead of peeling the label off the backing I carefully cut the label and the backing away from the rest of the labels with scissors. Then trim the label to size, peel it away it from the backing and attach it to the equipment. This proce-

dure avoids the photocopy and glue steps in John's procedure. —*Bryant C. Winchell, W2RGG, 2901 Via Alvarado, Palos Verdes Estates, CA 90274;* **bryantcw@cox.net**

## AN IMPROVISED RESISTOR

◊ A week or so before Field Day, I decided that I wanted to try something other than a dipole as an antenna. Living in the Pacific Northwest, I recognized that the vast majority of my QSOs would occur to my east and south. With limited time and a limited budget, construction of a multiband Yagi wasn't feasible.

Looking through a 1965 antenna guide, I came across a seemingly suitable design for a long-wire, terminated V antenna. The radiation pattern for this antenna consisted of a long main lobe and a virtually nonexistent rear lobe. On 20 meters, using leg lengths of 2 λ, the guide estimated power gains of around 8 dBd. Further, because this antenna is terminated (a "traveling wave" design), exact radiator lengths are not critical, giving it a fairly broad bandwidth.

So, I built the antenna, coiled my coax to form a balun and went in search of terminating resistors. The article suggested using non-inductive terminating resistors of about 500 Ω, each capable of dissipating $^1/_3$ of the transmitter power. Another

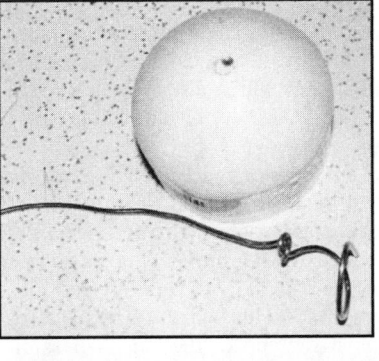

(A)

Figure 7.1—At A, the formed lower terminal and the drilled end cap. At B, the terminal has been inserted in the drilled cap and secured with silicone sealant.

(B)

article I read on this design suggested using resistors between 600-1000 Ω. To play it safe, I looked for 750-Ω resistors. My old Yaesu FT-107 can produce a maximum output of about 120 W, so the resistors must sink 40 W each.

With time running out, I searched RadioShack and local home-improvement stores for a resistor matching these specifications. Woe, my efforts were in vain.

The *Army Ranger Handbook*[1] discusses improvising resistors for long-wire antennas by putting a saltwater solution into an earplug case. Saltwater is a decent conductor whose resistance can be altered by changing the salinity of the solution. With this idea, I set out to build my own power resistors.

My main concern was the power capacity of the resistors. I wasn't concerned about burning out the resistors because (1) saltwater is cheap to replace, (2) destruction of the resistors would be immediately noticeable by a dramatic change in SWR, and (3) water doesn't burn. However, water *does* boil, and this could change the resistance or cause the enclosures to explode. Because of this, I decided to make the resistors with a much larger power-handling capacity than necessary.

One gram of water requires one calorie of heat to increase its temperature by one degree Celsius. One calorie is equal to 4.186 Joules. A watt is 1 J/s, or 4.186 cal/s.

Assuming that the temperature of the resistor starts at 20°C (about 70°F) and it boils at 100°C, its temperature can change up to 80°C. For a single gram of water, this will require the addition of 80 calories, which is about 335 Joules. This means that a single gram of water could absorb 40 W for about 8.3 seconds before boiling[2] (without cooling).

Assuming that I would transmit at maximum power for no longer than two minutes, each of my resistors would have to absorb 40 W×120 s = 4800 J. This converts to 4800 J/4.186 J/cal = 1147 cal. Again, assuming the temperature goes from 20°C to 100°C, the resistors would require a minimum of 1147 cal/80°C = 14 g (14 ml) of water. Again, this equation disregards cooling effects.

With such a relatively small amount of water being required for my worst-case scenario, it would be practical to exceed this volume by a couple of orders of magnitude.

After a few quick calculations, I headed to the hardware store where I bought 4 feet of 2-inch (OD), schedule 200 PVC pipe, four 2-inch end caps and a tube of silicone sealant. I chose the schedule 200 PVC because it is cheaper than schedule 40 and because it has thinner walls, allowing more rapid cooling of the saltwater. The 200 PVC is more than strong enough for this application.

For each resistor, I used a 2-foot-long piece of PVC. I drilled a $^3/_{32}$-inch-diameter hole in each of the end caps. I then cut two pieces of #12 AWG bare solid-copper wire and tied a knot about 4 inches from one end. The knot prevents the wire from pulling out of the end cap.

I coiled the short end of one of the wires so that the exposed conductor was as near the end of the cap as possible. Since the entire coil will be exposed to a conductor (saltwater) at roughly the same potential, the coil shouldn't act as an inductor. The length of wire here is not critical, just leave enough so that, as the saltwater corrodes the copper, you'll still have sufficient surface area on the wire to conduct.

I left the other wire straight. This wire goes on top of the resistor (assuming the resistor is placed vertically). The long wire ensures that if some of the water escapes the resistor,

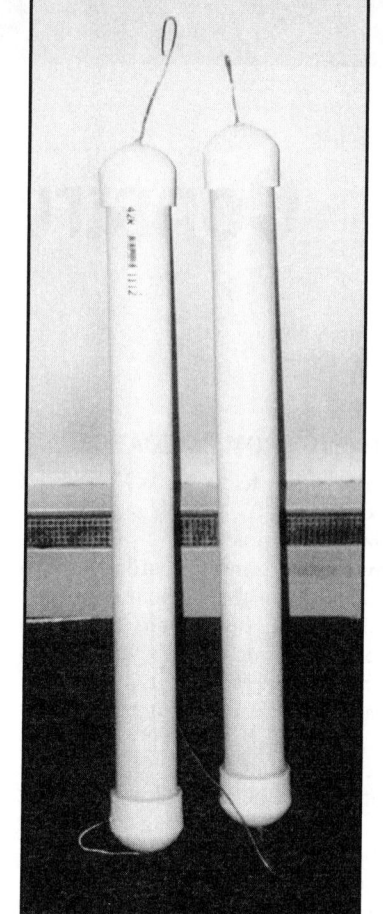

Figure 7.2—A pair of finished termination resistors.

enough of the wire will contact the water to conduct.

The long end of each wire was then fed through the end caps from the inside (see **Figure 7.1**). A liberal amount of silicone sealant was applied to seal the hole with the coiled wire. Seal both the inside and outside of the hole, but try to seal only the hole. Don't coat the entire wire, or it won't make contact with the saltwater. I allowed this cap to dry over night, added more silicone to the hole, and then secured this end cap on the pipe with silicone to keep it from leaking. This cap is the bottom of the resistor.

Note that I did not silicone the cap with the straight wire. You'll need a small vent when you put this cap on or it may pop right back off, especially if the resistor heats up. I let the pipe assembly dry overnight before mixing the saltwater.

The specific ratio of salt to water you should use is a complicated formula. Instead, I chose a less scientific, albeit effective method: Take a bunch of water and add a bunch of salt.

I boiled the solution to ensure that as much of the salt as possible would dissolve in the water. After it cooled, I poured the solution into the pipe, put the top cap (the one with the straight wire on it) on the pipe, and measured the resistance between the two wires with a VOM. I then adjusted the resistance as follows:

If the resistance of the solution is too high, pour it back into the pot you boiled it in, add salt, simmer and try it again. I don't recommend just adding salt to the pipe since it might take some time to completely dissolve, thus changing the resistance over time.

If the resistance is too low, pour some of the solution back in the pot, add water to the pipe, shake well, and measure it again. Note that you *can* add water do the pipe, since the salt in the pipe is already dissolved. Adding water simply dilutes the mixture, but you should ensure that the water and saltwater are thoroughly mixed.

After repeating the above steps three or four times, I read a resistance of about 750 Ω. I pushed the top cap onto the pipe (without silicone, so I could disassemble it later) so that it could support the resistor's weight when hung by the top conductor. The products are shown in **Figure 7.2**.

After operating for 12 hours, the resistors' values were still right where they belonged, *and* they were cool to the touch. The terminated V worked amazingly well using these resistors. I created a pair of high-power resistors for about $7!

I don't recommend using this type of resistor for anything really critical or expensive. However for antennas, where you

[1]*Ranger Handbook* by Department of Army (Apple Pie Publishers, LLC; ISBN: 0967512344).

[2]This formula is greatly simplified. It ignores cooling effects by the atmosphere and disregards the latent heat of vaporization, which would require an additional 2.3 J/ml to boil.

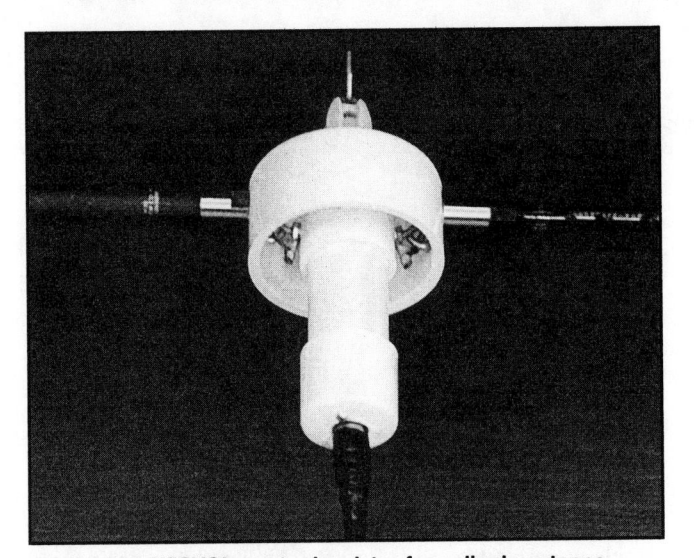

Figure 7.3—KØOVQ's center insulator for a dipole antenna made from two Hamstick whips.

get goofy impedances whenever elevation changes, it rains, or a particularly large bird flies overhead, this design is more than adequate.—*Scott Baker, AC7JC, 210 NW Anthony St #5, Pullman, WA 99163;* **srbi24@mail.wsu.edu**

## AN INSULATOR FOR WHIP DIPOLES

◊ Because of limited real-estate size and an unfortunate placement of overhead power lines, my HF antenna space is confined to a spot under the eaves only 20 feet in length and a mere 11 feet off the ground. I put a 10-meter wire dipole in the space, and it worked remarkably well, but as sunspots waned, I looked for a way to get on other bands. I decided to try two 20-meter Hamstick mobile antennas in a dipole configuration—certainly not an original idea.

In my case, the appeal is that Hamsticks are available for all the popular HF bands, and all are roughly the same length (about 7 feet). I could switch bands with a couple of wrenches and a relatively short ladder. My problem was that the commercial mounting brackets available for the purpose didn't suit my needs. I wanted a 1:1 balun at the feedpoint to limit feed-line radiation.

My solution was a Van Gorden balun with a top cover fashioned from a PVC cap for 3-inch ID pipe (**Figure 7.3**). I drilled a ⅝-inch hole in the top of the cap to clear the upper eyebolt and used a rotary tool to cut shallow grooves inside the cap that clear the side eyebolts. The antenna mounts are taken from RadioShack #21-961 feedthrough adapters (**www.radioshack.com**). I replaced the SO-239 sockets with short ⅜×24 bolts and solder lugs. Before soldering the balun to the mounts, I fastened the PVC cap in place with epoxy cement. (Tip: Use slow-drying epoxy so you can align the pieces carefully.)

The assembly hangs from an egg insulator. Rigid insulators and nylon cable ties near the center of each Hamstick prevent rotation in the wind.

My SWR is 1.1:1 in the center of the 20-meter phone band. The 2:1 bandwidth is 200 kHz. My first contact produced a 20-over-9 report from California. Subsequent reports have been entirely satisfactory.—*Roy A. Raney, KØOVQ, 600 Jackson St, Denver, CO 80206-4545;* **k0ovq@arrl.net**

## A PUSH-BUTTON MEMORY ANTENNA TUNER FOR $2!

◊ When I travel, I like to take along a simple, lightweight dipole. It usually serves my needs for average operation within a limited timeframe. Without fail, however, I always seem to

hear more activity on a band *not* covered by that particular antenna. Perhaps suddenly, one band goes dead and a different band springs to life! With (literally) all the "ups and downs" involved, changing bands or fine-tuning a dipole antenna can be a real pain, particularly in a vacation situation. It all adds up to lost operating time and increased frustration.

At home, my multiband antenna and autotuner provide me with push-button tuning. Traveling dictates small size and convenience, however, so I seldom haul along a tuner. Consequently, I quickly tire of wrapping, unwrapping and rewrapping wire dipole ends, measuring the resonant frequency, then doing it all over again. Plowing through the tuning process, the ends of the antenna wire always become twisted and kinked making adjustment increasingly difficult. One day, I stumbled onto a nifty solution to speed the tedious task of dipole tuning and found I had the basis for an inexpensive, multiband travel antenna as well.

While strolling with my wife through her favorite sewing store (trying *very hard* not to look bored), I noticed a package of the familiar little barrel-shaped, spring-loaded retainers used to keep drawstrings from pulling out. Commonly called "cord stops" or "stoppers," the devices are about an inch long, made of metal or plastic and, typically, shaped like a little barrel or antique milk can (see **Figure 7.4**). They have a single hole through the side to accommodate the drawstring and an internal spring to hold it snugly closed. You squeeze the two ends of the barrel together to release pressure on the drawstring, then reposition it. When you release pressure, it locks down on the drawstring again.

It occurred to me that these inexpensive retainers could easily hold the desired "resonant" position of a dipole-antenna end (similar to the cable clamps on a tower's guy wires), if the antenna wire were reasonably flexible. So, I bought a pack of "stoppers" for $2 and spent the rest of the day at the workbench experimenting. Since discovering these neat little retainers, I have used them on all kinds of portable and attic dipoles.

You can build a pocketsize, multiband travel dipole using cord stoppers. I have had particularly good results with Flex-Weave[3] bare antenna wire because the cord stoppers grip the Flex-Weave well and the wire is very travel-friendly.

Calculate the length of the element for the *lowest* frequency on which you want to operate. Cut two lengths of Flex-Weave 8-10 inches longer than your calculated element length and slip two or three "stoppers" onto each leg (see **Figure 7.5**). Pass the tip of the wire through the end insulator and fold it back along itself. Next, slide one "stopper" down the antenna element wire, (encompassing the excess wire as well), and right up against the end insulator. Wrap the wire once, *lightly* around itself and place another "stopper" at the tip of the excess wire, clamping it to the element wire.

[3]Flex-Weave is available from Radio-Ware, PO Box 209, Rindge, NH 03461; tel 800-457-7373; **www.radio-ware.com**.

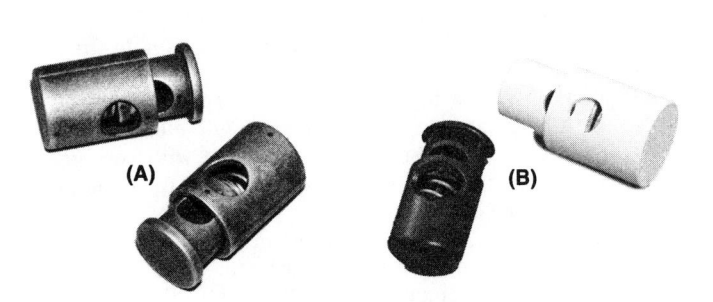

Figure 7.4—Metal (A) and plastic (B) push-button cord holders can be found at local sewing shops and outdoor stores.

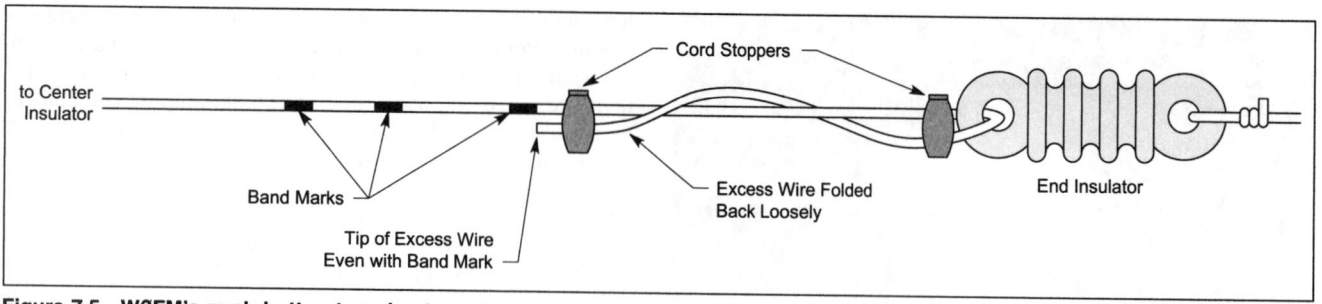

Figure 7.5—WØFM's push-button tuned antenna.

Fine-tune the length for minimum SWR on the lowest operating band of interest (longest element length) by releasing the "stopper" and slightly changing the element length as needed. Then, reposition the "stoppers" with one flush against the end insulator and another one at the tip of the folded-back wire, clamping the tip of the excess wire against the element wire. This shorts the wire out right at the end insulator, where it's folded back on itself, and, finally, at the other "stopper" at the tip of the excess wire. Therefore, all excess wire is electrically cancelled from the antenna's element length, but it's still available if you need to lower the frequency later.

Next, we borrow an age-old trick. Mark the point where the tip of the folded-back wire ends up on the element leg with tape or a permanent marker. This is the "memory" position for your lowest frequency band. Then, adjust (shorten) the antenna for the next *highest* frequency of interest, and, again, mark the spot where the folded-back wire tip ends up on the element. For example, the outer-most mark on each leg could indicate resonance on, say, 17 meters, the next mark toward the feed point might indicate 15 meters and the mark closest to the feed point could indicate 12 meters. You might do CW and SSB frequencies within the same band. Whatever your pleasure.

The marks on the wire, combined with the "stoppers," now provide for fast, easy "memory tuning" of a single dipole for multiband use! When you want to readjust the antenna's resonant frequency, simply position the innermost "stopper" just outside the desired band mark. Press the button to release the stopper and pull the antenna wire through the stopper to align the tip with the desired band mark. Then, simply reposition and release the outer stopper at the insulator, and *voila!* Your antenna is tuned for the new frequency.

"Stoppers" work best with center-supported dipoles or inverted Vs, where there is minimal pull at the ends of the antenna. Obviously, a heavy 80-meter dipole supporting the weight of the center insulator and feed line might not be a good candidate for the cord-stopper trick. Nonetheless, I have supported some reasonably heavy dipoles in my attic using three stoppers at the end of each antenna leg. (Thankfully, high winds and ice loading have yet to be an issue *inside* my attic!)

Operating from a hotel room during vacations to Grand Cayman, I have used stoppers to tune a single-element dipole for 20-17-15-12 and 10 meters, quickly and with very good results. This technique would also seem good for Field Day or QRP backpacking.

Add a "stopper" antenna to your travel bag. Imagine the looks when you tell your friends that you've built a multiband, push-button memory tuner for 2 bucks!—*Terry Schieler, WØFM, 104 Ladue Woods Estates Dr, St Louis, MO 63141; w0fm@arrl.net*

## A CURE FOR WORN LABELS

◊ I have one very well used handheld with the silk-screened labels worn off the keys. Because the key labels are gone, I could not figure out how to reprogram it when I decided to use it again. Several of the keys have multiple functions, so it is often necessary to refer to the manual when programming seldom-used functions. How could I read the keys and buttons? I went back through my old issues of *QST* to find the beautiful color advertisements for that model and clipped one out. I laminated it with clear plastic and presto! I can now look at the key labels on the picture while checking the manual and program the radio.

I have now done this for all of my equipment. I can read the labels now, but in a few years when those keys have the lettering rubbed off I will be able to check against the pictures from the advertisements.—*Avery M. Finn, KØHLA, PO Box 53, Hopkins, MN 55343-0053;* k0hla@arrl.net

## WILL IT FIT?

◊ Before committing a PC-board design to copper, I often print a component-side view on plain paper and glue it to a sheet of thin cardboard. I then punch holes with a sharp stylus and mount the major components (using TTL ICs as stand-ins for any CMOS devices).

This helps me verify that there's adequate clearance between components and between components and the enclo-

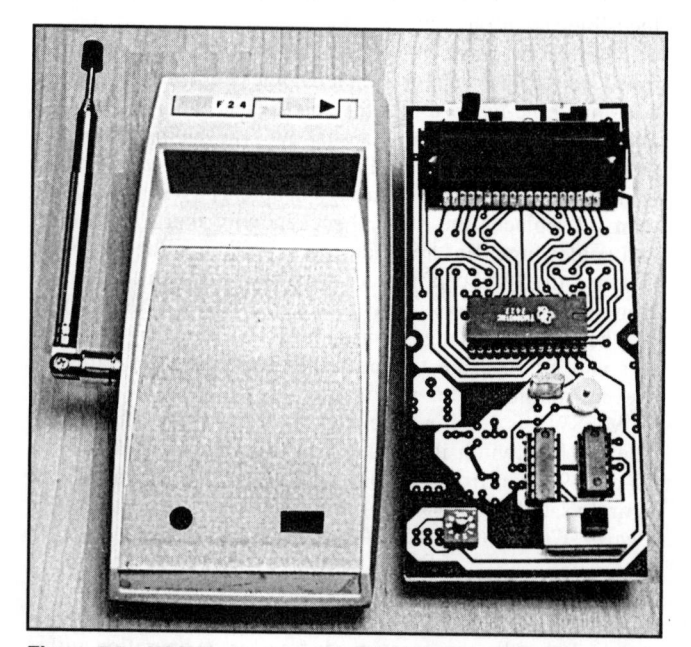

Figure 7.6—KØOVQ checks packaging issues with a paper and cardboard circuit.

sure. The method is particularly helpful when reusing an old enclosure. I can make sure that switches and control shafts line up with existing holes. **Figure 7.6** shows a mock-up of a frequency counter that I wanted to mount in a case from a defunct calculator. The mock-up demonstrated that one of the switches had to be moved to line up with a hole in the case. It also disclosed a problem I wasn't even looking for: The crystal was too tall. I wouldn't have been able to close the case! Fortunately, I discovered both problems at a point where they were very easy to fix.—*Roy A. Raney, KØOVQ, 600 Jackson St, Denver, CO 80206;* **k0ovq@arrl.net**

## A SUPER GLUE SOLVENT

◊ When working with super glue (cyanoacrylate) you should always have the solvent nearby in case you glue something that you shouldn't—your fingers, for instance. If you have run out of the solvent sold with the glues, acetone will serve. [It's also good for cleaning up epoxies *before* they've cured! —*Ed.*]—*Jim Martin, KC5ZL, 1801 Peaceable Rd, Apt 8, McAlester, OK 74501-7298*

## A PYRITE CRYSTAL RADIO

◊ Years ago, a crystal set was an excellent way to introduce a youngster to the mystery and excitement of radio. Today, it is not as easy to get a crystal set to work as it was sixty years ago. Antenna restrictions, as well as the lack of big trees on today's small house lots, make it difficult for kids to string a suitable antenna. Modern low-impedance headphones are another problem.

Hams can bring back the crystal set magic by letting children (in my case, visiting grandchildren) use our antennas. My rooftop multiband vertical makes a very good broadcast-band antenna when both feed-line conductors are tied together. The antenna (feed-line and all) is used together with a ground connection.

A rock of iron pyrite[4] (fool's gold) makes a simple AM broadcast-band crystal radio (see **Figure 7.7**). Use an alligator clip to make one connection to the pyrite diode. A *cat-whisker* should be used for the other end. The cat-whisker can be a needle or a straight pin (they're easier to find when dropped) held by a miniature alligator clip (see **Figure 7.8**). The radio operator moves the cat-whisker to hunt for a "sweet spot" on the pyrite. I find that resting the needle very lightly on the pyrite gives the best result.

Connect headphones in *parallel* with the pyrite crystal diode via the wire loop in Figure 7.8 and another out of view at the screw holding the large alligator clip. Then connect the antenna and ground to either side of the pyrite diode (using the same loops). That's all there is to this radio! It picks up

[4]Pyrite can be found in mine dumps near abandoned gold mines or it can be purchased inexpensively at rock and mineral shops. Galena was commonly used 60 years ago but is somewhat harder to find today. A parallel combination of four 1N34A diodes also works, but some of the magic is taken away.

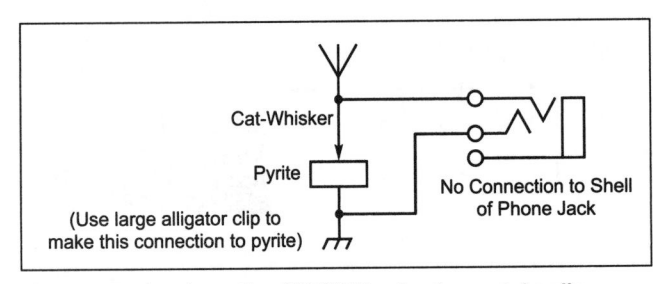

Figure 7.7—A schematic of N7KSB's simple crystal radio.

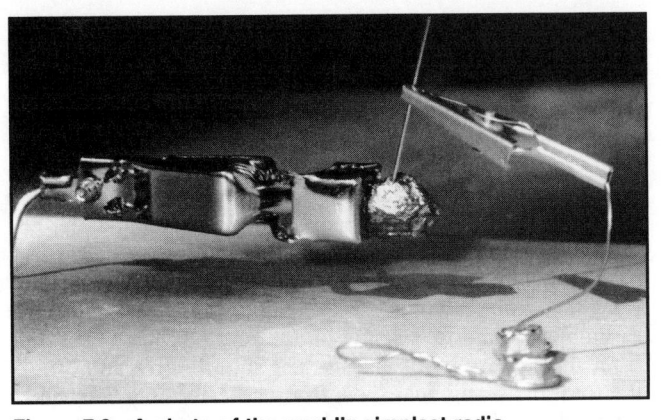

Figure 7.8—A photo of the world's simplest radio.

the strongest local signal with one or two weaker signals in the background. Except for tweaking the cat-whisker, there is no tuning. Best reception occurs during the day, before nighttime power reductions take place.

I use stereo headphones with the two earpieces connected in series. This is accomplished by connecting only to the "ring" and "tip" of the stereo phone plug. Leaving the "shell" unconnected results in a more sensitive 32 Ω headset. If more sensitivity is desired, add a small transformer (either one used for audio output matching or a small 12 V power supply) to transform the headphone impedance into the kilohm range.

More sophisticated crystal sets can be built, but until the Lone Ranger, Little Orphan Annie, and Captain Midnight return and kick the crude talk shows off the air, this simple radio will suffice.—*Lew Smith, N7KSB, 4176 N Soldier Tr, Tucson, AZ 85749;* **evieandlewsmith@aol.com**

## MOUNT PANEL CONTROLS PROPERLY

◊ Okay, call me a nitpicker. Ham equipment should not only work well, but should also look attractive. There is a right way and wrong ways to panel-mount components such as toggle switches, push buttons and jacks. Today for some reason, much ham-built equipment is assembled incorrectly. I have ignored the problem for a long time, but when I discover three prime examples of the same error in one copy of *QST*, I think it's time to speak out.

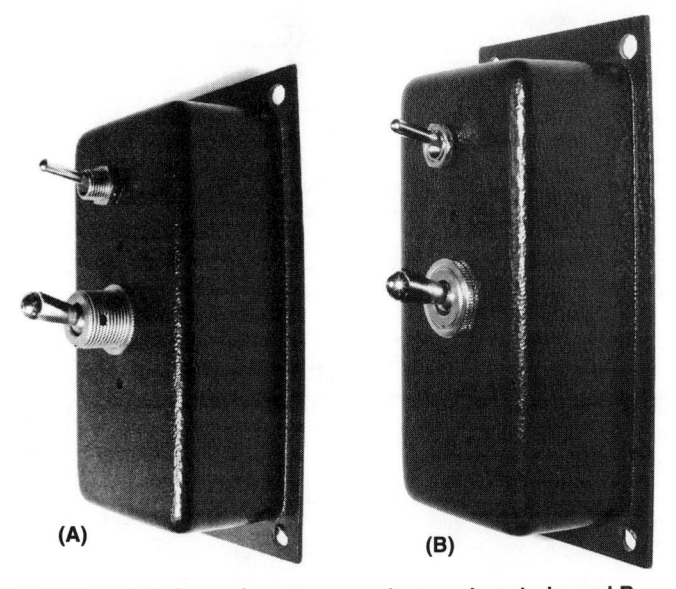

Figure 7.9—A shows the wrong way to mount controls, and B the right way. Any unnecessary control shaft length belongs behind the panel.

Components are to be mounted so that any unused portion of the threaded barrel is hidden behind the panel, not showing in front of it. In my opinion, the way it's often being done is just plain ugly. See Dec 2002 *QST*, pp 28, 39 and 62. These are examples of what I am sure is otherwise excellent home-built equipment. As supplied from the manufacturer, panel components usually come with three items: a front nut, which is either knurled or hex-shaped, a lock washer and a rear hex nut. Sometimes there is also a decorative flat washer or perhaps an ON-OFF indicator plate as well. **Figure 7.9** shows the right and wrong mounting methods. For proper mounting, the assembler should first screw on the rear hex nut so that the front of the barrel will end up just slightly protruding from the front mounting nut. Some trial-and-error may be needed. Then add the lock washer, and insert the component through the panel from the rear. Mount the washer or plate (if supplied), and finally the front mounting nut. Be careful not to mar the panel when tightening the front nut. When the rear is accessible, I tighten the rear hex nut after installing the front nut, using a small, flat hex wrench, to avoid scratches on the front. That's all there is to it. As a guide, most (but not all) commercially built equipment is done correctly.—*Sumner Weisman, W1VIV, 43 Agnes Dr, Framingham, MA 01701;* **w1viv@rcn.com**

## AN EASY HOMEBREW BURGLAR ALARM

◊ How about a neat little circuit, easily built, to protect your Amateur Radio gear? This is actually good for any place needing protection: swimming pool, gate area, etc. The project (see **Figures 7.10** and **7.11**) simply uses a low-cost motion-detector light fixture that is modified to power a 12 V wall transformer rather than its normal lamp. Choose a 12 V siren and the transformer to power the siren.

Here are the modifications:

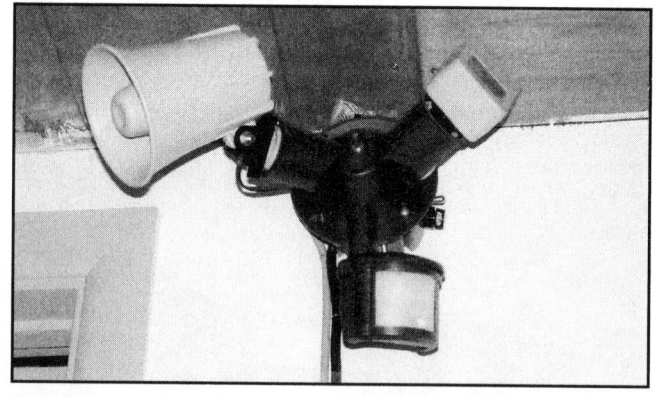

Figure 7.10—A photo of the W7VEW system at work.

1. Remove both black and white wires from one socket.

2. Fill the socket with strong and hard putty. Let the putty harden, then mount the siren to the putty-filled socket.

3. Leave the red and white wires connected to the other socket, screw a lamp-to-ac-socket adapter into it and plug the 12 V "wall wart" into the adapter.

4. Connect the wall-wart output to the siren's power terminals.

Mount the modified fixture to a standard deep octagon electrical box and add a cord set for power. Plug it into a nearby outlet.

With the motion detector switch in the normal position, the alarm will operate only in the dark and when triggered it will sound for the interval you select. With the switch in the TEST position, it will operate with lights on and sound for about 15 seconds. Mount the alarm so that S1 is hidden from view, away from the protected area.

This alarm system prevented a robbery only two weeks after installation at my son's construction office. The criminals defeated the door switches, but this ham project got 'em. —*Steve Kimber, W7VEW, 670 Garfield St, Lander, WY 82520;* **w7vew@arrl.net**

## SAND PAINT SMOOTH BEFORE LETTERING AND DECALS

◊ Gloss paint is a good surface for lettering but getting a glass-smooth surface is tough. Conversely, flat paint is easy to apply and flows out smoothly, but rub-on lettering doesn't adhere to it very well. My clever solution is to paint the panel with flat paint, then sand it down with ultra-fine 600-grit sandpaper. The sanding technique also works with metallic paint, which often dries to a rough finish. For a really smooth finish, I've purchased 1000 and 2000-grit sandpaper in the auto-finishing sections of big retail stores.

After applying rub-on labels, I protect the panel with a coat of spray clear acrylic, which produces a shiny finish. (Remember, paint compatibility varies as a function of how long the base coat has to dry—applying a top coat too soon can cause problems with otherwise compatible paints.) You can also use waterslide decal film labels—they can be protected with Future floor wax, a thin acrylic, after application.[5] Unlike rub-on lettering, decals are easily replaced if damaged. A sanded-smooth finish can make a good surface for peel-and-stick decals with clear areas—a notoriously difficult challenge.—*Zack Lau, W1VT, ARRL Staff;* **zlau@arrl.org**

[5]One supplier of waterslide decal media for ink-jet printers is Bel Inc, 10913 NW 30th St, Ste 103, Miami, FL 33172; tel 305-406-9507, fax 305-593-1011; **www.beldecal.com**.

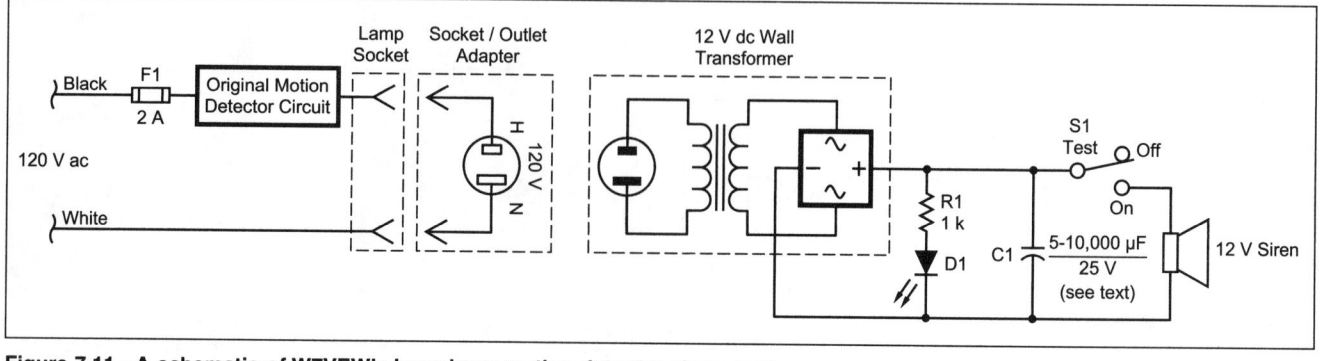

Figure 7.11—A schematic of W7VEW's homebrew motion-detector alarm system.

## MORE ON WORN KEYPAD LABELS

◊ Do you have an old radio with the keypad lettering worn off? Here is a solution for that predicament with possible applications for other projects where you need a neat, professional looking label for your radio equipment.

Go to your local stationery story and purchase a pack of self-adhesive labels (in whatever color you prefer) that are slightly larger than the size of the label you intend to make. Next, go to your computer and type out the label that you want to make, using a word processing or spreadsheet program. Adjust the word spacing and sizing of the label to suit your needs.

Here's the new twist: Go to the "Font Color" portion of the word processor menu and select white for the color of the type. Now go to the processor's "highlight text" portion of the menu. Select "black" and drag the highlighter through the text of your label. This should result in white letters on a black background. Now, load a sheet of the label paper into your laser printer and print your label onto it, and you will have a *black*-background label with type that is the color of the label you selected. A great variety of font and type sizes are available using this approach.

Now, carefully cut out the label (leaving a little margin around the perimeter of the text), position and mount the label, and voilá you have a neat, professional label (see **Figure 7.12**). If your label will be in a heavily used environment, cover it with a strip of glossy-surfaced, clear vinyl or Mylar tape and you have a durable, readable label.—*Allan M. Hale, WA9IRS, 1580 Basswood Ct, Florence, KY 41042;* **wa9irs@arrl.net**

**Figure 7.12—W9IRS repairs keypad labels with color.**

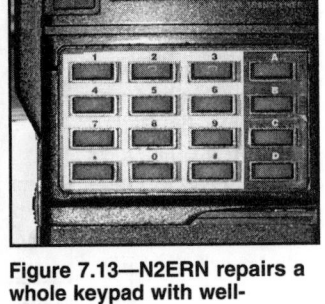

**Figure 7.13—N2ERN repairs a whole keypad with well-placed cutouts.**

◊ KØHLA's approach (Hints & Kinks, May 2003) to worn keypad identifiers doesn't really address the issue, since you're still left with a radio that has no identifying data on the keypad.

I used a different approach. I laid out the keypad on my Mac in a simple drawing program, printed the facsimile on peel-off label stock, put clear tape over the whole thing, and then cut out the holes with an X-Acto knife and stuck it on the face. The repair is fast, effective and fairly waterproof. You can print several copies and replace them as needed.

Draw the layout as large as you can—double, triple or quadruple size—and reduce it appropriately when printing. This will reduce your letters, "jaggies" and measuring errors to minuscule proportions when printing and give a *very* professional job. **Figure 7.13** shows my old IC-2GAT.—*Harris Ruben, N2ERN, 64 Apple Tree Row, Berkeley Heights, NJ 07922;* **n2ern@arrl.net**

## USING LINEAR POTENTIOMETERS FOR AUDIO APPLICATIONS

◊ Few things are more frustrating than trying to finish your latest project shortly after midnight and being unable to find that last necessary component in your parts bin or junk box. I

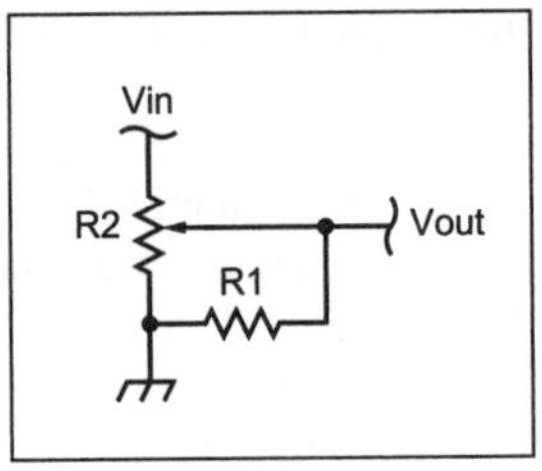

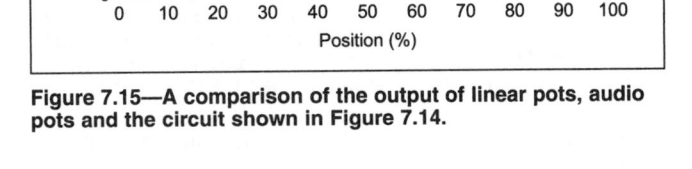

**Figure 7.14—A simple circuit allows the use of linear pots in applications normally needing audio pots.**

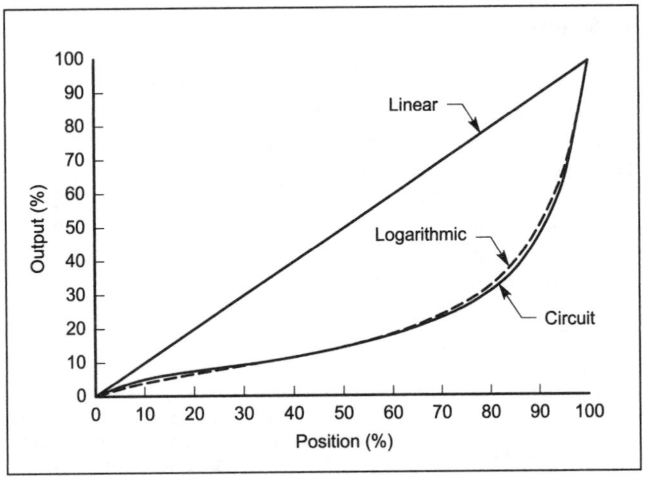

**Figure 7.15—A comparison of the output of linear pots, audio pots and the circuit shown in Figure 7.14.**

was in such straits one night, when I needed a potentiometer with an audio-taper but had only linear pots on hand. This circuit converts a linear input to a logarithmic output.

**Figure 7.14** shows a simple way to make a linear pot function like an audio pot. Select R1 with about one-tenth the value of R2 for best performance. For example, if you are using a 100 kΩ linear pot for R2, try a 10 kΩ fixed resistor for R1. **Figure 7.15** shows the percentage output related to percentage of available shaft rotation for linear and audio pots as well as this circuit.

Be aware that the stage feeding this circuit will see a varying load resistance. For example, the values above produce an input load resistance that can vary between 9091 Ω and 100,000 Ω (ignoring any loading caused by the following stage). I haven't observed any noticeable effect from this in my applications.

This idea is widely known among audio experimenters, but it doesn't seem to be used much by hams. I hope it will make your next trip to the junk box for a volume control more rewarding.—*Jim McClanahan, W4JBM, 300 Relais Trace, Alpharetta, GA 30004;* **w4jbm@arrl.net**

## ANOTHER PL-259 INSTALLATION TIP

◊ Like many others who dislike or cannot solder PL-259 connectors on to large coax cable, I have tried many techniques to make the job easier. I have found that the soldering is not the problem when using RG-213. The connector is just too difficult to mount on the coax because the diameter of the connector insert is too close to that of the coax (0.405 inch) and the cable jacket makes the job harder than it should be. I have seen many techniques, but none that worked for me until I found that the feed line to my vertical antenna had been sliced in half by an inattentive gardener.

All that is necessary is to take your electric drill and mount a bit that can be used to remove metal. (I have seen "hogging" bits and spiral cutters; I am sure there are many others.) Then make a pass or two with the cutting bit inside of the threaded barrel of the insert to the PL-259 and you will find that the coax maintains a tight fit yet permits you to insert the coax easily. You do not need to remove much of the metal. Now you can use your favorite technique to dress the cable to the dimensions for the technique you are using and insert the dressed cable and solder per directions. Finish up by using some coax sealing material around the barrel to seal the cable and connector at back of the connector.—*Bob Cowan, WB6DAC, 2740 Canary Dr, Costa Mesa, CA 92626-4748;* **wb6dac@attbi.com**

## WATERPROOFING FIELD DAY COAX CONNECTIONS

◊ After connecting two coax cables with a UHF barrel adapter during a Field Day exercise, you should waterproof it against the inevitable overnight rain (and morning dew). To accomplish this in less than 10 seconds, cut an 8 inch length of $^7/_8$ inch ID foam hot water pipe insulation (the non-split type), slide it over one

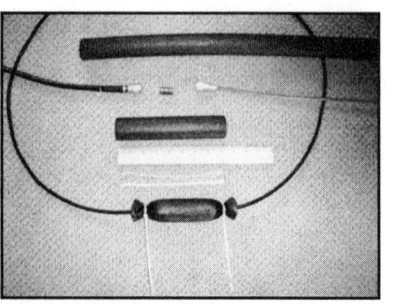

**Figure 7.16—A low-cost but effective way to waterproof cable connectors in the field. A short length of pipe insulation does the job.**

coax connector, join the coaxes with a barrel, slide the insulation over the joint and strap it *tightly* one inch from each end with nylon cable ties. Done. The result is shown in **Figure 7.16**.

A 5 foot length of pipe insulation costs $1.50 and it will provide up to eight pieces of section. Nylon ties are 5 cents each. That's 30 cents per connection…a small price to pay for an essential requirement. It's cheaper than electrical tape and coaxial sealing tape and much faster, both in application and removal. To disassemble, cut the ties with diagonal pliers. —*Jim Yuen, WH6GS, 91-1517 Halahua St, Kapolei, HI 96707;* **wh6gs@arrl.net**

## QUICK AND EASY CIRCUIT BOARD PREPARATION

◊ For the past 30 years, I've been making printed circuit boards using a method that is both simple and inexpensive, although it is only suitable for a few boards. It's very simple and works beautifully every time. There's no need for computers or programs. I've never seen anyone else use this method (at least in print). A quick step-by-step description follows:
1) Make a 1:1 scale drawing of the board.
2) Photocopy the scale drawing.
3) Cut the PC board to size.
4) Coat the PC board with a thin coat of rubber glue.
5) Cut out the photocopy, which should fit the PC board, and coat it with rubber glue. Wait for both the PC board and photocopy to dry.
6) Carefully place the photocopy on the PC board copper and rub it down.
7) Using a hobby knife, cut out the tracings. Even unsteady hands become steady because the knife is always on the paper.
8) Peel the cut tracings off.
9) Rub off the excess dried rubber glue.
10) Coat the exposed copper with fingernail polish. I use red because it's easy to see.
11) Peel off the rest of the photocopy paper.
12) Etch!

I've been able to make dozens of boards using this method with no mistakes and no badly etched boards. Lines as close

as 1 millimeter can be accommodated.

Try it and you'll see that it's simple, easy, and costs little, particularly when you keep the rubber glue. I've used it for all varieties of circuitry.—*Jack Thomas, 3008 Westfield Ave, Baltimore, MD 21214*

## A PORTABLE OPERATING LAMP

◊ Do you like operating at night while camping, but you can't see your log in the dark? Here's a neat little project that doesn't cost very much and recycles one of those ever-present Altoids tins that are finding their way into a lot of low-power (QRP) projects these days. It's a simple construction project that's easy to build. **Figure 7.17** is a picture of the completed project.

First, procure one high-intensity white LED, 8 inches of RG-402 ($^1/_8$ inch miniature, semi-rigid coax), one SPST toggle switch, and your choice of batteries and holders to fit in the Altoids tin. If you can't come up with a piece of RG-402, use small-diameter copper tubing. Use the smallest you can get from your local plumbing supplier and thread an appropriate length of Teflon insulated wire through the center of it. (Use Teflon-insulated wire because you will be soldering to the copper tube and you don't want to melt the insulation on the center wire.) If you wish, you can substitute a high-intensity yellow LED for the white one—as a "bug light."

Prepare the ends of the RG-402 by carefully removing $^1/_4$ inch of the outer jacket from one end and $1^1/_2$ inches of the jacket from the other end. Shorten the anode lead of the LED to about $^1/_4$ inch and solder it to the center conductor of the RG-402. Leave the

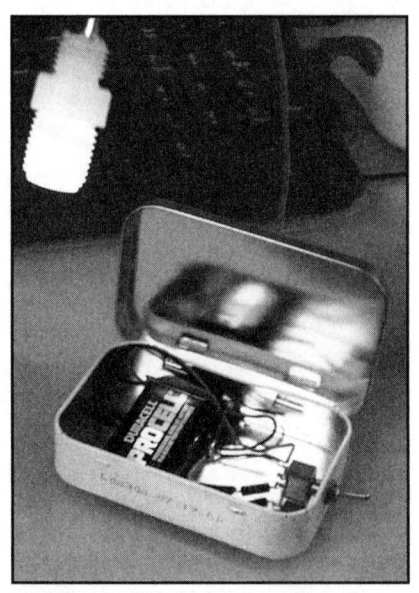

**Figure 7.17—A photo of WØEB's battery powered operating light.**

cathode lead of the LED long and solder it along-side the shield of the RG-402. Cover this joint and—all but the very tip of the LED—with appropriately sized heat-shrinkable tubing. Or, if you can find a translucent nylon plumbing fitting, use it for a cute shade, as I did. Use your imagination. I've found that "hot" glue works wonders to attach things like this.

Carefully punch a very small hole in the rear (not the bottom) of the Altoids tin. Insert the RG-402 or copper tubing through this hole and carefully solder it to the bottom of the tin. I also soldered the jacket to the can where it comes through the small hole in the back. This helps stabilize the "gooseneck."

Install the toggle switch in another hole that you have carefully punched or drilled in the can. Connect the normally open switch contact to the center conductor of the RG-402 through a 1 kΩ, $^1/_4$ W resistor (if using 9-12 V), or a 100 Ω, $^1/_4$ W resistor if you're using a couple of AA cells. [The value of the current limiting the resistor will depend on your power source and the specific LED you use—it will range anywhere from 33 Ω to 1 kΩ.—*Ed.*] Connect the positive lead of your battery connector to the "common" terminal of the switch and solder the negative supply lead directly to the tin.

Check to be sure you've assembled everything correctly,

then install your battery or batteries. The LED should light nicely when you close the switch. If you use a 9 V battery and a 1 kΩ resistor, you can also install a coaxial power connector to externally power the LED. In this case, use an SPDT, "center-off" switch, connect the 1 kΩ resistor from the center (C) contact of the switch to the center conductor of the "gooseneck," connect the positive lead of the 9 V battery to one of the normally-open (NO) contacts, and the positive lead of the coaxial power jack to the other NO contact. With all of the negative leads grounded to the tin you shouldn't need a wire from the negative terminal of the coaxial power jack, unless the mounting nut is internally isolated from the negative contact (some of them are). The switch center position is now OFF and the NO positions select between battery power and the external power supply.—*Jim Sheldon, WØEB, 2029 East Evanston Dr, Wichita, KS 67219;* **w0eb@cox.net**

## HOMEBREW THUMBSCREWS MADE WITH "WIRE NUTS"

◇ The radio I recently purchased for mobile use includes a mounting bracket with small metric screws to attach the radio to the bracket. I didn't want to purchase a quick release bracket, so I needed a way to easily remove the radio without the need for a screwdriver. I couldn't find thumbscrews to fit the radio, so I built my own. Each is made by using a wiring nut as the knob and fixing the screw inside the nut with epoxy. (Rather than wire nuts, you could use caps from toothpaste tubes, or anything of appropriate shape. Since wire nuts and caps come in many different colors, you can select a color that works well for your application.)

After mixing the epoxy, I filled the wire nut with it and inserted the screw into the nut. (Be careful to orient the screw so that it's coaxial with the nut.)

After allowing the epoxy to set (even "5 minute" epoxy is stronger after curing 24 hours) the screw-nut interface seems strong enough hold the radio with no problem.—*Dan Trigilio, W6DAN, 948A Kennedy Dr, Capitola, CA 95010-12317;* **w6dan@ arrl.net**

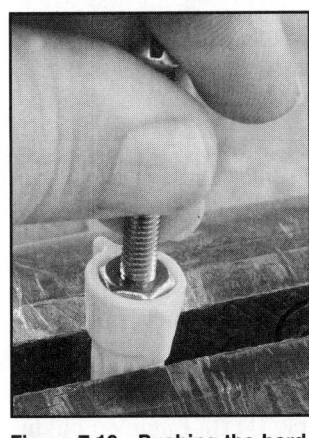
**Figure 7.18—Softening the wire nut plastic with a heat gun. Epoxy is used to bond the hardware to the wire nut.**

*Editor's note:* This is a wonderful idea! Soon after receiving it, I was installing a whip antenna on my station wagon (a Subaru Legacy). My Rube Goldberg solution required some weather-tolerant hardware that could assemble and disassemble without tools. I purchased suitable stainless-steel hardware, then attached wire nuts as shown in the photos. The result is hand-friendly hardware that is completely rust free. (Because this was for use on a moving vehicle, I chose aircraft nuts, which have nylon inserts to prevent them from working loose.)

In addition, I chose the

**Figure 7.19—Pushing the hardware nut into the softened wire nut. This ensures that the plastic conforms to the outside dimensions of the nut. The same technique can be used for screws.**

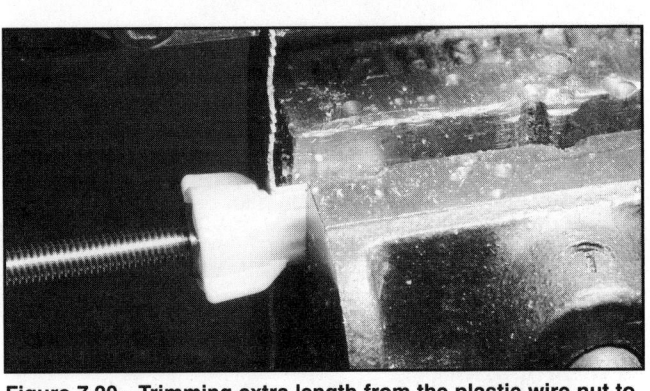
**Figure 7.20—Trimming extra length from the plastic wire nut to make a smaller fastener.**

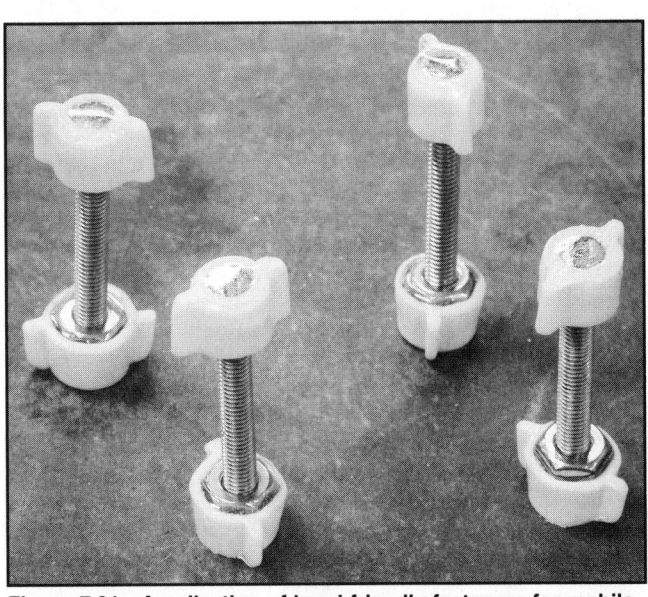
**Figure 7.21—A collection of hand-friendly fasteners for mobile and portable installations.**

nuts and wire nuts for a tight fit. I softened each wire nut with a heat gun (**Figure 7.18**) and pushed an aircraft nut into it (**Figure 7.19**). This makes the wire nut conform to the shape of the aircraft nut for more strength.

For looks, I trimmed away the extra length of the wire nut (**Figure 7.20**). Several of my completed fasteners are shown in **Figure 7.21**. They assemble and disassemble quickly when I must remove the antenna from the car.

## A PARTS HOLDER FOR TOWER WORK

◇ A common aggravation in tower work is finding a place to put small parts or tools while working on something else. During a recent session 100 feet up on a friend's tower, my mental light bulb went on with a solution to the problem.

I took a spring clamp large enough to clamp to a tower leg and attached a small plastic storage container to it. To

**Figure 7.22—The parts holder in use, mounted to a tower leg.**

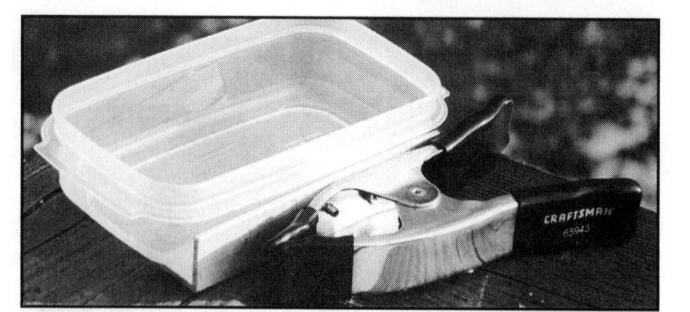

Figure 7.23—The assembly configuration for the tower-mounted parts holder. Note the aluminum angle stock screwed to the clamp and the container.

facilitate mounting the container to the clamp, I used a 1 inch × 1 inch aluminum angle bar stock. This adapted the curved clamp to the straight-sided container and gave support to the bottom of the container. You'll find assembly easier if you tap the holes in the clamp to accept the mounting screws. **Figures 7.22** and **7.23** show the assembly configuration and the holder mounted to a tower leg.

With the matching container lid, parts can also be stored in the container for the trip up the tower. Using the holder doesn't guarantee that parts or tools won't fall, so remember to exercise caution while on the ground below a tower and wear a suitable hard hat.—*Jim Stahl, K8MR, 30499 Jackson Rd, Chagrin Falls, OH 44022;* **jimk8mr@aol.com**

# The Doctor is IN

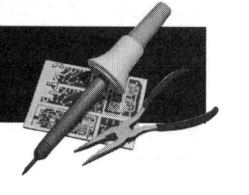

**Q**B.R. Bear Carson, AC7HI, writes, "I have looked through *The ARRL Handbook, The ARRL Antenna Book, QST* and TIS pages and cannot find a really informative article on how to select good relays for a remote antenna switching system. There are several tidbits here and there, but nothing I could find discussed the physical properties needed for a good RF relay and how RF affects the performance specifications of various relays. How can one minimize the RF "bump" the relay might cause on the system impedance? There's a lot of stuff out there about relays for conventional ac/dc applications but RF applications seem to be lacking. I think I remember something about how to build a switch box somewhere, but its source eludes me. Anyway, with all the relays on the market, how do I pick the right one? Also, is there anything about how to fabricate your own coax switches?"**

**A**To be ideal, coax switch contacts should maintain a constant impedance throughout. To do so requires transmission line type of construction, which is why regular relays always present an impedance bump. The only way around it would be to construct a relay exclusively for this purpose. Such RF relays do exist commercially, but they can be expensive, even for a simple 1-port in, 2-port out arrangement.

The best a homebuilder can expect to do at reasonable cost

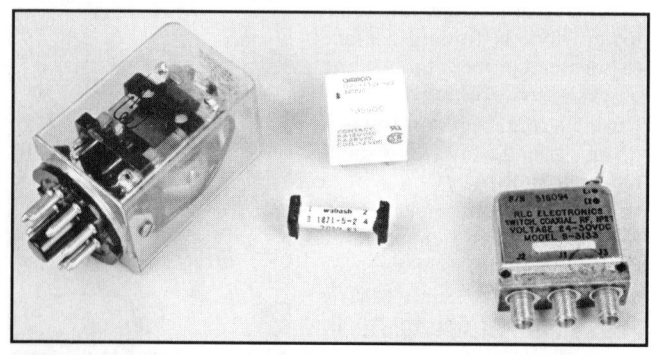

Figure 7.24—The RF characteristics of these different relay types will be very different from band to band. For UHF and microwave, relays with integral RF connectors, as seen on the relay on the right, are a must.

is to minimize the losses inside conventional relays, making the impedance bump insignificant. Transmission line should be used at the inputs and outputs of the relays to confine the effect to the relay itself. In fact, some of the commercially available remote switch boxes (such as the units available from Array Solutions) use this technique, except that these switches often use circuit board traces to form transmission lines.[6]

*QST* has had a number of projects for antenna switches, most recently, H. Rosenthal, W5AN, "A Remote Antenna Selector Switch," *QST*, Aug 1997, p 40.

The relays in these switches should be suitable for any sort of design you might care to come up with. None of the published designs use any circuit boards, however, so you would be on your own if you wanted to take that approach. Personally, I would just stick with sections of good quality coax at the relay input and output terminals.

**Q**From Richard, KC2HZW, comes an observation. I am interested in constructing the 40 meter Yagi as shown in *The ARRL Antenna Book*, 19th Edition.[7] It would appear that the taper schedule "D" is incorrect. After the 1″ × .058″ wall tubing, the next size would be ⅞″ and then ¾″ (not the ¾″ and ½″, as shown). Are the tubing sizes in the book correct, or do I have to use reducers to keep the tubing sizes as shown? Thanks!**

**A**Gee, I'm sorry to say that little boo-boo has been in the book for a long time, for almost 9 years!

It should be just as Richard says. The section labeled ¾″ should be ⅞″ OD, and the end (variable) tip should be ¾″ OD instead of ½″. The wall thickness should be 0.058″ for both, so they should telescope fine.

I'm working on rewriting chapter 11 as we speak, so Richard's timing is superb.—*Dean Straw, N6BV*

**Q**Joe, N1KHB, asks: Doc, I'm looking to make some plastic insulators to support wire antennas at my QTH. I plan on buying a quantity of either Lexan or

---

[6]Array Solutions, 350 Gloria Rd, Sunnyvale, TX 75182; 972-203-2008; **www.arraysolutions.com/**.
[7]*The ARRL Antenna Book*, 19th Ed, p 11-22, Fig 18 (D).

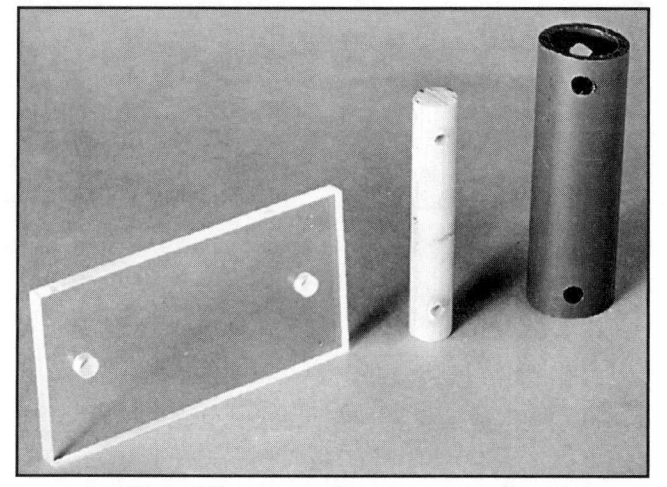

Figure 7.25—Here are some homemade antenna insulators made of acrylic and polycarbonate plastics. They are easily machined, have good weathering characteristics and are fairly strong.

Plexiglas, but I haven't decided which. I've heard that Plexiglas is not as good as Lexan for projects involving exposure to the weather—can you give me some guidance?

A The Doctor doesn't claim to be a plastics expert, but I can advise you on a couple of points. I don't think UV or weather exposure is much of a problem with Plexiglas or Lucite (which are trade names for clear acrylic) or else it wouldn't be used for windows. Lexan (a trade name for polycarbonate), however, is much stronger than Plexiglas and will hold up to much more physical strain and abuse as would occur when it's used as an antenna insulator. For more information on the properties of plastics, the doctor suggests contacting a plastics distributor or manufacturer. You can locate several using the TIS Find Web page at **www.arrl.org/tis/tisfind.html**. Some antenna insulators made of these materials can be seen in **Figure 7.25**. The nice thing about them is that they're easily configurable to custom requirements that the commercial products might not be able to meet.

Q Danny, KD5UJ, writes: I have acquired a new Hammond HV transformer with a secondary rated at 2800 V at 5 kVA. The amplifier I want to build uses a 4CX250 tube which requires around 2000 V dc of plate potential. Will this transformer be suitable? If so, how do I reduce the secondary voltage? I've thought about attempting to build a power supply that could run both an HF and a VHF amplifier—one amplifier would require the 2000 to 2200 V dc and the other around 3200 V dc. Can you help me with this project?

A I assume the transformer rating you give is the ac rms output voltage. A 5 kVA transformer is one large device, capable of sourcing almost 2 $A_{rms}$ of current at that secondary voltage—*be careful!* A transformer of that power rating will most certainly have a 230 $V_{rms}$ ac primary winding. Your amplifier will require about 1400-1500 $V_{rms}$ ac before the filter capacitors, with the full-wave rectified and filtered output bringing the dc voltage to about 2000 V dc. Accordingly, you can operate the 230 $V_{rms}$ primary on 115 $V_{rms}$ ac. That will give you the necessary 1400 $V_{rms}$ ac output voltage prior to rectification and filtering. Be sure that the primary ac supply circuit can support the current requirement of the tube or tubes you are supplying. Another option, and one that is often used, is to power the primary through a Variac or Powerstat variable voltage auto-transformer. Auto-transformers for 230 $V_{rms}$ ac are

available on the surplus market, or you can use a 115 $V_{rms}$ ac auto-transformer with an isolation transformer to convert the 115 $V_{rms}$ to 230 $V_{rms}$. Just remember to allow adequate current ratings. That would let your transformer operate at any voltage within its maximum ratings, providing the current capability of the Variac or Powerstat is sufficiently high. It would also let you continuously vary the secondary voltage from near zero to the rated output voltage, 2800 $V_{rms}$… in effect, a variable voltage HV dc supply. Lastly, and once again, I stress, *be careful—* transformers of this power capability and voltage rating can be lethal and are not forgiving; there's usually no second chance, so remember—*switch to safety!*

Q Bob, KD3JK, has a question regarding meters: I found a meter calibrated for 50 A dc with the notation at the bottom reading USE WITH EXTERNAL SHUNT, FS=50 MV. I figure the FS=50 means full scale = 50. I am unsure as to MV. Is that microvolts or millivolts? Can you suggest what I need to do to make the meter useable with my battery back up power supply?

A The meter in question is most certainly a voltmeter having a full-scale reading of 50 mV (millivolts) or 0.05 V. In order to use this as an ammeter, you'd need an external shunt, which, unfortunately, it appears you don't have. We can use Ohm's Law, however, to calculate the resistance of the external shunt to make the meter read 50 A full scale.

$R_s = V_{fs}/I$, so $R_s = 0.05$ V/50 A = 0.001 Ω. In other words, the external shunt resistance would have to be 1 mΩ (0.001 Ω) to give the meter a 50 A full-scale reading. It's not easy finding a 0.001 Ω shunt, so I'd suggest using a piece of copper wire across the meter terminals. Using the copper wire tables from *The ARRL Handbook*,[8] p 24.8, we see that #16 copper wire has a resistance of 4.018 Ω/1000 feet at 25° C. Dividing by 1000, that equals 0.004018 Ω per foot. Dividing again, by 4, we find that the same 16 gauge copper wire has a resistance of 0.001 Ω for a 3 inch length. We should also concern ourselves with the power handling capability of the shunt. The maximum power that the shunt will dissipate at full current is $P_s = I^2 R_s$. In this case that's $(0.001) \times (50)^2$ or 2.5 W. Three inches of 16 gauge wire will easily dissipate 2.5 W, although at 20 A this will be less than 0.5 W. Put that wire across (in parallel with) your meter and you'll have a usable ammeter with a full scale current reading of 50 A.

In order to use the same meter as a higher voltage (50 V)

[8]Available from your local dealer or the ARRL Bookstore. Order no. 1964. Telephone toll-free in the US 888-277-5289, or 860-594-0355, fax 860-594-0303; **www.arrl.org/shop/**; **pubsales@arrl.org**.

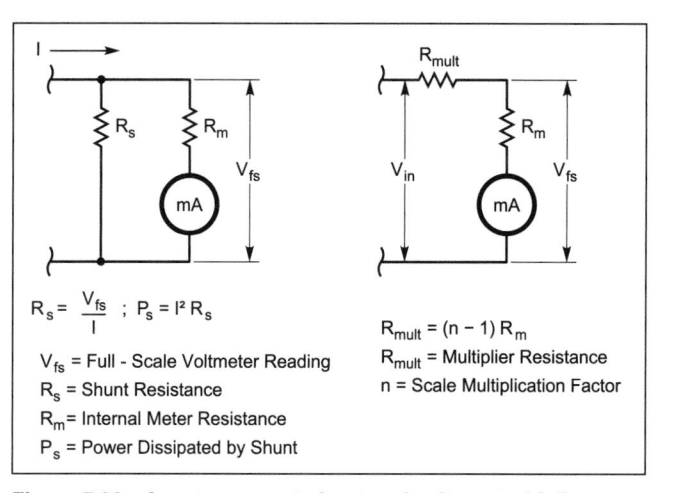

$$R_s = \frac{V_{fs}}{I} \; ; \; P_s = I^2 R_s$$

$V_{fs}$ = Full - Scale Voltmeter Reading
$R_s$ = Shunt Resistance
$R_m$= Internal Meter Resistance
$P_s$ = Power Dissipated by Shunt

$R_{mult} = (n - 1) R_m$
$R_{mult}$ = Multiplier Resistance
n = Scale Multiplication Factor

Figure 7.26—A meter current shunt and voltage multiplier.

voltmeter, you'd have to know its internal resistance—not always easy to measure safely without damaging the meter. *The ARRL Handbook*, p 26.4, describes a test setup to measure the internal resistance of a meter safely. My guess is that meter has an internal resistance of about 1000 $\Omega$, but this still needs to be measured. After the internal resistance is determined, the value of the multiplier will be $R = R_m (n - 1)$, where $R_m$ is the internal resistance of the meter and n = the multiplication factor of the scale (1000, in this case, to result in a full scale reading of 50 V). An educated guess would be that a 1 M$\Omega$ ($1\times10^6$ $\Omega$) multiplier resistor would result in a 50 V full scale reading for this instrument. You could try that, using a 2 M$\Omega$ potentiometer and a variable power supply. Set the power supply voltage to the full-scale reading you want and vary the potentiometer until the meter reads that voltage full scale. Then accurately measure the potentiometer reading and use the measured value for your multiplier. Be sure to set the potentiometer to its maximum resistance value first and set the power supply to its lowest voltage reading. Gradually bring the supply up in voltage and bring the potentiometer down in resistance. Remember that the voltage multiplier goes in *series* with the meter, while the current shunt is in *parallel* with the meter. The **Figure 7.26** schematic shows both voltage multipliers and current shunts. I hope this helps. Good luck!

Q Alan, KB2HEI, asks: I would like to build the power supply shown in the Beginner and Novice column of the April 1961 issue of *QST*. The transformer shown in that article has a 365 V ac secondary on either side of the center tap. The one I have available is 600-0-600 V ac. Also, the filter choke in the article has an inductance of 2 H while mine is 4.5 H at 200 mA and rated at 3000 V. My question has to do with the other components of the supply. What, if any, modifications are needed to build a dc power supply using the components I have on hand?

A Your filter choke should be fine, but you would most certainly need to reduce the secondary voltage coming from the transformer by about 40%. There are several ways to do this. You might be tempted to put a series resistor in the transformer primary to lower the input voltage. It's not a good idea. That would seriously affect the input voltage regulation and it isn't recommended. Similarly, a resistor at the secondary would seriously degrade the output voltage regulation. Rewinding the transformer is also not a good idea at these power levels, as the effort is very time consuming and difficult.

I would try to locate a small 220/120 V ac isolation transformer and apply the 120 V ac to the 220 V winding—use the 120 V winding to feed your transformer primary. This will give you about the right voltage at the secondary of your transformer. Conversely, you could also try to find a small Variac or Powerstat auto-transformer. These are sometimes available on the surplus market. Use that to feed the transformer primary and you'll have a variable voltage power supply. An-

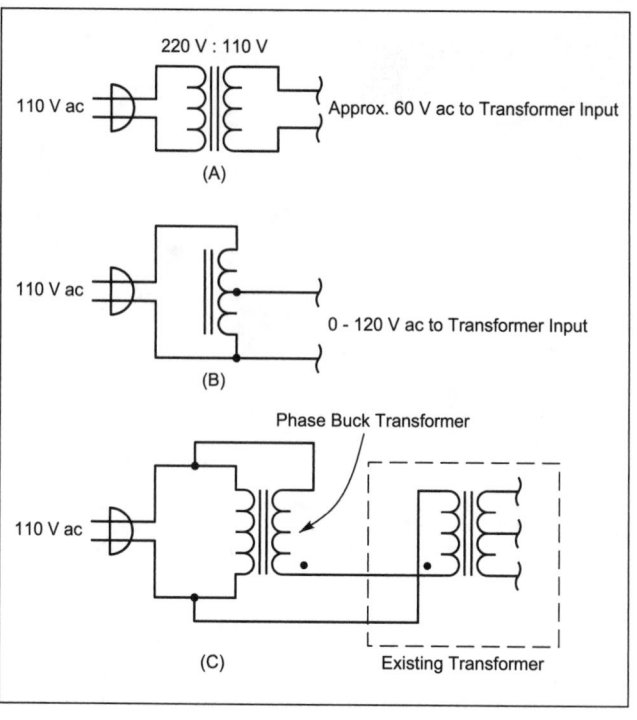

Figure 7.27—(A) A simple 220:110 V ac isolation transformer lowers the primary voltage if 110 V ac is fed to the 220 V winding. (B) A variable autotransformer configured to supply primary voltage. (C) An out-of-phase transformer winding can also be used to lower the primary voltage.

other technique is to connect a transformer out of phase with the input primary, so its voltage effectively "bucks" the input voltage. In this case, you'd need about a 50 V ac transformer. Connect its winding in series with the input, while monitoring the output voltage. If the output voltage increases, reverse the series connection windings—the output voltage should now drop. **Figure 7.27** shows some approaches to lowering (or, for that matter, boosting) the primary voltage.

Be aware that all of these techniques will affect *all* the secondary voltages coming from the transformer. That includes any 6.3 V filament windings and the rectifier tube filament voltage (usually 5 V). You would then need a separate transformer to supply these voltages. Or, in the case of the vacuum tube rectifier that is used in this supply, replace the tube rectifier with solid-state diodes, making sure that the PIV and current ratings of the diodes are sufficient for your application and the surge current drawn by the filter capacitors. In this case I'd recommend a full-wave bridge rated at 800 V PIV at 3 A, or, if you go with discrete diodes, use a type 1N5408 diode. Have fun, good luck and, as always, be careful around those high voltages!

# Chapter 8

# Antenna Systems

## A HANDY WAY TO INSTALL INSULATORS ON LOOP ANTENNAS

◊ When setting up a portable station for Field Day often the configuration of a loop antenna must be altered to fit the situation. With the traditional method of wiring the insulators on, it is difficult to move them, or remove them. The following simple method avoids the problem, and makes it easy. With this method it is not necessary to open the loop in order to move an insulator. It works well with stranded or flexible wire, but probably not with stiff copper coated steel wire. Refer to **Figure 8.1** while reading these instructions:

1. Bend the antenna wire double at the desired location of the insulator, and pass the doubled wire through the opening at the end of the insulator.

2. Pass the insulator through the loop of wire, and pull the wire tight. This makes a secure connection to the insulator. It will not slip, but is easily undone if you need to move the insulator.

3. Insulators that you want to be able to have loose, so that the wire is able to move, should be threaded on the wire before assembly of the loop antenna.

This method also works well if you want to add a new insulator to a loop. It helps, too, if you want to move the antenna to a new location, and need to change its configuration so that it will fit. It does not seem to make any significant difference to the function of the antenna. It can be used with insulated or uninsulated wire. It shortens the antenna a little, but loop antennas are broad-banded, and no problems seem to result.

Considering how well this works, it could be applied to fixed location antennas as well.— *Hugh Inness-Brown, W2IB, 5351 State Hwy 37, Ogdensburg, NY 13669*

## USING SWR TO MEASURE LINE LOSSES

◊ As described in *The ARRL Antenna Book*, losses in the line connecting a transmitter to an antenna reduce the actual SWR at the antenna to some lower value seen at the transmitter. Greater loss more greatly reduces the SWR. You can use this fact to get a direct measurement of the loss in a line. Create an approximately infinite SWR at one end by shorting the line. The short must be heavy and direct (very-low inductance) so that it closely approximates zero impedance, especially if the expected line loss is low. (In theory, you could use an open line, but capacitive effects make it difficult to create a good infinite impedance.) Then measure the SWR at the transmitter end of the line. **Table 8.1** relates the line loss—in decibels—to the measured SWR.

As you can see, when the line loss is high, a very accurate SWR reading is needed, but if the loss is that high you probably ought to replace the line anyway (or use it as a dummy load!)—*Edward K. (Ned) Conklin, KH7JJ, 2969 Kalakaua Ave #1004, Honolulu, HI 96815; ekc@forth.com*

(This technique assumes the line impedance is the same as the system impedance. It won't work with 75-Ω coax and a 50-Ω SWR meter.— *Zack Lau, W1VT, ARRL Lab*)

## HANG WIRES FROM TREES FLEXIBLY

◊ I have several Beverage antennas and elevated radial wires in old woods surrounding my home. "Old woods" means there are many dead branches that frequently land on my wires and break them. The following scheme prevents the wires from breaking and makes repairs easier when they are necessary.

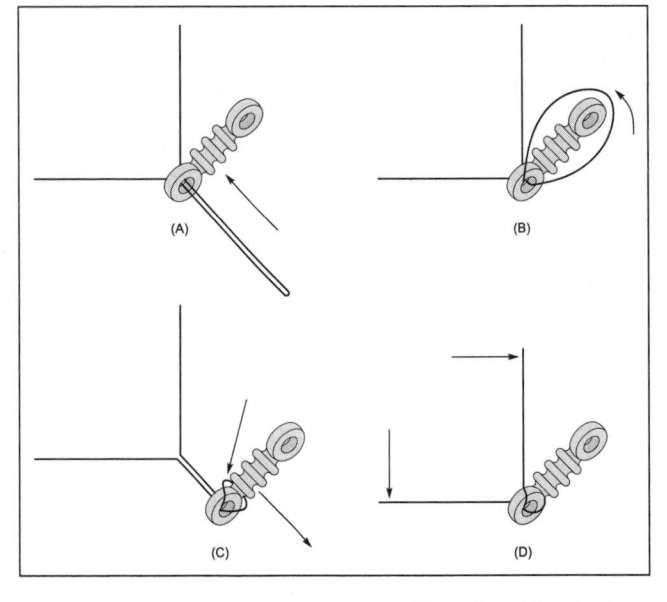

**Figure 8.1—Install insulators on loops without breaking the loop conductor. For flexible conductors, this method makes it easy to reposition the insulators as needed on portable antennas.**

**Table 8.1**
**SWR versus Line Loss**

| SWR | Line Loss (dB) | SWR | Line Loss (dB) | SWR | Line Loss (dB) |
|---|---|---|---|---|---|
| 40.00 | 0.22 | 5.00 | 1.76 | 1.80 | 5.44 |
| 30.00 | 0.29 | 4.50 | 1.96 | 1.60 | 6.37 |
| 20.00 | 0.43 | 4.00 | 2.22 | 1.50 | 6.99 |
| 15.00 | 0.58 | 3.50 | 2.55 | 1.40 | 7.78 |
| 12.00 | 0.73 | 3.20 | 2.81 | 1.30 | 8.85 |
| 10.00 | 0.87 | 3.00 | 3.01 | 1.25 | 9.62 |
| 9.00 | 0.97 | 2.80 | 3.25 | 1.20 | 10.41 |
| 8.00 | 1.09 | 2.60 | 3.52 | 1.15 | 11.56 |
| 7.00 | 1.25 | 2.40 | 3.85 | 1.10 | 13.22 |
| 6.00 | 1.46 | 2.20 | 4.26 | 1.05 | 16.13 |
| 5.50 | 1.60 | 2.00 | 4.77 | | |

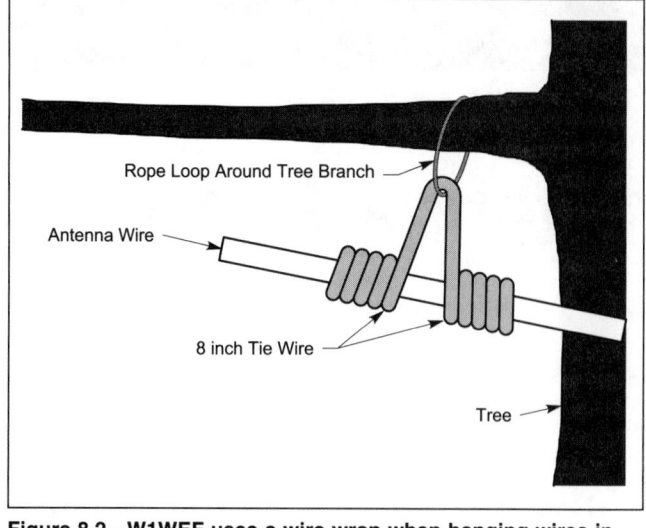

**Figure 8.2—W1WEF uses a wire wrap when hanging wires in trees. When a deadfall strikes the antenna, the wrap can unravel, releasing the antenna wire before it breaks. It is then simple to repair the antenna by replacing the wrap.**

For those unfamiliar with Beverages, they are receiving antennas that are typically suspended 6 to 10 feet above the ground, running in a straight line toward the desired direction from which they are to receive. My European Beverage is 550 feet long, running through the woods and supported by trees along the way.

My 32 elevated radials are on a four-square antenna for 80 meters. The four-square is a phased array of four λ/4 vertical wires, suspended in trees, with eight wire radials sloping up from the base of each vertical to a height of 6 or 7 feet above the ground. Each radial is λ/4 long, or about 66 feet. Trees along the way support the elevated radials.

If the Beverage or radial wires were simply stapled to trees and a branch was to fall on them, they would likely break. If the staple is left loose so the wire can move, the tree eventually grows around the staple (if it's up long enough), making it tight. Then when a branch lands on the wire it breaks. After years of playing with wires in the woods, I found the following to work pretty well. (All of my wires are #14 or #12 AWG insulated stranded wire.)

I put a galvanized fence staple in the tree where I want to support the wire. [**Figure 8.2** shows the arrangement with a tree-friendly rope loop in place of the staple.—*Ed.*] I then use an 8-inch piece of solid #14 AWG insulated wire to secure the antenna to the staple. Pass the wire through the staple and wrap 4 inches on each side of the staple tightly around the

wire to be supported, with four or five turns on each side. Now, when a branch falls on the wires, the antenna wire pulls out of the wrap. All I need do to fix the damage is clear a fallen branch and refasten securing wire. This sure beats bringing the torch out to the woods or using split-bolt connectors to splice broken wires!—*Jack Schuster, W1WEF, 408 Thompson St, Glastonbury, CT 06033;* **w1wef@arrl.net**

## BUILD A PARALLEL-WIRE DIPOLE

◊ **Figure 8.3** shows a multiband dipole antenna I've been building for some folks around here. **Table 8.2** shows measured values from one I built for Brian, K4BKG, who lives in Sampson County, North Carolina. I put the dipole up between a few pine trees at about 40 feet above ground level. It is mounted in a flat-top configuration with the center supported via an eye-ring on the center insulator. It could be built in an inverted-V configuration also.

The center insulator (no balun) that I use is from The Wireman (#800 at **www.thewireman.com**), but there are many others available elsewhere. [If you're concerned about antenna-pattern uniformity, use a balun at the feed point.—*Ed.*] You can also get the bare #14 AWG hard-drawn copper wire, end insulators and pulleys from there. My contributions to the original concept are the weed-trimmer line, spreaders and wire sizes. The trimmer line is stiffer and neater than string or twine. The spreaders are made from small-diameter PEX or PVC tubing secured by filling them with hot glue. The wire passes through them via holes positioned to stabilize the antenna. The bare stranded 80 meter wire serves as a messenger cable to support shorter wires via the spreaders. The other wires are #16 AWG insulated wire I purchased at the local hardware store.

When you purchase the wire, check the diameters of both sizes before you buy the drill bits. Keep the hole size as close as possible to the outer diameter of the wire; you'll see why later. The bottom wire holes are spaced a bit from the top wire (see **Figure 8.4**) to lower the center of gravity. This helps keep the antenna from twisting on itself! After drilling and cleaning the holes, I used a .22-caliber gun-cleaning rod and bore-brush to remove the plastic burrs from the center of the tubing. Next, cut two wires for each band, but be sure to allow a little extra length. You'll need it for terminations at the center and pruning at the end insulators.

I've found it best to cut the wires and thread them through the spreaders first. Lay your wires out as shown in Figure 8.3, 80 meters on top and the higher frequency wires downward in succession. Thread the first spreader on, making sure you are using the *top* hole and the bare wire for 80 meters. Once you have all the wires started through all the spreaders on that side, grab each wire and pull about 2 feet through the spread-

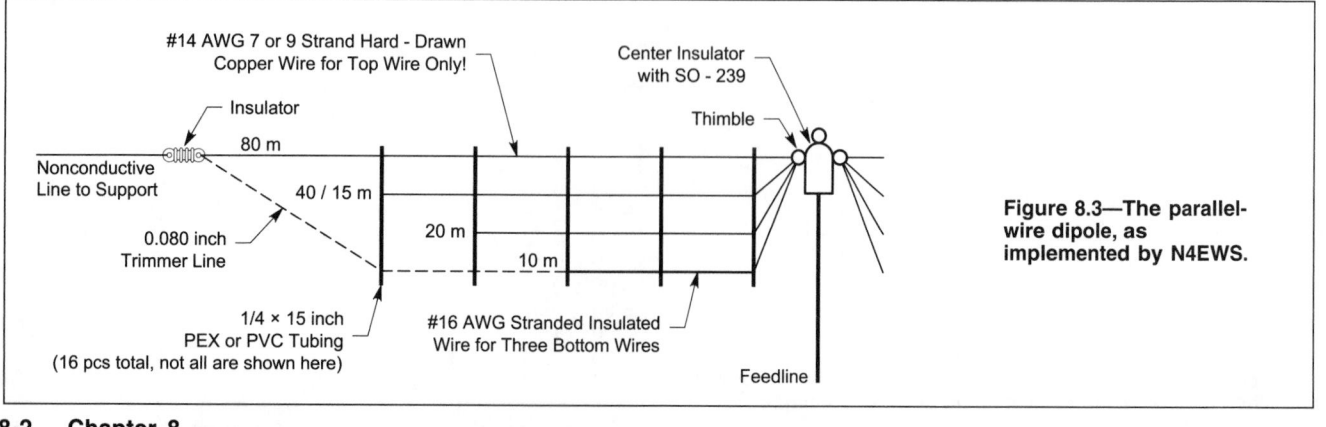

**Figure 8.3—The parallel-wire dipole, as implemented by N4EWS.**

**Table 8.2**
**Parallel Dipole Data**

| Band (m) | Leg Length | $f_0$ (MHz) | SWR@MHz (Phone Subband) | |
|---|---|---|---|---|
| 80 | 60' 8" | 3.880 | 1.1@3.850 | 1.3@3.980 |
| 40 | 33' 6" | 7.225 | 1.4@7.230 | 1.9@7.300 |
| 20 | 17' 0" | 14.260 | 1.2@14.200 | 1.1@14.345 |
| 15 | (See 40 m) | | 1.7@21.300 | 1.8@21.450 |
| 10 | 8' 7" | 29.000 | 1.1@28.200 | 1.5@29.000 |

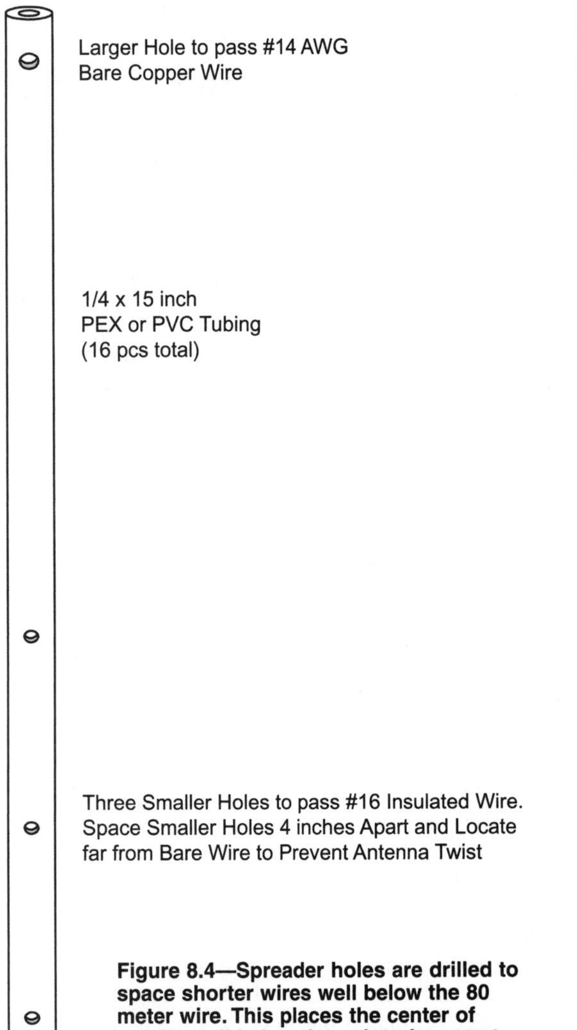

Larger Hole to pass #14 AWG
Bare Copper Wire

1/4 x 15 inch
PEX or PVC Tubing
(16 pcs total)

Three Smaller Holes to pass #16 Insulated Wire.
Space Smaller Holes 4 inches Apart and Locate
far from Bare Wire to Prevent Antenna Twist

**Figure 8.4—Spreader holes are drilled to space shorter wires well below the 80 meter wire. This places the center of gravity well below the point of support and prevents the antenna from twisting.**

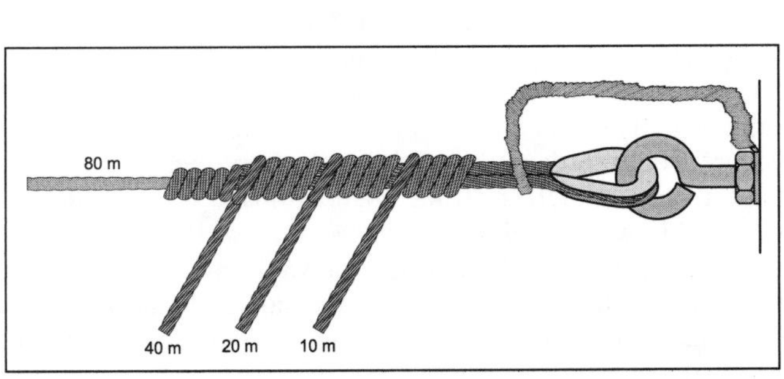

80 m

40 m    20 m    10 m

**Figure 8.5—Details of the wire connections and thimble at the center insulator. The 80 meter wire is wrapped about 3 inches from the center insulator, and the shorter wires are wrapped around the double wire in that 3 inch space.**

ers from that end. You may want to do this work a few spreaders at a time, depending on how well the holes are aligned. Now, strip about 4 inches of insulation from each of the bottom wires. If you are not already using wire thimbles on your wire antennas, I suggest their use. They reduce wire fatigue.

Place the thimble through one of the eyes on the center insulator. Tin about 6 inches of the bare 80 meter wire using a high-wattage soldering gun or a small gas torch and some rosin-core solder, then let it cool. Wrap the tinned wire around the thimble and leave about 3 inches extra from the thimble junction before you begin the wrap (see **Figure 8.5**). Compress the thimble ends as much as possible, but *do not* use pliers! Pliers may nick the thimble edges. Start a tight wrap, one turn right next to the other! When finished, apply more heat and solder to the junction if needed to fill any voids. Don't use too much heat, as you don't want to soften the wire! Make sure to check for voids and fill where the wires come together at the thimble ends; this will improve the strength.

Next, place all the wires flat as they would hang from the top: 80-40-20-10. *Make sure the thimble and center insulator are oriented properly before you start!* The PL-259 should be at the bottom, just as it would hang when in use. Hold the bottom wires by the insulation, keeping them flat, perpendicular and underneath the end of the 80 meter wrap. The 40 meter wire should be the first and outermost wire, next to the beginning of the 80 meter wrap. Do a flat spiral wrap from each wire around the double wire leading back to the thimble. Keep the wires as flat as possible, and wrap towards the thimble. Snip any extra and solder. Do the same for the other side. Now, attach and solder the pigtails from the center insulator to each side.

It's just about time for testing, but before you do, ensure that the lengths of both antenna sides are equal. I did this by folding the antenna over onto itself, but measuring would be simpler and should be sufficiently accurate. Check each set of wires according their band, and be careful not to cut the wrong wire.

Now, grab a couple of end insulators and install them on the 80 meter wires. Pull 1 1/2 feet of wire through the end insulator and loosely wind it back onto itself; then do the same on the other side. Connect the feed line, and your antenna is ready for tests. If you use coax, make a shield choke near the transmitter by wrapping six loops of the coax at about 8 inches in diameter and taping them together. [Eight inches is good for small-diameter coax, but always conform to the minimum bending radius specification for the cable you're using.—Ed.] This ensures that your SWR measurements won't be disturbed by stray shield current.

Hoist the dipole into operating position and give it a test. Remember, the antenna height and configuration affects the impedance. When testing, measure the SWR on all the bands and record the results after every test. You need to see how much the wires interact before final pruning for resonance. When you start cutting, keep a close eye on 10 meters. I have found that it can really interact with the other bands. [I have not experienced this with the wires spaced apart by 4 inches or more and when pruning in order from shortest wire to longest.—Ed.] Leave an extra 1 1/2 inch on the outer ends of the insulated wires. This is for securing the wire end at the spreader. To do this, strip the insulation from that 1 1/2 inch of wire previously mentioned, twist the stripped wire into a small ball and then apply some solder. You don't need to cut the 80 meter wire yet; just unwrap, move the insulator in or out and rewrap until the adjustments are complete.

When adjustments are complete, it's time to run the string trimmer line and glue everything down. Lower the antenna and position the spreaders evenly. Fire-up the 80 W hot-glue gun while you're feeding the string-trimmer line through the holes in the spreaders. Allow some extra line for tying to the end insulators. When you get to the end of the 10 meter insulator, you can either make a loop around it and/or drill another hole to terminate it there. You can drill it about an inch above the 10 meter hole, pass the line through it, make a knot and glue it. It's kind of like bobbing the ends of the wires, but you use hot glue instead of solder.

Now grab your heavy-duty glue gun and get to work on the spreaders. Make sure the glue gun has a full reservoir, a fresh stick in the feed handle and there's a good supply on hand! You'll need a lot of glue to fill the centers of the spreaders. Wear work gloves to do this next part, and be very careful; it can get hot. Start with the first spreader near the center on either side. Hold the spreader from the top, horizontally with your covered hand between the 80 and 40 meter wire or lay the spreader on a table. Tilt it upward slightly, so that the 10 meter wire end is slightly elevated. Be careful not to let the wires slip from side to side, as this will cause one or more wires to be slack. Insert the glue-gun nozzle firmly into the top of the spreader. Squeeze the trigger, filling the entire length of the tubing. Don't stop until you see glue coming out the other end and don't move it until the glue cools and starts to solidify!

Some of the glue will be squeezed out the holes, where the wires and string trimmer line are passing through the insulator. This is okay. In fact, it's the reason why I used bare stranded wire for the 80 meter span! The glue forced into the wire strands will help it stay in place.—*Joe Deaton, N4EWS, 107 Nature Trail, Louisburg, NC 27549;* **n4ews@mindspring. com**

## TOWER FOOTING HINTS

◊ I enjoyed Bart Pulverman, WB6WUW's article "Self-Supporting Tower and Antenna Installation" (*QST*, July 2003, pp 33-37). It reminded me of the cold January evening years ago when I used a wheelbarrow to move 12,000 pounds of concrete (by myself!) from the ready-mix truck to my crank-up tower foundation; the reason I had to do that is a story in itself.

Nonetheless, I have a few suggestions to make the excavation easier if you plan to dig by hand as I did. Because the space to work is so limited (in my case, the hole was only 42 inches on a side), I found an old garden shovel and then sawed off most of the handle. This produced a "shorty" shovel with which I could easily move the loosened soil up and out of the hole. I encountered fairly hard clay at a depth of about two feet, which made hand digging slow and difficult even though our wet Pacific Northwest winter ensured that the soil was wet and well lubricated. A helpful tool rental center owner suggested a solution: an electric jackhammer equipped with a spade tip. For $45 (1991 prices), I rented the machine for a day and quickly completed the excavation. Because of the restricted workspace, I rigged a block and tackle to lift the jackhammer out of the hole before using the shorty shovel to remove the loosened soil.

By the way, the best method I have found to drive ground rods is to remove the tip from the electric jackhammer and then place the machine on top of the ground rod. Pull the trigger and down goes the rod! When it encounters a buried rock, the rod pauses until the jackhammer pulses fracture the rock, then rapidly continues burying itself. I took advantage of the tool rental to drive three eight-foot ground rods near the tower foundation and three other ones around the property. The total time to drive six rods was under half an hour! Resist the temptation to place your tower ground rods in the foundation hole; a lightning strike could severely damage the concrete.

My tower manufacturer's hole dimensions required 2.5 cubic yards of concrete, but my concrete supplier quoted the same price for 3 yards as for 2.5. I decided to accommodate the additional half-yard by digging the hole a few inches deeper and then expanding the bottom outward, giving the excavation a "bell" shape and lowering the foundation's center of gravity significantly. Although not at all necessary, this change provided a significant safety margin for the tower's stability.

Finally, on advice of a friend who was an industrial bricklayer, I decided to rent an electric vibrator (known as a "stinger" in the trade) to ensure that the concrete would be as dense as possible. I was amazed at the large volume of trapped air that the vibrator released. I believe that the vibrator was essential to produce a foundation of the highest integrity, and it was much faster than using the manual method suggested in WB6WUW's article.—*Michael Mraz, N6MZ, 15526 SE 50th St, Bellevue, WA 98006-3611;* **n6mz@arrl.net**

## PUT YOUR BUTTERNUT VERTICAL ON 60 METERS

◊ If you've got a Butternut vertical, you can be on 60 meters in literally minutes. Just take a clip lead and short 11 of the 16 turns of the 80-meter coil. One end of the clip lead should be clipped to the screw at the bottom of the 80-meter coil, and the other end of the clip lead is connected up 11 turns. Use an antenna analyzer to find the exact point for lowest SWR at 5365 kHz. I was able to get less than 1.5:1 SWR at resonance and less than 2:1 at the band edges. Mark the turn with a permanent marker, so it is easy to find when you want to get on 60 meters. If you have some Solder-It aluminum solder, you can solder a tab to the aluminum 80-meter coil at the appropriate place (**www.solder-it.com**).

My Butternut is mounted about six inches from a cedar fence. To make things a little easier, I mounted a 12 V SPST relay in a plastic box to the fence near the 80-meter coil. The relay contacts are connected across the 80-meter coil as described above, letting me remotely switch in 60 meters from my shack. See you on 60 meters!—*Phil Salas, AD5X, 1517 Creekside Dr, Richardson, TX 75081-2913;* **ad5x@arrl.net**

## WATER AND HYGAIN TH-7 TRAPS

◊ After having my TH-7 in the air for almost a year, I began encountering a rising SWR during long, heavy rainstorms. At first, I suspected that water was getting into the BN-86 balun enclosure. So I lowered the antenna and inspected the balun, but it showed no signs of water having settled in it. After some head scratching, I raised the antenna back to the top of the tower. A few days later, another heavy rainstorm came along, and again my SWR rose to above 3 to 1 on 15 and 20 meters. This time I suspected that I was getting water into the traps of the dual driven elements. I again lowered the antenna; and when I pulled off one of the end caps from a trap, water came pouring out. I had found the problem, but how was water collecting in the traps when they have drain holes on the bottom? Furthermore, what would be the solution?

As illustrated below (see **Figure 8.6**), I surmised that water was collecting on the outside of the traps and that the droop of the element caused the traps to lay somewhat less than fully horizontal. Thus, any water that accumulated in the trap enclosure would settle toward the outside. The pitch of the trap made it impossible for all the water to make it to the drain holes. This was certainly the case; as all of the traps I inspected, the ones that showed signs of water collecting in them was always found to be on the outside half of the trap.

Actually, the solution is quite simple. At the bottom of each plastic trap cover, I drilled a ⅛ inch hole to drain any water. I did this to all of the traps throughout the antenna. Don't be fooled into thinking that sealing the trap covers will solve the problem. If moisture accumulates in the trap, sealing will make

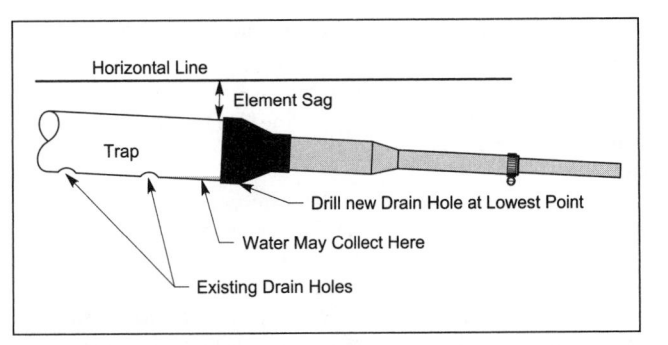

Figure 8.6—Element sag permits water to accumulate in traps away from the existing drain holes. By drilling an additional hole as shown, the trap can drain.

it impossible for water to make its way out. If you do seal the covers, add the drain holes too. Since making this adjustment to my TH-7, I have had no problems with SWR during long, heavy rainstorms.—*William J. Thomas, K1XT, 810 Selma, Webster Groves, MO 63119*

## IMPROVEMENTS TO THE 2 METER CU LOOP

◊ The assembly and alignment of the 2 meter Cu loop antenna ["Try Copper for 2 Meters—The Cu Loop," *QST*, Dec 2002, pp 46-48] can be simplified by making the following changes to the gamma matching system. These changes eliminate forming the gamma match tube shape and delete the shorting strap and its adjustment completely. The center frequency can then be set by a simple adjustment of the end caps. If the SWR is not very low after completion, the center wire insulation is probably different than on those antennas tested. If that's the case, change the wire size in $^1/_8$ inch steps until the SWR is minimum. All other parameters of the design remain the same. **Figure 8.7** shows a drawing of the modified match.

1. Drill a $^1/_4$ inch hole on the centerline of the elbow and tubing and $^3/_{16}$ inch below the edge of the elbow. The gamma rod should then be spaced $^9/_{16}$ inch from the OD of the lower antenna element, as shown. Place the $^1/_4$ inch gamma tube through the hole so that $4^{15}/_{16}$ inch is exposed outside the elbow. The tube should not touch the back wall when inserted.

2. Solder it in place, with the gamma tube parallel with the element. Do not heat to the point that you loosen the elbow. Insert 6 inches of sleeving against the element back wall. It should be exposed about $^3/_{16}$ of an inch at the connector end of the tube.

3. Insert a $4^7/_8$ inch length of #16 (AWG) vinyl covered

wire and solder it to the coax connector center pin. The length of this wire is critical and includes $^1/_8$ inch excess, which is stripped for soldering to the connector. Both the back of the connector and the exposed end of the gamma rod should be sealed against moisture entry.—*Dick Stroud, W9SR, 3139 S Main, Box 73, Liberty Center, IN 46766;* **w9sr@arrl.net**

## TUNING A WIRE J-POLE ANTENNA

◊ There have been many good 2-meter, or 2-meter/70-cm J-pole construction articles published in Amateur Radio magazines and numerous club newsletters. Unfortunately, they all fall short by not telling readers how to tune the new antenna.

I built two J-poles shortly after becoming an Amateur Radio operator. One tuned up just as advertised, the other was a lost cause. This antenna was constructed the same as the first, and I used the same batch of 300-Ω ladder line for both. I put this antenna aside for about three months, until one summer day I decided to discover just how to tune a J-pole antenna, first time *every* time.

### Minimize SWR

I found that the distance between the feed point and the shorting bar determines the minimum SWR. If the antenna is too long or too short, the lowest SWR may be nowhere near 1:1. If you've followed the instructions and your dimensions are correct, however, that should not be the case.

I find it best to keep some extra wire at the bottom of the antenna matching section (about 2 inches). That lets me move the shorting bar up and down to find the minimum SWR. Do *not* use the stripped wire at the end of the matching section to form the shorting bar. Leave it straight and tack on a moveable shorting bar.

### Resonant Frequency

Once you have the shorting bar set, do *not* cut off the extra wire at the bottom of the antenna. Move the shorting bar and the feed point *together*. Move them upward (shorter single wire) if the tuned frequency is too low, downward (longer single wire) if the tuned frequency is too high. Either way, maintain the distance between the feed point and the shorting bar. This insures that the SWR does not change.

The overall length of the antenna, the length of the matching stub, and the distance between the feed point and the shorting bar are not independent of one another. Since the construction-article authors have spent the time to optimize the antenna dimensions, however, you can treat these lengths as independent for the small changes needed to tune a J-pole.

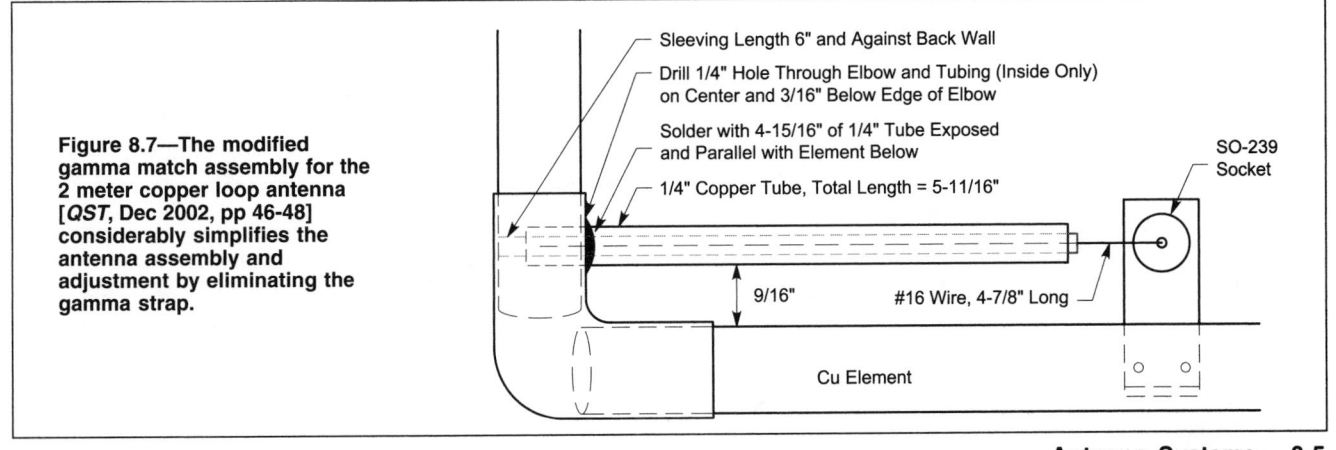

Figure 8.7—The modified gamma match assembly for the 2 meter copper loop antenna [*QST*, Dec 2002, pp 46-48] considerably simplifies the antenna assembly and adjustment by eliminating the gamma strap.

Sleeving Length 6" and Against Back Wall

Drill 1/4" Hole Through Elbow and Tubing (Inside Only) on Center and 3/16" Below Edge of Elbow

Solder with 4-15/16" of 1/4" Tube Exposed and Parallel with Element Below

1/4" Copper Tube, Total Length = 5-11/16"

SO-239 Socket

9/16"

#16 Wire, 4-7/8" Long

Cu Element

## A Bit More Information

I once constructed a J-pole antenna that was 3 inches too long, but with a matching stub of the correct length. The minimum SWR was about 3:1, and it would not resonate on 146 MHz, as expected. When I removed the extra length, it could achieve resonance on 146 MHz with a 1:1 SWR. Therefore, if an antenna cannot achieve a 1:1 SWR after you perform the steps above, check the overall length of the antenna again. The resonant (minimum SWR) frequency tells you if the antenna is too short (the frequency is too high) or too long (the frequency is too low).

I've built—or helped build—over 100 wire J-pole antennas, and I've yet to find one that couldn't be tuned using this method. If you have a problem wire J-pole in the closet, get it out and see if these instructions help.—*Phil Karras, KE3FL (OES, ORS, VE, and AEC), Carroll County, Maryland;  ke3fl@juno.com*

## THE "TENNA-TUNE": A SIMPLE CONTROL/SWR INDICATOR FOR SCREWDRIVER ANTENNAS

◊ Antennas based on Don Johnson's (W6AAQ) "screwdriver" design have become extremely popular because of their performance and remote-tuning abilities. Miniature versions of these antennas have recently become available from numerous sources.

These miniature antennas interest me because I like to operate mostly "mobile-at-rest." Therefore, I want a small antenna package that I can easily remove and install on my car.

After considering several of the different antennas currently available, I settled on the Little Tarheel "screwdriver" antenna (**www.tarheelantennas.com**).

I like to pair my Little Tarheel with the MFJ-1954 10 foot telescoping whip (**www.mfjenterprises.com/products. php?prodid=MFJ-1954**). This combination makes a very effective mobile-at-rest/portable package, with operation down to 60 meters (and even 80 meters if you don't mind changing the base-matching coil for that band).

Rather than purchase a commercial tuning device, I decided to build a simple, effective and inexpensive tuning indicator to help me tune the antenna remotely.

I normally operate mobile with either an SGC-2020 or an IC-706MKIIG, so my circuit is built to key my IC-706MKIIG in its 10-W tune mode.

### The Tenna-Tune

The circuit is shown in **Figures 8.8** and **8.9**. The parts list is in **Table 8.3**. The circuit is simply a resistive 50 Ω bridge coupled with an IC-706MKIIG "tune" interface.

The bridge is the same circuit I used in an absorptive SWR indicator for the MFJ-902.[1]

The advantages of the resistive bridge are that it is simple, and it protects your radio during high-SWR conditions. (The worst-case SWR presented to the radio should be only 2:1.) The disadvantages are that two of three resistors must dissipate up to 100% of the tune-up power, and it can be difficult to find the suitable resistors.

This circuit is based on three Caddock 50-Ω 15-W power resistors in TO-126 packages (Mouser #684-MP915-50 at $2.78 each). These are excellent, noninductive power resistors. (If you want more power dissipation, a 30 W, TO-220 version is available—Mouser #684-MP930-50 at $3.58 each.) The 15 W resistors are fine for short periods of up to 25 W, if they have appropriate heat sinks.

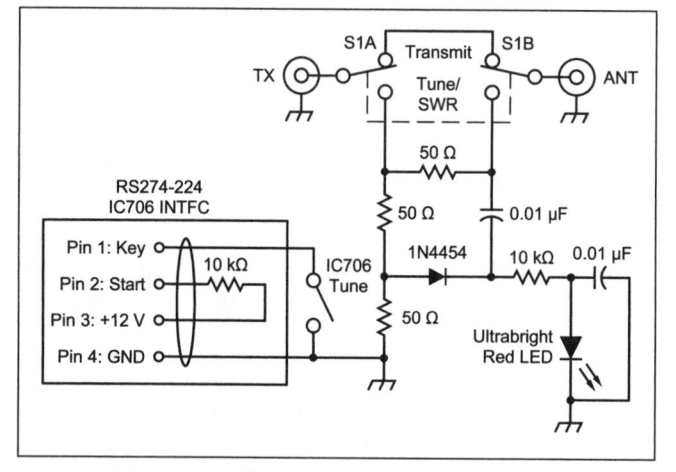

**Figure 8.8—The Tenna-Tune schematic.**

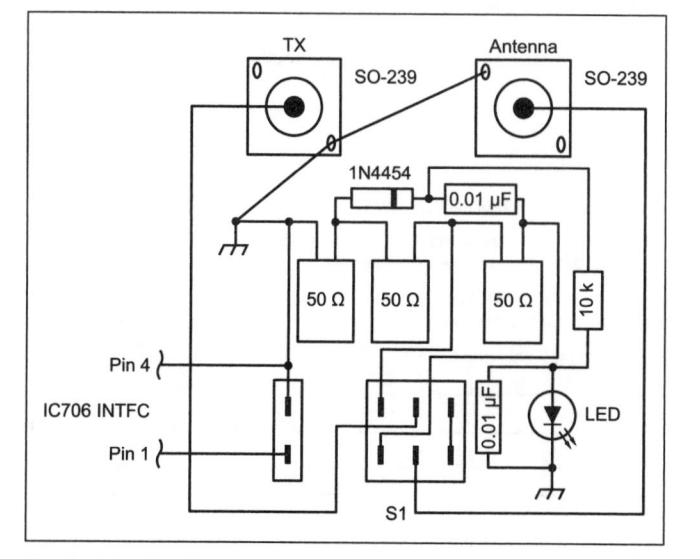

**Figure 8.9—The Tenna-Tune wiring diagram drawn as if the box were folded flat.**

[1]P. Salas, AD5X, "An SWR Indicator for the MFJ-902 Antenna Tuner," *QST*, Oct 2004, pp 58-60.

---

**Table 8.3**
**Tenna-Tune Parts**

| Qty | Description (Source) |
|---|---|
| 3 | 50 Ω 15 W resistor (Mouser 684-MP915-50) |
| 1 | DPDT slide switch (Mouser 611-S602031SS03Q) |
| 1 | SPST toggle switch (Mouser 1055-TA1120) |
| 1 | Mini-box, 2.25×1.5×1.38 inches (Mouser 537-M00-P) |
| 2 | 0.01 µF, 500 V capacitor (Mouser 75-5HKSS10) |
| 2 | 10 kΩ resistor (RadioShack 271-1335) |
| 1 | 6000 mcd red LED (All Electronics LED-94) |
| 1 | Terminal strip (RadioShack #274-688)* |
| 1 | Heat-sink grease (RadioShack #276-1372) |
| 3 | #2 screws (RadioShack #64-3010) |
| 3 | #2 nuts (RadioShack 64-3017) |
| 1 | 4-pin Molex plug (RadioShack 274-224) |
| 2 | SO-239 connectors (All Electronics SO-239) |
| 1 | 2-piece LED clip (All Electronics HLED-4)* |

*Optional—see text.

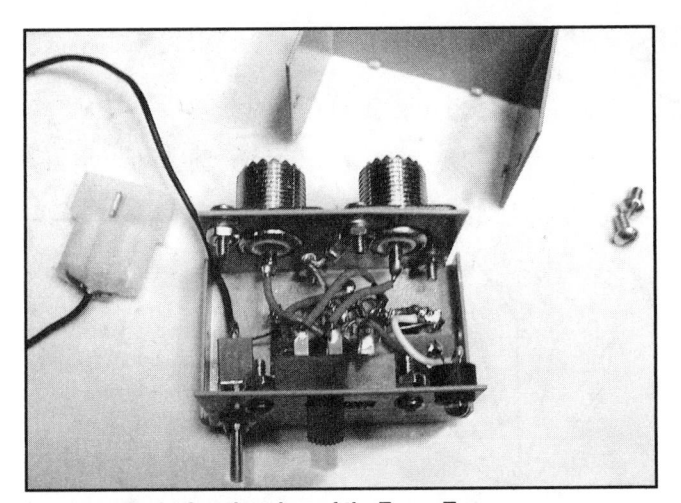

Figure 8.10—An Interior view of the Tenna Tune.

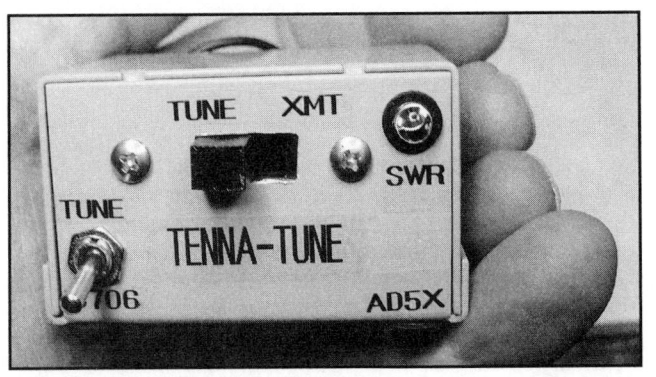

Figure 8.11—The Tenna Tune front panel.

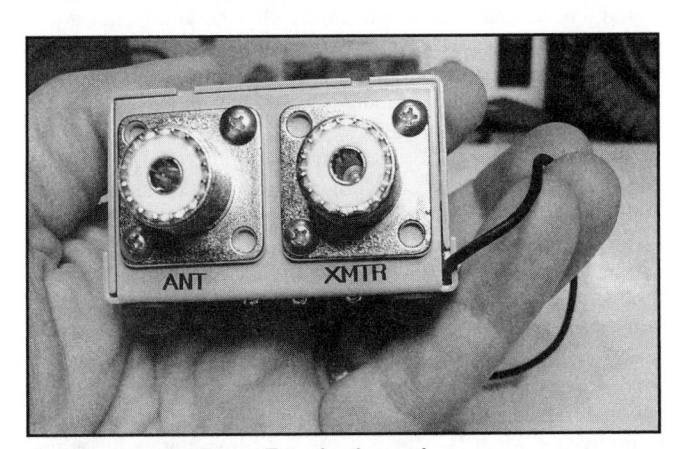

Figure 8.12—The Tenna Tune back panel.

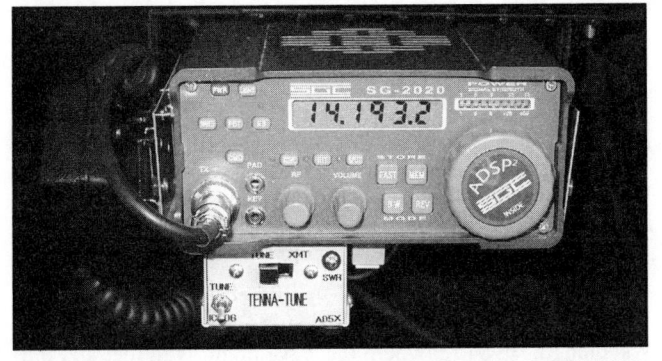

Figure 8.13—The Tenna Tune installed with the author's SGC-2020.

### The Interface

The IC-706 tune interface is very simple. A 10 kΩ resistor "fools" the radio into "thinking" that a tuner is connected, so the radio is keyed in the 10-W CW mode whenever pin 1 of the antenna-tuner interface is grounded by the SPST toggle switch. I mounted the 10 kΩ resistor directly on the 4-pin plug, so only two wires need connect run to the Tenna-Tune.

The most difficult assembly task is cutting a rectangular hole for the DPDT slide switch. You may want to use a toggle switch (round-hole mount) to make things easier—I prefer the look of the slide switch.

I built everything into the tiny aluminum box in the parts list (see **Figure 8.10**). If yours is painted, scrape the paint away where the connectors and power resistors touch the box. (Use heat-sink grease under the power resistors.)

I chose a 6000 mcd ultra-bright red LED. This LED requires minimal current to give a good SWR indication. It's at the upper-right corner (see **Figure 8.11**). The LED clip in the parts list requires a 1/4 inch hole. You could drill a 3/16-inch-diameter hole and hold the LED in place with some hot glue if you prefer. The two SO-239 connectors just fit on the back panel as you can see in **Figure 8.12**.

The wiring diagram is shown in Figure 8.9. This figure is drawn as if the aluminum box were laid out flat. Wiring should be as direct as possible, but it is not shown that way for clarity. While I did use a terminal strip to mount some of the parts (see the parts list), this is probably not necessary. There are enough stiff leads on the 50 Ω resistors, SO-239s and the slide switch to support the few parts required. I also nibbled a little aluminum from the corner of the aluminum box cover so that the IC-706 interface cable can easily exit the box. Figure 8.10 gives you an idea of what my final wired unit looks like. All labeling "black on clear" tape from a Casio label maker. I also used stick-on rubber feet on the bottom of the unit. **Figure 8.13** shows the Tenna-Tune mounted with my SG-2020 in the car.

### Operation

I start with the antenna in its minimum-length position, which resonates with the fully extended 10 foot MFJ whip just above the 17 meter band. I always return the antenna to this minimum length position when I'm through operating so the antenna takes up as little room as possible in my trunk when I remove it from the quick-disconnect mount.

To tune the antenna, I push the slide-switch on the Tenna-Tune to TUNE, flip the IC-706 toggle switch to TUNE (when using the IC-706MKIIG), and then run the antenna motor up until the SWR LED dims noticeably or, preferably, goes out. I then turn off the IC-706 TUNE toggle switch, flip the slide switch to XMT, and I'm ready to go. This entire process is very easy, and takes very little time. I've had no problem with warming of the Tenna-Tune case during the time it takes me to tune the antenna. Obviously, the Tenna-Tune will work with all screwdriver antennas and other brands of radios. Just limit your tune-up power to no more than about 25 W. A good SWR indication occurs with 2-5 W of power.

This simple unit permits rapid tuning of screwdriver antennas. For IC-706 owners, it also sets the radio to the 10 W tune mode. While this unit does not provide automatic operation, it is easy to use and inexpensive, and it protects the radio during the tuning procedure.

If you have a screwdriver antenna and don't yet have one of those automatic tuning interfaces, give the Tenna-Tune a try!—*Phil Salas, AD5X, 1517 Creekside Dr, Richardson, TX 75081-2913;* **ad5x@arrl.net**

# The Doctor is IN

**Q** Bill asks, "Where can I find information on how to tune a trap vertical antenna with or without an antenna analyzer?"

**A** information on tuning an antenna is the antenna's manufacturer. Failing that, you want to mount the antenna up in the clear and check SWR on the highest band on several frequencies across the band. If the SWR is lowest at the low end of the band, then you want to shorten the section of the antenna that operates on that band. Conversely, if the SWR is lowest at the high end of the band, you would want to lengthen that section.

**Figure 8.14—The MFJ-259B HF/VHF SWR Analyzer.**

Once you get the SWR where you want it for that band, you should move down to the next lower-frequency band and adjust that in the same fashion. Repeat for the remaining bands.

Depending upon the antenna's design, the adjustments may be interactive and in that case, you may have to repeat the whole process (starting with the highest band and working downward) several times to get the tuning just right.

This can be done with a transmitter and SWR bridge, although if you use an SWR meter and your transmitter, you are limited to transmitting only in the ham bands for which you hold a license. If you use an antenna analyzer, you can check the SWR outside the ham bands, in case the initial tuning is so far off that the SWR is high across the entire ham band. If you are using a transmitter, see which end of the band has the highest SWR and make the adjustments as described above.

**Q** Chester, KD5TFK, asks: I am presently using a multi-band mobile antenna mounted about 15 feet high as my base station antenna. I find that I work more DX than local stations on 10 meters using 100 W. Is this normal considering I have a very simple antenna setup? Would a low angle of elevation or the antenna's polarization have anything to do with it?

**A** Ten meters can be open for worldwide communications when conditions are right. Part of what you are seeing is the fact that there are a lot more DX stations in the world than the number of hams near you. Even a modest antenna and 100 W can work the world when the band is open.

DX communication on HF involves the ionosphere. The ionosphere consists of several layers at varying heights above the earth, from about 50 to over 200 miles. The layers are known as the D, E and F layers, with the F layer usually combining at night—the F1 and F2. The layers bend or reflect radio energy back toward the earth. The actual reflection is usually from the F2 layer. This is shown in **Figure 8.15**, which shows how signals can travel from one point to another by reflecting off an ionized layer in the ionosphere.

Not all angles are actually reflected, though. Note that energy that is sent upward at high angles can be bent into space rather than returning to the earth. There is a "skip" zone where

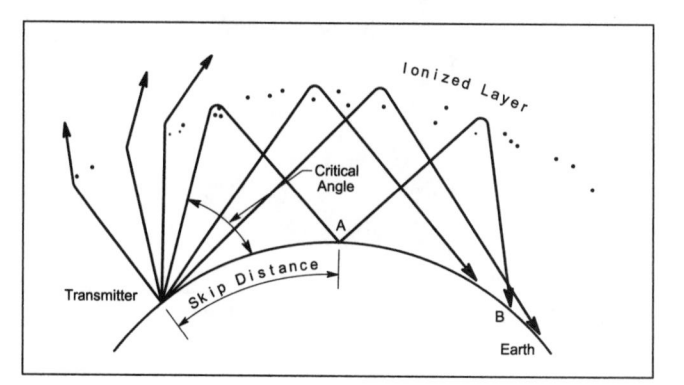

**Figure 8.15—How signals can travel from one point to another by reflecting off an ionized layer in the ionosphere.**

no signals can be heard at all. Near your station, the signal from your antenna can travel directly to another local station (this is often termed the "ground wave," indicating that the signal has traveled close to the earth). In the skip zone, no signals can be heard (or a very faint signal might be audible from various scatter effects). At longer distances the signals become loud and strong. At higher frequencies—10 meters for example—the skip zone can be hundreds of miles.

The vertical antenna also produces more low-angle radiation than high-angle radiation, so it does not send as much signal upward that could be heard by closer stations, nor does it hear them very well. The relative number of DX and local stations, the skip zone and the low-angle performance of your vertical antenna both contribute to your hearing more DX than stateside QSOs on 10 meters.

For true local work on 10 meters, you and the other local stations should use the same polarization. For local 10-meter FM, vertical polarization is almost universal. If, however, the local stations you want to communicate with use horizontal antennas, you should, too. For local work, you should mount this vertical as high and in the clear as reasonable, to help get your signal more directly to the other station by avoiding the losses caused by buildings and other ground clutter.

For DX work the antenna polarization doesn't matter because the reflections off the ionosphere change the polarization anyway. Most DX takes place with low angles of radiation from the antenna. A vertical generally has good low-angle performance in all azimuth directions. Over ground with average characteristics, a high dipole can actually be a better DX antenna than a vertical antenna, but it attains that performance only in directions broadside to the antenna. Off the ends, the DX performance suffers.

**Q** W4FTP wants to know: What are the formulas for calculating full wavelengths and partial wavelengths? I'm interested in building a wire antenna in some trees in my backyard.

**A** The answer depends on what you are trying to calculate. In free space (that is, traveling through the air or a vacuum), the formula to calculate 1 wavelength is:

Wavelength = 984 / F where the wavelength is in feet and the frequency is in MHz.

It is easy to calculate fractional wavelengths from this formula by multiplying the numerator (the 984) by the fractional wavelength you want to calculate. For example, a half wavelength = 0.5 wavelength = $(0.5 \times 984) / F = 492 / F$

A free-space ¼-wavelength in feet would be 246/F.

However, when you are talking about wire (or coax), additional factors have to be considered. For antennas using straight wires, the open wire ends exhibits a "self-capacitance" (commonly known as *end effect*) that causes them to appear electrically longer than they are physically. To compensate, the calculated physical dimension must be shortened about 5 percent.

So for half-wave dipoles, the correct formula is $0.95 \times 492/F = 468/F$ and for ¼ wave, the formula is 234/F. For a ⅝-wave vertical, it would be $0.95 \times 985/F \times ⅝ = 584/F$.

In a closed loop antenna, the loop does not exhibit end effect, but the loop adds some inductance. To compensate, the antenna must be made somewhat physically larger, hence the one wavelength formula of 1002/F. HF loops are usually close to 1005/F.

**Q** Richard, W4MUR, writes: I have encountered an antenna problem that has me totally buffaloed. The design is electrically a J-pole (15 meters), but the matching stub is run horizontally. The radiator consists of a half-wave vertical made of a 10 foot section of ½-inch electrical conduit with threaded nuts brazed to each end for mechanical and electrical coupling. To the top of this is screwed a 12 foot length of WW II surplus mast sections. The matching section consists of 11 feet of open wire feed line (12 gauge wire spaced 3½ inches, fed with 50 Ω coax near the shorted end).

The antenna sits on top of a 14 foot fiberglass vaulting pole and sticks through a short section of ABS pipe bolted to the edge of the garage roof and is about 2 feet from the brick wall of the garage. Additionally, there is an 18 inch wide horizontal trellis of galvanized mesh attached to the wall at the 7 to 9 foot level for some vines in my yard. Near the bottom of the vertical radiator is a triangular metal vent.

In order to tune the antenna, I brought the base of the antenna away from the wall, lowering it to a convenient tuning height. The top part was still run through the ABS pipe. I was able to get a 1.1:1 SWR using an antenna analyzer.

Upon raising the antenna to vertical, the SWR increased and no matter where I connect the coax to the open wire, the best SWR I can get is 2:1. Simultaneously, the resonant frequency decreases from the lowered position to the vertical position. I tried coiling the coax to act as a choke balun and manipulating the antenna position so that it no longer touched the ABS support pipe. Raising the antenna incrementally to the vertical position, I observed increasing SWR as it became more vertical. Changing the position of the matching section to vertical had no effect. What's going on?

**A** I definitely recommend using a balun for this antenna for a permanent installation, although it is not likely the cause of your problem. Coiled coax would certainly suffice, but it *must* be wound in adjacent, neat turns in order to get the proper choking action (using some sort of coil form would be a good idea). *The ARRL Antenna Book*[2] suggests using 6 feet of coax wound in 8 turns as being the optimal configuration for a 15 meter choke balun (this applies to both RG-8 and RG-58 type coax).

What is the most likely cause of your grief is the metal vent

[2] *The ARRL Antenna Book*, 20th ed., is available from your local dealer or the ARRL Bookstore, order no. 9043. Tel (toll-free in the US) 888-277-5289 or (from elsewhere) 860-594-0355; **pubsales@ arrl.org**; **www.arrl.org/shop**.

**Figure 8.16—A portable antenna analyzer is a useful device for determining antenna and transmission line characteristics. It generates its own signal, so transmitter RF isn't required.**

at the peak of the garage roof. This piece of metal will act as the plate of a capacitor, with the antenna as the other plate—as if you had added a small capacitance hat at that point of the antenna. This, in itself, is not so much the problem, but rather, the different position of the antenna from where you tuned it to where it was finally mounted. The electrical position of this capacitance hat is changing with respect to the antenna and that is most likely changing the antenna's resonant frequency.

What I would suggest is to make note of where the resonant point is now (in the permanent mounting position). Don't worry about the actual SWR for the moment—just note where the impedance is pure resistive. The use of a portable RF antenna analyzer, similar to the one shown in **Figure 8.16**, is recommended. Then, lower the antenna, change the length of the radiator by several inches and raise it back up. Relocate the resonant point and note how much it's moved. This should give you a pretty good idea as to how you need to change the length of the radiator to get the exact resonance you desire, although it may require a couple of tries before you get it exactly where you want it.

Once you get the radiator where you want it, adjust the position of the feed point on the ladder line. Since the ladder line is not a radiating section (not significantly so, anyway) it should not be affected by the proximity of the wire mesh for the vines, especially if you are using a balun on the coax. The Doctor hopes that helps and good luck!

**Q** From Jack, W1TEC, comes this: I had always thought that the ARRL had a policy of not allowing antenna gain values to be published as part of advertisements published in *QST*. In a full page ad on page 8 of the July 2003 issue there are free-space gain values given in dBi for each band. Is this a change in policy I have missed, or, since they specify gain in dBi, is that acceptable?

**A** That advertiser was kind enough to provide the information needed for the ARRL Lab to employ computer antenna modeling techniques to verify the gain figures claimed in that ad. This is in accordance with the ARRL's advertisement acceptance policy. Several other antenna manufacturers have also met this requirement. For the complete text of our Advertising Acceptance Policy (AAP) and for further information on how it is applied in the case of antenna gain figures, please see AAP (**www.arrl.org/ads/#policy**) and "Antenna Ads in ARRL Publications" (**www.arrl.org/ads/ antenna**). It is worthwhile to quote a portion from these: "…at least one fundamental property *must* be shown if *any* performance claims are made—the gain in free space at a specified frequency. This must always be shown referenced to a free-space isotropic antenna, meaning that gain must be shown in dBi. If the advertiser wishes to show, in addition, the gain with reference to a half-wave dipole in free space, he can do so by showing both dBi and dBd…"

Of course, the advertiser is free to, and encouraged to, provide more than this basic data to enable a member to make an intelligent decision on a purchase. Performance claims must be verifiable by accepted modeling software or by actual measurement on a certified antenna test range. That test range must meet EIA standard RS-329, Part 1. In lieu of RS-329 certified results, the advertiser may advertise performance figures derived from specific antenna modeling programs and all advertising performance claims derived from antenna modeling must indicate that they are calculated.

**Q** Nathan, KA3MTT, writes: Greetings and thank you for an excellent column every month in *QST*! I really enjoyed the recent article in *QST* that compared the different high power antenna tuners. Would you have any information, however, that compares low power (300 W and less) tuners? I think I'm in the market for a new tuner, and any info would be greatly appreciated.

That brings my next question. I just converted my delta loop antenna into a regular loop antenna fed with ladder line. I really don't have a specific measurement on it—I simply made it as long as possible. By doing this, I gained 80 meters, but there are a couple of bands (10 and 20 meters) that don't tune as well as they did when it was a delta loop. I can get them to tune down to an SWR of about 1.8 or 1.9:1 or so. I would like to have a better match than that, and was wondering if a better tuner would help. I currently have a tuner that is not the roller inductor type, and was wondering if one of those would possibly help out more. Thank you in advance for your help!

**A** First, the Doctor thanks you for your kind words. The antenna impedance matching range of a tuner is generally determined by the maximum and minimum values of the capacitors and inductors used in the tuner. There are cases where a tapped inductor (L) can be the limiting factor in achieving a good match. A tapped L may not be capable of reaching a proper value because a tap may fall between the needed inductance. If you should find that one of the capacitors in your tuner is running out of range between two inductor settings (if you can't get exactly the right setting), then trading for a roller inductor tuner could be useful. A roller inductor allows for an infinite value of L settings (or as fine as that roller can select). If you find, however, that either capacitor (C) (especially on the antenna side) is at maximum for multiple inductor settings, then you just don't have enough capacitance available and you need a tuner with more C.

Along with a higher power rating, the larger tuners often also have more C and L available.

I would not spend time trying to get that SWR below 1.8:1, however—there's really not much to be gained, unless your transceiver is reducing power output (going into power "foldback") at that SWR.

As far as your new delta loop antenna is concerned, I would advise you to try to model the antenna using one of the several antenna-modeling programs available, like *EZNEC* by W7EL.[3] You'll then have a good feel for its gain and SWR characteristics. If you do this, you'll see that you will be able to vary both the SWR and antenna pattern with the feed line impedance and the loop feed point. It's an interesting exercise and will teach you a lot about that antenna and others like it.

**Q** Donald, KJ4PO, asks: How do you calculate the impedance of a whip antenna? Let's say a 108 inch whip at 7250 kHz?

**A** The general formula for the radiation resistance ($R_r$) of a short dipole is:

$R_r = 790 \times [L / \lambda]^2$ where L = 108" = 9 feet, and $\lambda$ = 136.5 feet, so $[L/\lambda]^2 = 0.004$ and $R_r = 3.16 \ \Omega$.

[3]www.eznec.com

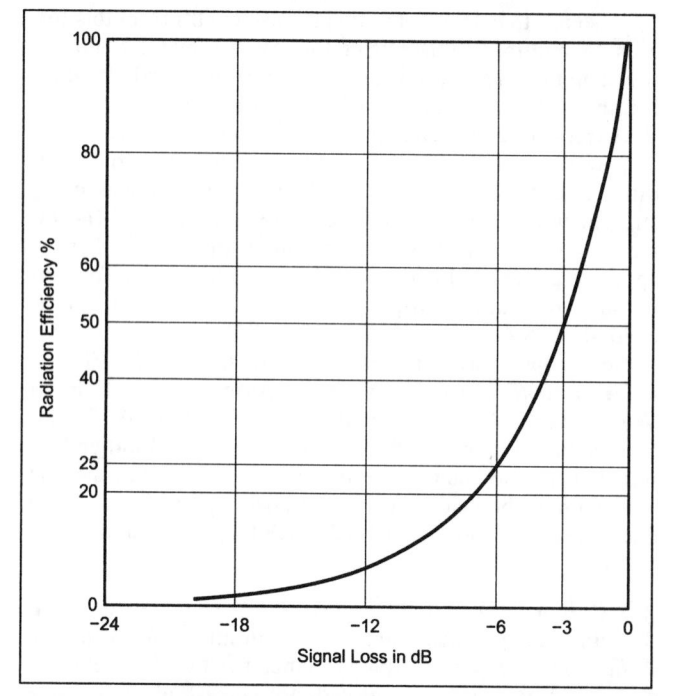

Figure 8.17—A plot of antenna efficiency in percent versus signal loss in dB compared to a quarter-wave vertical over perfect ground.

When used above an ideal ground, the whip acts as half of a short dipole; thus the radiation resistance is approximately half this value or 1.58 Ω. A more accurate and practical approach may be the formulas and graphs in Chapter 16 of *The ARRL Antenna Book*, which covers maritime and mobile antennas.[4] Referring to Eq 4 (page 16-5), $R_r = h^2/312$, where h is in degrees, so h = [L/984]×f (MHz)×360 and L = antenna length in feet. Running this calculation out, we find the radiation resistance = 1.82 Ω. This is close to the value presented by Figure 11 (page 16-8) for a 9 foot whip at 7.225 MHz.

In any case, you can see that the radiation resistance of very short whip antennas is indeed very low, something on the order of 2 Ω or less. The antenna efficiency expressed as a function of radiation resistance ($R_r$) and total loss resistance ($R_t$) is η = $[R_r / (R_r + R_t)] \times 100\%$. Assuming a total loss resistance (including ground loss) of 6 Ω and a radiation resistance of 2 Ω, we arrive at an antenna efficiency of about 25%. **Figure 8.17** presents the signal loss as a function of radiation efficiency and you can see that antenna efficiencies of 25 percent represent a loss of 6 dB compared to a ¼ wave vertical above perfect ground.

**Q** Paul, W8TM, writes: On page 4-12 of the 19th edition of *The ARRL Antenna Book*, it says, "When window-type line is suspended from an antenna in a manner such as that shown in Figure 14, the line should be twisted—at several twists per foot—to prevent stress hardening of the wire because of constant flexing in the wind." Yesterday, my first-ever installation of 450 Ω ladder line rode out its first wind/thunderstorm. The transmission line is not twisted and runs about 25 feet from the antenna to a window. I'd like to improve its ability to withstand wind effects, but that "several twists per foot" has me confused. So much twisting would turn the ladder line into a pretzel. Might you be able to give further suggestions for weather-worthy installations of ladder line?

[4]See Note 2.

A The technique of twisting window line is only appropriate where all slack in the line can be taken up so as to prevent the pretzel effect. Where the line is run horizontally, that just isn't practical. In fact, you will probably get wind flexing in that type of installation no matter what you do. However, you can still put a few twists in the line (say one every 3 to 5 feet) to reduce the amount of wind flex. The idea is to eliminate constant pounding due to the wind. Not only do you want to eliminate stress hardening, you also want to limit the ladder line motion with respect to its immediate surroundings. Local influences of walls, wires and pipes will affect the characteristic impedance of the line, and this is something you don't want to change randomly.

Ladder line standoff insulators are available or you can make your own. A 2-3 inch PVC pipe T, cut lengthwise with a hacksaw, down one side, makes one type of ladder line support. The hacksaw cut makes it easy to insert the line after the support is mounted. The coupling can be supported with a 4-inch length of PVC pipe attached to the building wall with a wood screw angled through the pipe.

Television type standoff insulators can also work (RadioShack[5] 15-854), although these must be used with care so as not to deform the line. It should be possible to carefully position a standoff over one side of the line (through the "window" of the ladder line) and tighten around one conductor only. Try to keep the ladder line spaced at least 3-4 inches from any adjacent structure.

The object is to keep the line motionless within the vicinity of local supports. This also applies when the line enters the house. If it's impossible to eliminate the proximity to wires and pipes within the structure or at the entrance, a better solution might be to use an outside-mounted balun transformer and revert to coaxial cable when the feed line enters the house. Try to keep the coax length as short as possible, as coax has substantially more loss than ladder line.

Q From Greg, K9ON, comes this: I had no problem in getting a permit for a tower but my local ordinance required that I put it within 10 feet of my house. At the time, I saw no problem with that, but once I put my antenna up the birds came from everywhere. Now my wife is about to evict me! The problem is the birds sit on the antenna and our deck has become almost unusable because of bird droppings. I have tried a fake owl on top of the boom but the birds only built a nest in the base of the owl. I've also tried a sonic bird repeller that emits calls of predator birds. After listening to it for a couple weeks, my nerves are shot.

[5]www.radioshack.com.

DAVID PINGREE, N1NAS

**Figure 8.18—A hawk visits one of the W1AW antenna towers.**

A At W1AW, we just let the birds roost as they will, but we don't have a backyard deck under the antennas. A visiting hawk surveying the scene up high on one of the W1AW towers can be seen in **Figure 8.18**. The owl usually works, but apparently you've got some pretty smart birds or that owl is simply not realistic enough. Perhaps you should try a hawk! However, here are some suggestions for other methods to try:

1. Run fishing line or other nylon/dacron line slightly above the horizontal elements and parallel to them. If the line is thin enough, the birds won't roost on it or the beam elements and boom. A suitable support for the line at the element and boom ends would have to be designed, however.

2. You can try a sticky bird-repellent liquid applied to the beam elements.[6] The problem is that this would have to be renewed periodically.

3. Plastic tubing sections can be placed around the beam tubing. The downside to this is that the tubing can rattle with the wind.

Q Allan, KF9RA, writes: Doctor, can this possibly work? My mag-mount antenna is on a steel plate about 6 inches square, just barely larger than the base. The plate is attached to the top of a plastic tool box that sits in the bed of the truck. The antenna is a long way from the center of the roof, but I have gotten favorable reports for the past 6 months. The SWR, as best as I can measure, is 1.4:1. I have to conclude that even though the antenna is separated from the body of the truck, the truck still acts as a suitable ground plane.

A A proper ground plane for a vertical antenna is essential for a low radiation angle and for a suitable match to the transmission line. In the case you show in your photos, it would not be possible to get an optimum or easily predictable pattern. I suppose some capacitive coupling to the truck body could work well enough to keep the SWR down, but the size of the plate and the distance it is from the truck bed precludes much coupling. While this is certainly not a desired or optimum situation, it may be good enough for nearby repeaters that have excellent receivers. That can be misleading, as repeaters frequently make even marginal signals sound good.

Another question is whether or not there is significant loss in the antenna or the coax. If the shield braid of the coax is simply left floating and not connected to the counterpoise or the plate, the mismatch would be significant. Even if it is connected to the plate, the plate area is too small and the spacing from the truck body is too great to be effective. This could result in a low SWR at the transmitter end of the cable—but a high SWR at the antenna end—not a good situation. I would suggest you measure the SWR as close as possible to the antenna, rather than at the transmitter. You'll then have a truer picture of what is going on.

I would not recommend the use of such a small ground plane. If you're forced to install the antenna this way, bring the plate as close to the truck or car body as you physically can.

Q George, KG4PIL, asks: What's the best feed line for a legal limit dipole? RG-213/U seems a little heavy to me. I used RG-8X with a foam center but it failed very quickly.

A The answer to that question depends on the anticipated SWR on the line. In addition, it depends on your budget and the amount of loss you can tolerate. A high SWR will contribute to the feed line loss and will result in a high voltage on the line and heating of the cable. The peak voltage will

[6]www.bird-x.com.

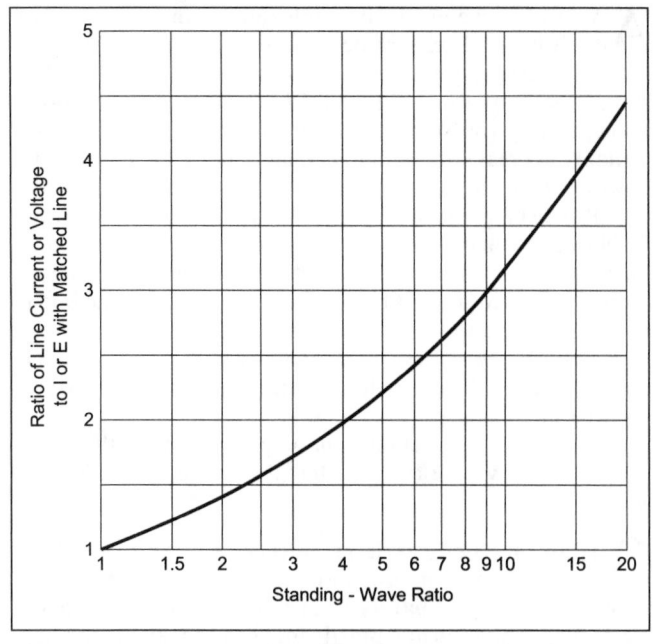

Figure 8.19—Here's how the SWR on a transmission line affects the voltage and current on the line. Note that the line voltage and current are directly proportional to the square root of the SWR.

be governed by the input power to the line, the characteristic impedance and the SWR. The following equation computes that voltage:

$$E_{peak} = \sqrt{P \times Z_0 \times SWR} \times 1.4$$

For maximum legal power (1500 W) and a $Z_0$ of 50 Ω, this becomes:

$$E_{peak} = 387 \times \sqrt{SWR}$$

A graph showing how SWR affects the voltage and current on a transmission line is shown in **Figure 8.19**. RG-8X coax is specified for a maximum voltage of 300 $V_{rms}$ or about 424 $V_{peak}$ (the Underwriters Laboratories specification). That peak voltage is already exceeded (458 V) with an SWR of 1.4:1 and that SWR would be expected when feeding a typical dipole at average height with a 50 Ω transmission line. The bottom line is that I would definitely not use RG-8X at maximum legal power to feed any antenna.

Ladder line is relatively cheap and very low loss, but that may not be something you would want because of its installation requirements (it needs to be kept clear of surrounding structures and it is a balanced feed line, requiring a balun transformer or a properly configured antenna tuner to interface to unbalanced output). 450 Ω ladder line with large enough conductors (14 gauge) will be able to handle a legal limit transmitter with ease. RG-213/U is a good coaxial cable that should do the job, as well. RG-8/U is popular and a bit cheaper, but it also has slightly higher attenuation characteristics. More information about cables and the effect of SWR on loss and voltage appears in both *The ARRL Handbook* and *The ARRL Antenna Book*.

**Q** Mike, KB1HIF, writes: I am installing a mobile ICOM IC-706 with a Pro-Am 20 meter whip antenna and I am having difficulty tuning the antenna—it has a high SWR. I'm operating one band only, without an independent tuner. How should this antenna installation be approached? Is the length of the coax critical?

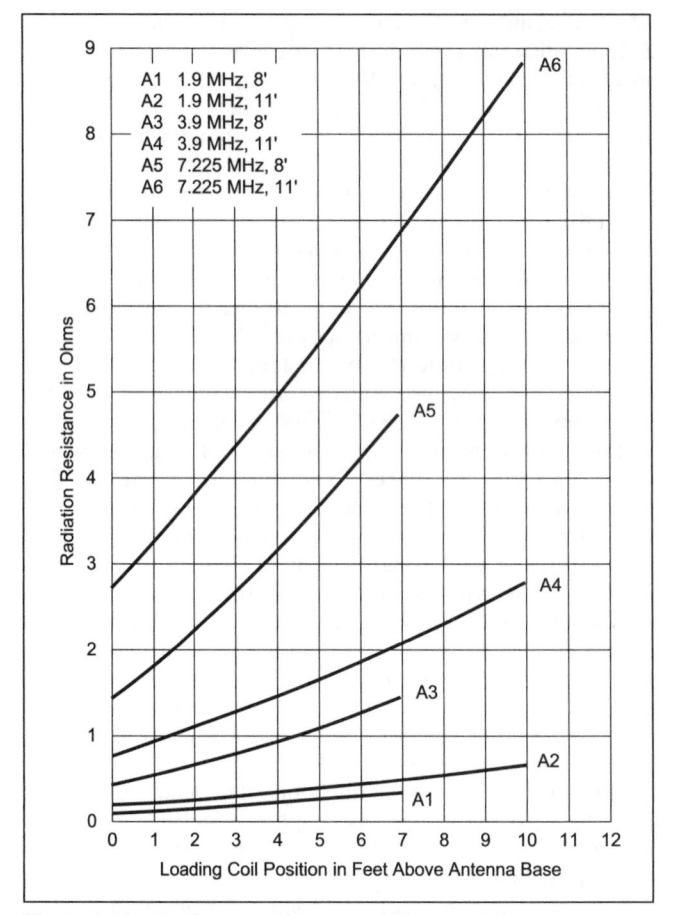

Figure 8.20—Radiation resistance of short mobile antennas.

**A** A high SWR indicates a mismatch between the antenna and the coaxial transmission line. That effect is to increase the existing cable loss. A loaded and short mobile antenna will have a radiation resistance somewhere around 3 Ω on 40 meters. **Figure 8.20** shows plots of radiation resistance versus coil position at several frequencies for short mobile antennas. Ground losses and loading coil Q will bring the base feed impedance to about 20 Ω, uncorrected.[7] I say "uncorrected" because this base impedance is normally lower than the output impedance of most transmitters (50 Ω). If you're using 50 Ω coaxial cable to feed the antenna (a common choice), that combination will give you an uncorrected SWR of 2.5:1. Without some form of antenna tuner, the IC-706 power foldback circuit will most certainly restrict the output power of the transceiver. Yes, the length of the coax will be critical, but only if the SWR is high.

My suggestion is to determine the actual feed point impedance of the antenna with an RF analyzer. Once you know the feed point impedance of the antenna, try to correct it with a matching network. If the antenna is inductive (too long), a shunt capacitor at the base will correct that reactance. If too short (capacitive), an inductor will be needed. The feed impedance is usually easier to correct with a capacitor. The capacitance value will depend upon frequency, antenna length, loading coil Q and ground loss. It could range from 50 pF to about 700 pF, with lower values of C at higher frequencies. Use a 600 V dc disc ceramic or mica capacitor. You might be tempted to use a quarter-wave coax transformer to match the antenna impedance to the feed line. That long coax can, however, make for a very lossy transformer and I would not advise doing this. Chap-

[7]See *The ARRL Antenna Book*, Chapter 16, Table 1, p 16-5.

ter 16 of *The ARRL Antenna Book*, 20th Edition, makes for worthwhile reading. My best advice would be to try to tune the antenna and bring the impedance closer to the feed-line impedance of 50 Ω.

Another answer, of course, is to use an antenna tuner. (It really doesn't *tune* the antenna, although it's called that. An "impedance transformer" would be a better name, but that applies to other devices, as well. So, I suppose, we're stuck with antenna tuner!) This will make the transceiver "see" a 50 Ω resistive load and will keep the transceiver power foldback circuitry from scaling back power (it does that to protect the output devices from high reflected power). Although a 1:1 SWR is preferable, a moderate SWR is normally not a problem at HF—mobile feedline lengths are normally short, thus limiting losses and the power levels are low enough to limit cable heating.

*Clarification:* After reading "A Mobile Antenna Base with Internal Capacitive Matching" and the Doctor is IN [Feb 2004, pp 43-46 and 65], Alan Applegate, KØBG, reminds us that there's another virtue to inductive, not capacitive, antenna matching. With an inductor shunted to ground, the mobile antenna is dc grounded. DC grounding can reduce static build-up and "grounds" the antenna should it contact any low-hanging power lines.

**Q** KR4ST writes: I built a 2 meter antenna into a small Hula Hoop. The wire inside the hoop is 84 inches long. I use a shorted 3¹/₂ inch stub made of 300 Ω twin lead with a 9-35 pF capacitor as a matching system. Is this antenna vertically or horizontally polarized ?

**A** The polarization is horizontal. It will be vertically polarized if you stand it up and rotate it so that the feed point is midway between the top and bottom. By the way, you've a good idea and I've taken the liberty of including a picture of your antenna. It can be seen in **Figure 8.21**. A Hula Hoop makes for an interesting radiator!

KR4ST

Figure 8.21—KR4ST's Hula Hoop 2 meter antenna.

**Q** KØJDW asks: Would there be an advantage in placing a ¹/₄ wave vertical HF antenna in shallow lake water (with or without ground radials) as opposed to dry land with ground radials?

**A** The Doctor advises you to see Chapter 3 of *The ARRL Antenna Book*,[8] which discusses this topic in detail.

The RF waves behave like sunlight striking a reflecting

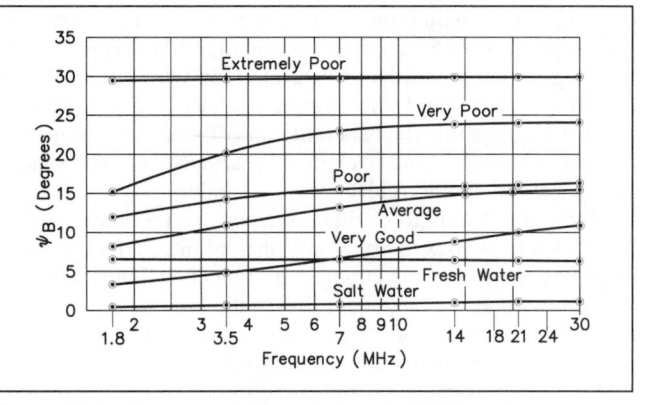

Figure 8.22—The pseudo-Brewster angle (PBA) versus frequency for various soil qualities.

plane, as on a lake surface. The angle at which the reflected wave is 90° out of phase with respect to the direct wave is known as the pseudo-Brewster angle (PBA). The vertically reflected wave subtracts from the direct wave at angles below the PBA and adds to it above the PBA, and the in-phase addition is what is desirable, because it enhances the signal strength. The PBA tends to increase with frequency, assuming other conditions remain equal. Thus, where low radiation angles are valuable for DX work (the higher frequencies), the PBAs are, unfortunately, the highest. Also poorer earth conductivities yield higher PBAs, as you would expect.

Above 7 MHz, fresh water is a better reflecting surface than very good soil, while it is slightly worse below 7 MHz. Typically, you will get good results down to a PBA of 6.4° with fresh water, while the PBA varies between 30° and 9° with soil at 14 MHz. Thus, for most hams (those that don't have access to salt water), fresh water is better than soil (above 7 MHz). **Figure 8.22** shows PBAs at various frequencies for different soil qualities. The bottom line is—for frequencies above 7 MHz, the vertical antenna is better off above fresh water than most soils.

Radials are still needed, however, even over fresh water. While you can get away with only two radials if you're fortunate enough to have your vertical located over *salt water*, which has very high conductivity, you need (arguably) at least four (and preferably eight or more) radials over fresh water. A vertical over regular soil requires a minimum of eight and preferably 16 or more, radials for decent efficiency. AM broadcast stations often use 120 or more radials for their high-efficiency vertical systems.

**Q** From Mike, W7KOL, comes the following: I constructed a loop skywire antenna from the pages of *ARRL's Wire Antenna Classics*.[9] The loop is 43 feet high on four poles with 272 feet of copper wire fed at the corner with RG-8/U coax into a 1:1 balun. The coax from the shack to the feed point is 145 feet in length. I have a tuner, but I cannot get the antenna tuned to an SWR of 1:1. Do I need to recalculate the copper wire length? The article said to let the tuner do the work and not to worry too much about wire length, but the author is obviously not at my site.

**A** If you model the antenna (*EZNEC*[10]) given those parameters, you'll find that the SWR is significantly better with a feed line impedance of about 300 Ω. With a coax feed line

[8]Available from your local dealer or the ARRL Bookstore. ARRL order no. 9043. Tel 888-277-5289 or 860-594-0355, fax 860-594-0303; **www.arrl.org/shop/; pubsales@arrl.org**.

[9]Available from your local dealer or the ARRL Bookstore (see footnote 8 for ARRL contact information). Order no. 7075.
[10]**www.eznec.com**.

of 50 Ω your existing tuner may not be able to transform the line impedance to 50 Ω resistive when the SWR is high. My first suggestion would be to feed the loop with either 300 Ω or 450 Ω ladder line. Either bring the ladder line directly into the shack and go into the balanced input of your tuner or mount a 4:1 balun outside and use 50 or 75 Ω coax into the shack. The 4:1 balun should replace your 1:1 balun.

If you don't want to go this route you can try adding about 15 to 25 feet of coax to your existing feed line and see if your tuner has an easier time coping with that "new" impedance. I would advise going the ladder line route, however, as the significantly lower loss of the ladder line under high SWR conditions will result in more power getting to the antenna. You'll find that loop to be an excellent and highly effective antenna if you can maximize the power getting to it. You can do that by reducing the SWR that the transmitter sees and reducing the transmission line loss by using ladder line. And, incidentally, one of the newer crop of auto tuners would be ideal for this sort of installation. That configuration with a ladder line fed loop is what I use very successfully on all of the HF bands. I hope this helps and good luck!

**Q** Homer, WB4UHV, asks: I recently built a quad for 2 meters (7-element) from an ARRL link. There was no mention of any probable matching difficulties but my SWR is way out of line (using a Bird meter). I have looked for matching systems for quads but can't seem to find any. All the references seem to say that a quad's feed impedance is 52 Ω. Is that correct?

**A** Yes, many quad designs are a relatively decent match to 52 Ω with a direct feed. The impedance of a full wave loop ranges from 100 to 300 Ω, depending on its height above ground. Adding the reflector and directors generally lowers that impedance to a value around 50 Ω. The direct feed is the simplest and easiest to get working—so it is the most popular. Here is a link, however, for feeding a quad with a gamma match: **www.cvarc.org/quad/cubquad.html**. You should view the formulas for matching networks as starting values—a bit of trial and error is often needed to get a good match.

You might try building another antenna and start with just the driven element, so you can measure the impedance of a single quad loop. Then you can add elements and see the SWR drop. Pay particular attention to the driven element's proximity to surrounding objects, its height above ground, and the dressing of the transmission line away from the feed point. Use a VHF RF analyzer (like the Autek RF5, Kuranishi BR-200 or the MFJ-249) to determine the real resonant frequency of the antenna, its feed impedance, and the SWR. Good luck!

**Q** Sherman, KA6EOW, asks: What is a current balun and where would it be necessary to use one? Can you point me to any references about baluns?

**A** A current balun is designed to produce currents that are equal in magnitude and opposite in phase and transform a balanced load or source impedance to an unbalanced one. It would be necessary to use one when you have undesirable shield currents on the outside of a coaxial transmission line—when trying, for example, to couple a so-called "balanced" antenna to an unbalanced transmission line. Also, when coupling to an antenna that is unbalanced because of its surrounding environment, like a nearby structure, or when you need to transform a balanced impedance to an unbalanced one (like a 300 Ω balanced line or antenna to 75 Ω unbalanced coaxial cable).

Current baluns are generally preferable to voltage baluns (in antenna use) because the current balun acts like a constant current source, forcing equal *current* into both antenna halves,

regardless of their impedance. A voltage balun will provide equal *voltage* to both antenna halves, but the current will be unequal if the impedances are different. If the SWR is very low and the antenna halves are truly balanced, the voltage balun will generally perform as well as the current balun. A balanced antenna, however, is never perfectly balanced unless it is in free space—its real environment will cause the opposite halves to be of slightly different impedance. And, it is desirable to have equal current flow in both halves of the antenna, regardless of that impedance unbalance. Most manufacturers of antenna baluns now offer current baluns. They are available in various impedance transformation ratios—usually from 1:1 to 4:1, but they can be obtained in ratios as high as 6:1 or 9:1.

There is an excellent article on antenna baluns in the Jan/Feb 2004 *QEX*, pp 55-58, "Why Do Baluns Burn Up?" W1VT points out that practical multiband baluns usually fall short of expectations, especially in situations of high SWR. The choking impedance is usually lower than that expected, so the current flow is excessive. If the SWR is low, however, the balun will behave properly (like in a well-designed triband beam). The last line of that article is worth noting: "Ferrite-core baluns should not be used haphazardly at high power levels." In other words, do not run high power with any balun under very high SWR conditions.

A couple of Web sites good for balun theory, design and practice are the following: **fermi.la.asu.edu/w9cf/articles/balun/** and **www.eznec.com/miscpage.htm**.

**Q** Mike, G3IZJ, writes: Some time in the last couple of years I saw a tip in *QST* on reducing the visual impact of 400 Ω ladder line, I have searched my *QSTs* and cannot find it. But, as I gave away several copies, it's probably in one of those. This is a small island and our neighbors are rather nearer here than in the rather larger USA, so it's best not to get them excited!

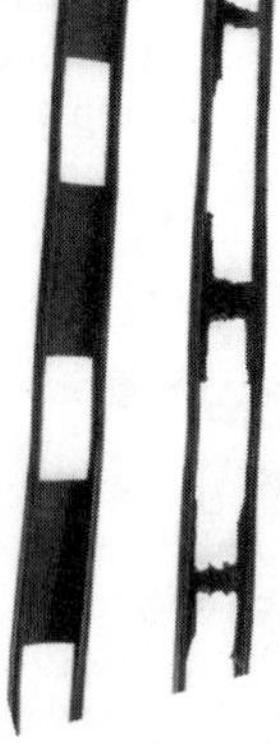

Figure 8.23—The "stealthy" ladder line on the right can be made by cutting the line with "nail-slot-hole pliers" used for punching oblong holes in aluminum and vinyl siding. The line is then sprayed with non-carbon pigment foliage colored paint.

**A** Hints & Kinks of Jan 2002, p 68, "Stealthy Ladder Line," has what you're looking for. The author, K9SQG, cut rough holes in the line with "nail-slot-hole pliers" to reduce the uniformity of the line. He also used some spray paint (he cautions to avoid paints like ultra flat black, which use carbon black for pigmentation; a conductor) to aid the line camouflage. This results in a line that's hard to see from a reasonable distance. The modified line can be seen in **Figure 8.23**.

**Q** Don, WA1ELA, writes: I've a question relating to dipole antennas. If I feed a dipole with 450 Ω balanced transmission line and use a balanced antenna tuner, is there an optimum length to operate, let's say, 160-10 meters, 75-10 meters or 40-10 meters?

**A** Yes, there is. The difficulty, however, is that typical amateur dipoles are installed too close to nearby objects to make them no-tune like, for example, a large Yagi that might be mounted on a tower free and clear of surrounding terrain. Even the tower-mounted Yagi often needs tuning if it has to share space with other antennas. Thus, while you can do the optimization with modeling programs like *EZNEC*[11]—even

[11]**www.eznec.com**.

modeling the effect of ground and wire insulation—the reality is often considerably different that what you think you are modeling.

Perhaps the best strategy is to put up your antenna and measure its impedance on all the bands you intend to operate. You can then simultaneously optimize the feed line length and choose the best compromise for your operating needs. The *TLW* program that comes with *The ARRL Antenna Book*[12] will model the feed line and matching network losses, given the load impedance.

**Q** Bill, N5DEE, asks: I'd like to clear up a question I've had for years and still don't know the answer to. When a commercially made W2AU balun is used on a 75 Ω, 40 meter dipole antenna, should the aluminum strap connecting the top to the bottom be left intact or not?

**A** Leave the strap in place. It's only a ground strap that connects the top mounting hook to the SO-239 coaxial socket shield. Its purpose is to act as a lightning discharge path from the top anchor to ground. In any case, it is balanced to either leg of the dipole and it won't hurt anything. The top anchor isn't connected to anything except that strap.

**Q** Scott, KBØFHP, writes: I have a wire vertical antenna that is resonant at 3.8 MHz. I want to switch in, via a relay, an extra length of wire for 3.5 MHz. What type of relay would I use? Can Potter & Brumfield (or equal) 10A, 110V SPST or DPDT relays work? I'd also like to add another antenna for 80 meters—and I'd like both to be switchable in order to change directions. Can I use similar DPDT relays to achieve that—or am I looking at the more expensive coaxial relays?

**A** The relays should work, with a few cautions. Try to avoid "hot" switching (switching with RF applied), as special contacts are required to do this if the power level is going to be moderate to high (100 W to 1 kW). RF tends to arc during "make" or "break" at these power levels and this will damage and "pit" standard relay contacts. Generally, at the kilowatt level, we're talking of upwards of 5 A of RF into a typical antenna impedance. Also, relay contacts usually develop a high-resistance insulating layer in an outside environment. Without adequate current to "punch through" that layer, this can be troublesome. Gold contacts may also be needed if you expect to dry switch to be able to do receive only testing with no current through the relay.

Moisture can also be a problem. Sealing a relay inside a box rarely works, unless you are in a very dry climate. In a wet climate, water vapor will condense inside the box and collect, and the enclosure will need to be vented. The commercial technique is to keep enclosures at a small positive pressure, usually using dry nitrogen. Broadcasters typically do this at their trans-

mitter sites with coaxial transmission lines (we're talking about 5-8" OD coaxial lines at power levels approaching 50 kW). The ham will rarely need to pressurize. Another concern is that the contact insulation may be inadequate for high voltage situations. Try to place the relays in locations where the RF voltage is not excessive.

Aside from the contact requirements, the coil voltage is another issue. I'd try to stay with low voltage dc coils (12-24 V dc) for outdoor use. It is safer, and it makes it easier to run the dc control voltage along with the RF with a suitable decoupling/isolation circuit. A circuit for doing this appeared recently in *QST*.[13] The basic idea is shown in **Figure 8.24**. The inductors (a *high* impedance at RF) and capacitors (a *low* impedance at RF) isolate the dc from the RF. It thus makes it unnecessary to decouple and choke the control cables that carry the coil voltage. RF getting into these lines tends to be a problem, especially if they are in close proximity to the antenna system.

You can probably use DPDT relays if the leads are kept short on 80 meters. On 10 meters, there may be a significant impedance discontinuity from the relays. There may also be isolation issues on receive—I wouldn't expect a lot of isolation from an open frame DPDT relay, even on 80 meters. This, of course, is where the coaxial relay shines, if used on a coaxial line. The isolation is high (especially at HF) and the impedance is nearly constant through the relay. Nevertheless, hams have been using open-frame relays to switch wire antennas for years, so good luck!

[13]P.Salas, AD5X, "Remote DC Power Through Your Coax," *QST*, Jul 2004, pp 35-37.

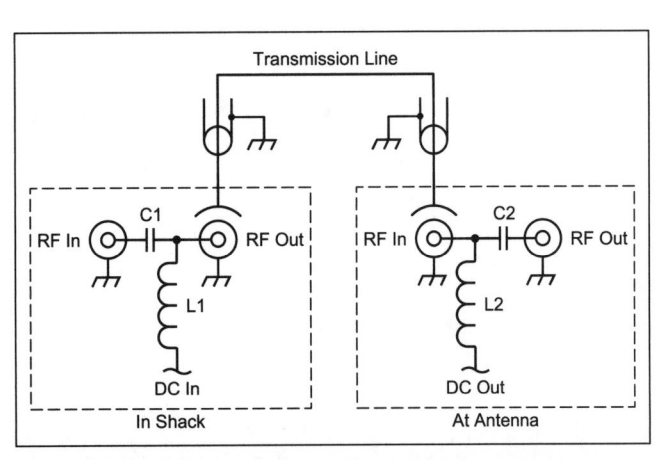

**Figure 8.24—The basic technique used to send dc power on an RF transmission line. At the sending end a capacitor (C1) and a choke (L1) are used for coupling and isolation. At the receiving end a choke (L2) and capacitor (C2) decouple the RF and dc. The capacitors have *low* impedance at RF—the inductors *high* impedance. The circuit was described in detail in *QST* (see text).**

[12]Available from your local dealer or the ARRL Bookstore. Order no. 9043. Telephone toll-free in the US 888-277-5289, or 860-594-0355, fax 860-594-0303; **www.arrl.org/shop/**; **pubsales@arrl.org**.

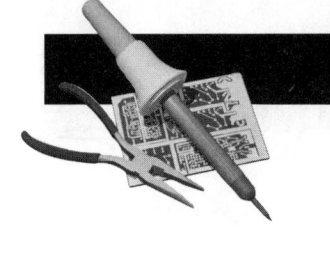

# Chapter 9

# Operating

## SPEED PSK-31 TRANSMIT TIME WITH LOWER CASE LETTERS

◊ PSK-31 and its phase-shifted brethren are becoming very popular for ragchewing in the digital subbands. Yet, because its duty cycle is 100%, my trusty old ICOM 751's fan will roar to life to cool torrid transistor finals during particularly long—and enjoyable—PSK conversations.

While thinking about how PSK-31's Varicode (character set) is set up, I realized that the time-honored RTTY practice of sending upper-case letters is not the most efficient way to transmit. In the traditional Baudot code, all characters are five bits long. As the name implies, the PSK Varicode, invented by Peter Martinez, G3PLX, has characters that vary in length from two bits ("e") to 10 bits ("Z"). A glance at the Varicode character table shows that lowercase letters clearly use fewer bits than uppercase letters.

A little math showed me how much shorter. Lowercase letters average 5.96 bits in length, while uppercase letters average 8.23 bits. It sounded good, so I decided to make a "practical test." I disconnected the soundcard interface and just sent the phrase "The tired old ham lumbered over the lazy dog to get another 807" through the PC speakers. It took 21 seconds to send the phrase in uppercase; it took 16 seconds to send it in lowercase.

After that, I released the Caps Lock key on the computer. Sending all lowercase letters might look a little odd, but it's more efficient, and I can tell you that the final of my transceiver is 24% happier!—*Dave Hassler, K7CCC, ARRL Staff;* **k7ccc@arrl.org**

## POOR MAN'S QRP

◊ Many of my friends have built QRP transceivers from kits and have managed to decrease their signal strengths enormously. Sadly, I am not good at constructing, and I am also chronically short of cash. My ICOM transceiver only cranks down to 12 W output, which does not qualify as QRP, but I hit on a way to achieve QRP operation with no fuss or mess: build an attenuator.[1]

All you need is a box, two SO-239 sockets, three resistors and a switch to flip the attenuator in and out. Connect the resistors in a π network as shown in **Figure 9.1**: R2 should be 68 to 75 Ω, 4 W dissipation; R1 is 100 Ω (6 W) and R3 is 100 Ω (0.7 W). Resistors of lesser dissipation may work for

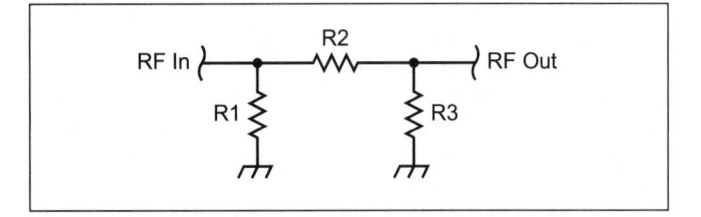

**Figure 9.1—A simple π-network attenuator reduces a transmitter's 12-W output for QRP operation.**

SSB (or CW provided you don't hold the key down too long). *The resistors should be carbon*, not wire wound. If you only find wirewound resistors, all is not lost! Pick a value between 20 to 30 Ω for R2 and (omitting R1 and R3) install it between the attenuator sockets, set the rig to its lowest power at 7 MHz and measure the power output of the attenuator with a wattmeter. Change R1 until you get about 4 W out. On 14 MHz, you will have 2 W out and on 28 MHz, you'll have about 1 W—that's all good QRP! Install the switch to flip between QRO and QRP. This technique reflects power to the transceiver, but with the rig running 12 W, it's not a big deal.

On receive, the attenuator reduces the incoming signal too. There are two ways to handle this: either flip the switch to the "QRO" position when receiving, or use a separate receive antenna (some transceivers are equipped with a socket for this).

Once you have the Poor Man's QRP you, too, will be able to drop your signal into the noise. (Thanks to Frank, VE6CB, for calculating the resistor characteristics.)—*Bruce Fleming, KI7VR, 7401 NW 16th Ave, Vancouver, WA 98665;* **Fleming@ pacifier.com**

[Bruce's friend, Frank, gave him an attenuator using standard-value resistors that drops his signal level by about 10 dB. Also, the resistor dissipations shown are adequate for light duty cycles only. Good engineering practice doubles the required dissipation, so R1 should be about 12 W, R2 8 W and R3 2 W. Personally, I would rather set the output at 5 W: R1 = 220 Ω 6 W; R2 = 27 Ω 10 W; R3 = 220 Ω 2 W. While checking the numbers on this hint, I developed a simple spreadsheet that yields the resistor values from the power input and desired power output. It also computes attenuation in decibels, given the resistor values. Finally, it gives the resistor dissipation with a safety factor of two for both scenarios.[2]—*Bob Schetgen, KU7G]*

---

[1]For folks who can't set their transceiver's output so low, an earlier hint suggests ways to economically attenuate 100 W to QRP levels. Check out Jay Jeffrey, WV8R's hint "Operate QRP with an Easy-to-Build Attenuator," *QST*, Feb 1993, p 75.

[2]You can download this package from the ARRL Web **www.arrl.org/ files/qst-binaries/**. Look for Pi-Atten.zip.

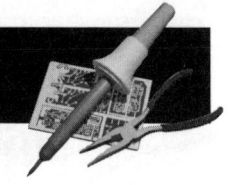

**Q** Ken and Joann Earle, KC0KPB and KC0KPA, ask: We live and cruise on our sailboat. We have an ICOM IC-706 transceiver with a Comet SB15 triband antenna mounted on the stern rail. Realizing the '706 has an internal antenna tuner, I still find it difficult to use the transceiver either on the boat or at home. People are telling me to buy a tuner and hook the tuner to the '706 and run a wire to a steel side stay or back stay of my sailboat and this will allow us to use the transceiver. We have a wooden mast and apparently this helps (according to other hams). Will you please give us information as to the type of tuner to buy and is the hookup correct as stated.

**A** The Comet SB15 is a vertical, ground-plane type 6-meter, 2-meter, 70-cm mobile antenna. It sounds like you want to operate on HF, and this antenna really won't work well on bands for which it wasn't designed. Even on VHF/UHF, the antenna needs a ground or ground-plane connection. If the rail is metal, it will be enough ground plane to work.

On HF, many hams do indeed load a backstay as a good all-band HF antenna. The internal antenna tuners in transceivers are quite limited in the amount of mismatch they can handle. Beyond a certain point—typically about 4:1—they may not be able to achieve a match, and the transmitter's internal SWR protection will reduce output power to protect the transmitter. The tuner may also achieve a match to a load outside its rated range, but the tuner internal components could fail as a result.

Feeding a backstay results in a "random" impedance that may or may not be outside the range of the internal tuner. Most hams who use this set-up use an external tuner, which almost always has more matching range than internal tuners. The Doctor recommends a good quality tuner with large spacing in the capacitor to prevent arcing. Any good quality antenna tuner capable of full legal limit will be fine to handle extreme mismatches at the 100-W level.

A wire can run from the lower end of the backstay to the operating position, but keep in mind that this will be a radiating part of the antenna system. It is also possible to connect an external antenna tuner to the bottom of the backstay. See *The ARRL Antenna Book*, 19th Edition for more information.

To end feed a wire as described, you need to provide an RF ground. Even though it may be difficult to find places to run ground-plane wires in the boat, your work done laying out such wires will pay off with better results than so-called "ground-plate" systems for HF communications. Be sure to tie in any large metal structures to form a reasonable ground plane, including engine(s), tanks, etc.

**Q** A member who wished to remain anonymous asks, "I received a notice from an Official Observer (OO) that my CW signal has key clicks. I asked a number of hams on the air about the key clicks, and only one of them told me that he heard clicks on my signal. What are key clicks, and why do I care?

**A** If a constant carrier is transmitted, it occupies only one frequency. Even a few Hz away, there is no signal. However, a carrier is not very useful because it doesn't contain any information. If that carrier is modulated, however, it does contain information that permits hams to communicate. The term "CW," or continuous wave, is somewhat of a misnomer for a Morse-code signal. The act of turning the carrier on and off is indeed modulation. The process of modulation creates sidebands—the modulated signal occupies a band of frequencies, the nature of which depends on the modulation.

In the case of an on/off keyed CW signal, the modulation is contained in the code elements and spacing. If the carrier were turned abruptly on and off, it would be modulated by a slow square-wave, at the "dit" and "dah" element rate. A square-wave contains a fundamental signal and all odd harmonics; therefore, transmitting a perfect square-wave requires infinite bandwidth. So, if that on/off keying is not shaped in some way, the keyed CW signal will take up lots of room (bandwidth). Each time the carrier turns on or off, the modulation process creates modulation sidebands up and down the band. This will sound like a click each time the carrier is turned on or off. If a ham tells you that your signal has key clicks, it means that those signals are loud enough to be objectionable.

Most of the modulation (and consequent RF energy) contained in these key clicks is wasted because it can't be heard by a receiver tuned to the desired signal. It is, in fact, more than wasted, because the clicks can interfere with other communications taking part elsewhere on the band. Fortunately, if the keyed signal is filtered (to "soften" the rise and fall times) so that it is no longer a "hard" square-wave, the level of the modulation sidebands is greatly reduced.

**Figure 9.2** shows the square-wave modulation that results from an unfiltered key line. The waveform rise and fall times are very short; this signal has key clicks. A properly shaped keying line results in the signal shown in **Figure 9.3**. Notice the longer rise and decay times.

**Figure 9.4** shows how the strong key clicks generated by unfiltered keying take up unnecessary spectrum space. In **Figure 9.5**, proper transmitter design results in much less noise up and down the band.

The OO listens up and down the band and when clicks are heard, he or she can quickly tune around and find the signal that is generating the clicks. However, if you ask most hams to listen for clicks, they don't know that they need to tune away from your signal to hear them. If you ask them for a click report, they will listen to your signal and won't hear any clicks when you transmit, so they will tell you that your signal is fine. The OO and the one ham who told you that you had clicks did it right and listened above and below your frequency.

It may not be possible for operators to do much about key clicks if the internal transmitter design does not properly shape the keying waveform. In some modern rigs, the selection of CW rise and fall time can be controlled through a menu selection. In some equipment, the transmitter ALC is active in the CW mode at high drive levels. This can clip the keyed waveform, generating clicks. Turning down the drive control to just below the point where the ALC is active may help. If adjusting the drive control or the rise ane fall times (for rigs with this capability) doesn't help, the internal circuitry may have to be modified. In most cases, this is a job for the equipment manufacturer...if they have developed a cure for the key click problem.

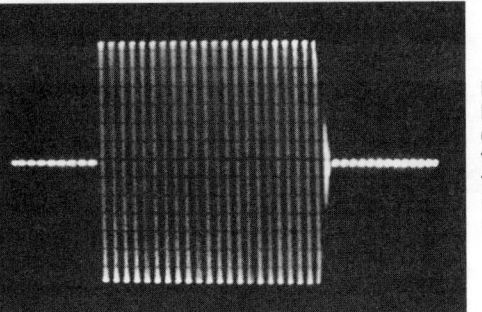

Figure 9.2—Modulation (square-wave) that results from an unfiltered key line.

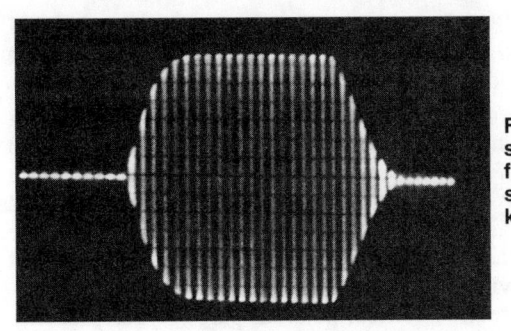

Figure 9.3—A shaped and filtered square-wave keying signal.

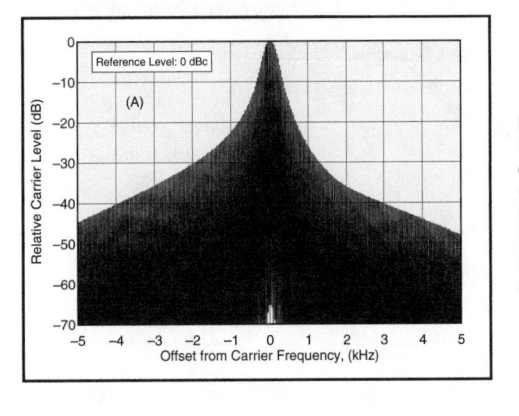

Figure 9.4—Key clicks caused by unfiltered keying result in a wide noise spectrum.

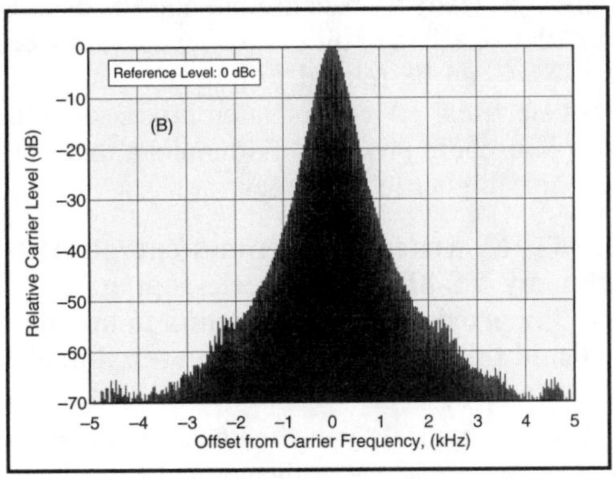

Figure 9.5—A filtered keying line reduces these spurious signals noticeably.

**Q** Brian Ward, KG4KGW, has a legal operating question: "I am a General Class operator and am trying to find the answer to an operating question one of my Technician friends had the other day. The FCC rules clearly state that a non-ham may operate from your station as long as you are the control operator and are at the control point of the station at all times while they are using your station. I would have to assume, in this scenario, that they would be operating with your license. What do you do when it is another ham? For example, my Technician friend wants to try his hand at the HF bands just to get a taste of it. When operating would he use his call sign? Could I act as the control operator for his/my station while he operates on the HF bands? What would be the proper procedures for this type of operation?"

**A** No non-amateur may *operate* an amateur station, even if you are present. Such "third parties" can *participate* in the operation of an amateur station as long as a licensed amateur is present and in control of the station operation. (Third-party communication can only take place with countries with which the US has a third-party agreement.[3]) If a licensed amateur wants to use your station, there are several

Figure 9.6—*The ARRL's FCC Rule Book* answers most questions about the FCC rules.

[3]www.arrl.org/FandES/field/regulations/io/3rdparty.html

different ways that this can be done legally. They, too, can be third-party participants. In that case, they would use your call sign and you would be the control operator. With your permission, they can be the control operator of your station, using your call sign, but only in the parts of the band where their license authorizes them to operate. You could also loan them all of your equipment and they could use their call sign from your location again under their own privileges.

You can also operate the station of a lower-class licensee. If you do, you can use his or her call sign in the part of the band they are authorized to operate. If you want to operate their station under your privileges, you can do so, but you then need to identify with their call sign, followed by your call sign (ie, KA1JPA / W1RFI). If you were W1RFI, on voice, you could say: "This is KA1JPA being operated by W1RFI." If the other operator loans you his or her equipment, you can also use your call under your own privileges.

In any case, no matter who is operating your station or what class license they hold, the designated control operator and the station licensee are jointly responsible for the legal operation of that station. If your call sign is being used, however, the FCC will contact you first for any violations, so you want to be careful about allowing others to use your station under your call.

This question is often asked of the ARRL HQ Regulatory Information Branch. They have answers to many common questions on their Web page at **www.arrl.org/FandES/field/regulations**. Every ham should also have a copy of *The ARRL's FCC Rule Book*, **www.arrl.org/shop/?item=7857**.

**Q** Tom, W8ESN, says, "I'm relatively new to 40 meters. That's kind of odd I guess, because I've been a ham for some 30 plus years. I've just not spent too much time on 40 over the years. Why is it that the background noise level on 40 is pretty consistently anywhere from S7 to S9? I don't have the same problem on 20, 15 or 17, for example. These bands are usually pretty quiet. The noise I'm speaking of isn't local QRN from power lines, etc or low level QRM buzz. It's simply inherent atmospheric noise on the 40 meter band. I just wonder why it's so loud."

A The lower one goes in frequency, the stronger the atmospheric noise becomes. In the summertime, 80 and 40 meters can have S9+ static "crashes," caused by lightning strikes over as much as a few thousand mile radius. The good news is that in the wintertime the band will be a lot more quiet. Forty meters is actually a decent QRP and DX band at night in the winter.

Don't discount electrical noise as part of your problem, however. Although static crashes can be tens of dB over S9, in a city environment a steady S9 background noise is usually caused by the cumulative effect of all of the electrical devices surrounding you. This can be related to power lines or the growing number of electrical devices and microprocessor chips found in everyday household products. Fortunately, that, too, gets lower as one goes higher in frequency.

Q Chester, KD5TFK, writes: I sometimes operate QRP at 5 W with my FT-817 using a telescoping whip antenna. Usually the proximity of the antenna to my body is fairly close. Would this be a hazard to me even though I am transmitting at a lowly 5 W?

A At 5 W QRP with a typical "whip" antenna, you will be well below the exposure levels. Although a quick calculation estimates that on 10 meters or VHF, you must maintain 6 inches between the antenna and any controlled exposure for 5 W CW, the exposure limits are based on a "whole body" exposure and it would be nearly impossible for the antenna to be 6 inches from your entire body. This is part of the reason that the FCC doesn't require evaluations for stations that use less than 50 W. There is one good safety practice you may want to use, however: It is not a good idea to operate that rig if the antenna were located very close to your eyes and head.

Q Again, from Chester, KD5TFK: If I am barely able to "hit" an out of town 2 meter FM repeater, would an amplifier help bolster my signal strength to bring up the machine? I am currently running 50 W and the amp is rated at 150 W with a 25 dB preamp. My antenna is a 2 meter mobile whip up about 15 feet on my roof.

A That is hard for me to answer because you give no clue how far "out of town" you mean. 10 miles? 50 miles? Nor do you hint at what the terrain is like. Flat? Hills? Buildings? Rural? City? All these things make a big difference in 2 meter work.

So let's talk in generalities. If you are in an area like Connecticut, there are many small towns located in very broad river valleys running north/south; 50 W to a mobile whip might get you 15 to 20 miles away and that could cover several towns within your particular valley. But getting from the Connecticut River valley to the Naugatuck or Thames River valleys would be a problem. If, on the other hand, you live on one of the ridges between the valleys, your range would be increased.

Remember, no matter what, you can't get a 2 meter signal through a hill or a mountain (not through, but perhaps "over" a mountain using knife-edge refraction, which takes lots of power and an antenna with substantial gain). Your antenna and the repeater antenna have to, for the most part, be able to actually "see" each other (except for trees and a few buildings).

So, if you've relatively clear terrain between you and the repeater, it's possible that the other antenna is beyond the curvature of the earth for your 15 foot height… get it up higher… say 30 feet. RadioShack sells a relatively inexpensive 36 foot mast. While you're at it, an antenna with a little more gain, a better pattern or even a better match to your feed line might help—like a ground plane antenna. I'm not sure if you are

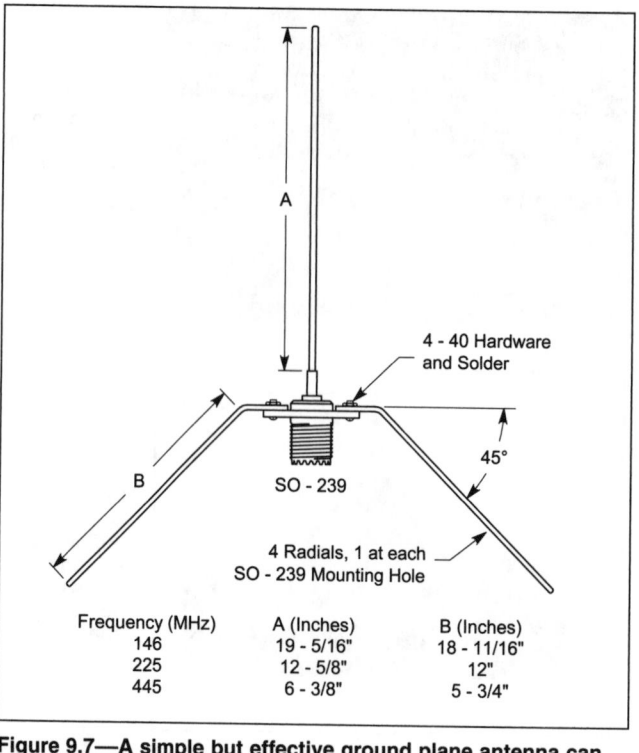

**Figure 9.7—A simple but effective ground plane antenna can be built with nothing more than an SO-239 connector and some heavy solid wire. Don't ignore the ground radials; they are critical to the antenna's performance.**

| Frequency (MHz) | A (Inches) | B (Inches) |
|---|---|---|
| 146 | 19 - 5/16" | 18 - 11/16" |
| 225 | 12 - 5/8" | 12" |
| 445 | 6 - 3/8" | 5 - 3/4" |

working that whip against a counterpoise (RF ground) or not. Remember, a mobile whip antenna is designed to use the vehicle body as a counterpoise. If it's just up in the air without a ground plane, it won't match your transmission line very well. A ground plane could not be easier to build. For 2 meters all you'll need is an SO-235 coax connector and some solid copper wire or welding rod or even five metal coat hangers from the dry cleaner (see **Figure 9.7**).

Q Ford, NØFP, says: I'm trying to organize a site plan for 2003 Field Day operations. We want to run multi-transmitter, and possibly more than one transmitter per band—a difficult task. I have been modeling different antenna designs and site plans, and can even model the amount of power present at the feed line of other antennas in the FD site. My question is, how much out-of-band or in-band signal can a typical rig tolerate before it starts to desense. What receiver testing parameter is appropriate?

We have several ICOM 746-class rigs that will show up during Field Day. The ARRL Lab has tested this radio and has even published an expanded report. Help me put this all in perspective. For example, if we intend to operate a station with 40 meter SSB, 40 meter CW and 40 meter PSK, simul-taneously, how much in-band interference can this radio tolerate before it is (a) dangerous to the radio, and (b) de-sensing from the other operating positions at the site?

A The only out of band tests we perform on receivers are IF and image rejection measurements, plus the second-order intercept. However, these figures don't tell you anything about de-sense.

For bands that are adjacent, the de-sense performance will likely be similar to the wide spacing (200 kHz offset) blocking dynamic range shown in the expanded test result report. For situations where you have CW and phone rigs on the same band, the spacing can potentially be much less.

An easy way to improve isolation between rigs on different bands is to use band-pass filters. Ed Wetherhold, W3NQN, had a two-part article in *QST* on this topic.[4] Of course, you could also purchase commercial filters.

Implementing a filter for a portion of the band is much more difficult. Zack Lau, W1VT, published a pair of projects in his *QEX* column, "RF," for the 80 and 40 meter bands.[5] A much easier solution is to try for a 90° orientation between the antennas (assuming you aren't using beams) or try for as much physical separation as possible.

With 100 W class rigs and reasonable antenna spacing, you shouldn't get anywhere near the levels that would damage a receiver.

**Q** Daryl Isbell, W4DAI, asks, "What antenna would you recommend for 20 meter phone operation for Field Day, 2003?"

**A** That is a pretty sweeping question, because the "best" antenna for Field Day depends a lot on what type of operating you intend to do. Some hams do Field Day working alone, perhaps even backpacking into a camping area and setting up a station by themselves. This will present an entirely different set of antenna challenges as opposed to the club that has a regular site with unlimited volunteers and resources.

The real fun in Field Day comes from trying different things, so don't be afraid to experiment and don't feel that you won't have a successful time unless you have the "best" antenna possible. Nearly any antenna will produce lots of Field Day contacts, so decide what you want to try and give it a go!

Some clubs have a ready-to-go antenna tower set up on a trailer. A small Yagi antenna can be easily set up and used for Field Day. For portable work, this may represent the ideal 20 meter antenna, as shown in **Figure 9.8**.

Many hams use wire antennas. For multi-operator Field Day stations, the use of separate antennas for each band can be helpful. To minimize mutual interference, these should be spaced as far apart as is reasonable.

There are a number of wire antennas that can be used on the HF bands. The simplest is a random piece of wire worked against earth ground with an antenna tuner. This antenna requires a good RF ground connection to work well. A simple ground rod is generally ineffective. Other hams use center-fed dipoles. These can be cut to a half wavelength and fed with coaxial cable. RG-58/U type coax works well for a few hundred watts, as long as the length of the feed line is not overly long. For higher power, longer coaxial runs or operation on the upper HF or VHF bands, use larger coax.

A nice multi-band HF antenna is a dipole of any length greater than a quarter wavelength on the lowest frequency to be used, fed in the center with open-wire or transmitting type ladderline. There are a lot of other interesting possibilities, from large loops to bobtail arrays to rhombics. In the past, the Meriden Amateur Radio Club of Connecticut has done quite well with 500 foot V-beams, although most hams don't have the space to put up an antenna that large.

The performance of a horizontal antenna varies a lot with its height above ground. At low heights, most of the RF signal is sent upward; relatively little is propagated at low angles, toward distant stations. But, higher is not always better! In the daytime, on 80 or 40 meters, the stations you will be working

are within a few hundred miles, so those high angles may be useful. On 20 meters, however, you should put a horizontal antenna up as high as possible in order to work stations nationwide. If you can get a horizontal antenna up a half wavelength or more (33 feet on 20 meters) it will generally work well. To help you plan, **Figure 9.9** shows an antenna elevation plot and

Figure 9.8—This small portable Yagi antenna is ideal for Field Day.

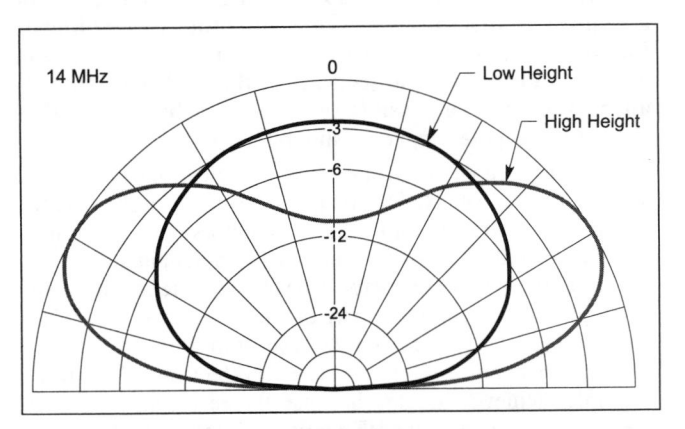

Figure 9.9—The low horizontal antenna is good for sky-wave communication with relatively close-by stations. As the antenna is put higher, its DX performance improves. The high-height line shows the performance of a half-wave dipole 33 feet in the air. The low-height line is the same antenna at a height of 8 feet.

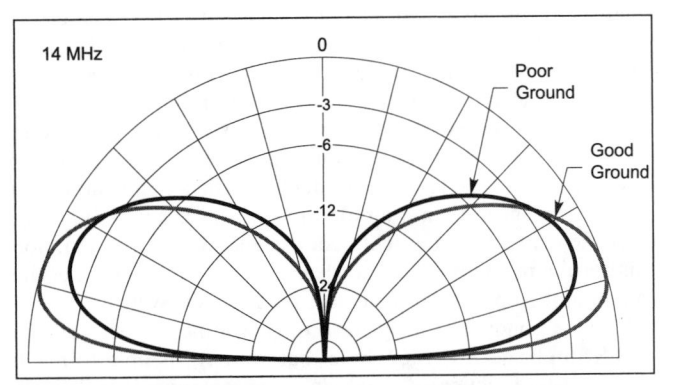

Figure 9.10—A vertical antenna over good ground can perform pretty well. Over poor ground, a vertical may be an omni-directional antenna that performs equally poorly in all directions. This compares the performance of a vertical with a short ground rod operated over good and poor ground.

[4]E. Wetherhold, W3NQN, "Clean Up Your Signals with Band-Pass Filters, " Part 1, *QST*, May 1998, pp 44-48; Part 2, *QST*, Jun 1998, pp 39-42.
[5]Z. Lau, W1VT, "A Narrow 80 Meter Band-Pass Filter," *QEX*, Sep/Oct 1998, p 57, "A Narrow-Bandwidth 40 Meter Band-pass Filter," *QEX*, Nov/Dec 1998, p 58.

the difference between a horizontal half wave dipole at both low and high heights. Note the low-angle radiation, concentrated at the horizon (toward distant receivers) for the high height. Conversely, note the relatively high angle of radiation, away from the horizon, for the low height.

Vertical antennas can also work well for Field Day. Most require a good ground system for the best performance, however. A simple ground rod will not usually be effective. Use one of the "end-fed" half-wave type verticals, or those fed in the center, so you can eliminate part of the grounding losses. Vertical antennas generally have a good low-angle launch, making them good DX antennas. However, that DX performance is dependent on the characteristics of the ground many wavelengths away from the antenna; impossible to control in most cases. If you are in a rocky area with poor ground, a vertical antenna may not be a good choice. In a swamp, the vertical can really work well for DX, although the mosquitoes might get you! **Figure 9.10** shows the performance of a vertical antenna over both poor and good ground.

The antenna patterns were produced using one of the several antenna-modeling software packages that are available. See **www.arrl.org/tis/info/HTML/antenna-modeling/index.html** for information and articles.

**Q** Ralph, W6DV, sends this in: I am considering a vertical dipole for 10 meters near my garage door—just for experimenting—not serious operating. The bottom leg will have to be near some roof flashing and on the side of a wall where there are paint cans and other metal objects. I know the radiation pattern will be poor, but my question is: How will the metal objects affect the feed-point impedance? Would it be possible to improve it by cutting that side of the dipole longer or shorter?

**A** When you apply RF to an antenna, an electromagnetic field is created. That field propagates away from the antenna and induces currents into other conductors. In some cases, that's a desired effect—at the antenna of a distant station, for example. If another conductor is near your antenna, however, it could become an active part of the antenna system. That could change the pattern and the feed-point impedance of the antenna. In some cases that's a desired effect, too. A Yagi, for example, achieves its gain because the reflector or director elements interact with the RF energy transmitted by the driven element, forming a pattern that concentrates signal in one direction.

How much the presence of these nearby conductors will affect your antenna depends on their proximity and dimensions and, to some extent, their orientation. Typically, long conductors within about a quarter wavelength or so—about 8 feet on 10 meters—will have a significant effect. The effect will usually be to lower the feed-point impedance and change the antenna's resonant frequency. Conductors that are at right angles to the antenna will have the least effect.

If the effect on the frequency is minor, you may be able to bring the antenna back to resonance by adjusting the side of the antenna closest to those conductors. The antenna may then be less balanced than a dipole in free space, now being fed, electrically, off center. This could cause feed line radiation and problems with RF in the shack. A 1:1 choke balun at the antenna feed point will take care of that, however.

These conductors may have only a minor effect and the SWR might be low enough so that your rig is able to reach full power. Practically speaking, most antennas for the low frequency bands do have other conductors within a quarter wavelength of their radiators and most usually work quite well. For example, on 80 meters a quarter wavelength is 66 feet. On a small residential lot it's difficult to isolate an 80 meter antenna more than 66 feet from other conductors!

**Q** Steve, AD4E, of Tallahassee, Florida has a question for our Product Review engineer: For HF radio product reviews, the ARRL publishes a graphical depiction of "worst-case composite-noise" while the radio is in the transmit mode. Is composite-noise synonymous with "phase-noise?"

Although I know how a transmitter with a "dirty" local-oscillator (high phase-noise) can affect nearby receivers, is this measurement indicative of the radio-under-test's received phase-noise, too? Is there a correlation between composite-noise and minimum discernible signal (MDS)? After comparing the MDS of several radios, that correlation is not readily evident.

**A** To answer your second question first, the two are not related. MDS (noise floor) depends on the gain of the receiver and the noise components of the amplification stages in the receiver. Phase noise is the noise (combination of changes in amplitude and shifts in frequency—also effectively a shift in phase, hence the name) of the receiver's local oscillator only. Also, the MDS is measured in a narrow pass-band, so the bandwidth of the contributing noise is small, whereas phase noise and transmitted composite noise are typically measured over a wide frequency range.

The transmitted composite noise is usually a good indicator of phase noise because phase noise makes up most of it. However, as the transmitter also has amplification, some additional noise is added, so it can't really be called phase noise.

It is possible to measure receiver phase noise more accurately than can be done using a transmit test, but it is more difficult and time consuming. However, you can be sure that, in a transceiver with a common or related oscillator, when transmit composite noise is high, the receiver phase noise is also high.

**Q** From George, VK5KGC: I have two different HF transceivers, made by two different manufacturers. After carefully setting all the necessary controls for the microphone gain, compression, etc, to ensure that the units are not being overdriven, the power meters in the transceivers do not show full power during normal speech/SSB. When I speak with a normal voice, the FT-1000D power meter shows 150 W and the IC-781 indicates 100 W. The specifications for the rigs are 200 W for the FT-1000D and 150 W for the IC-781. I also have an external power meter that indicates power output in *excess* of the tranceiver's specifications! I do not understand how this can be.

**A** In the July 2002 issue of *QST*, we had a Product Review on a number of popular peak-reading wattmeters (**www.arrl. org/members-only/prodrev/pdf/pr0207.pdf**). During testing, the ARRL Lab found inaccuracies in displaying peak-envelope power (PEP) under voice modulation. The reason for this has to do with their designs relative to reading peak signals. Those are often merely based upon the addition of a capacitor in the meter circuit—resulting in a displayed value much closer to average power rather than true PEP for some signals.

As to the differences between meters and referring to the same Product Review, note that most power meters have a basic accuracy of ±10-15%. One would expect, therefore, that any two meters would certainly disagree, perhaps by as much as 30%. **Figure 9.11** shows the power meters that were reviewed in the July 2002 issue of *QST*. And, as can be seen from that Review, the accuracy can be even worse for some meters.

Bird Electronics (**www.bird-electronic.com**) makes a very

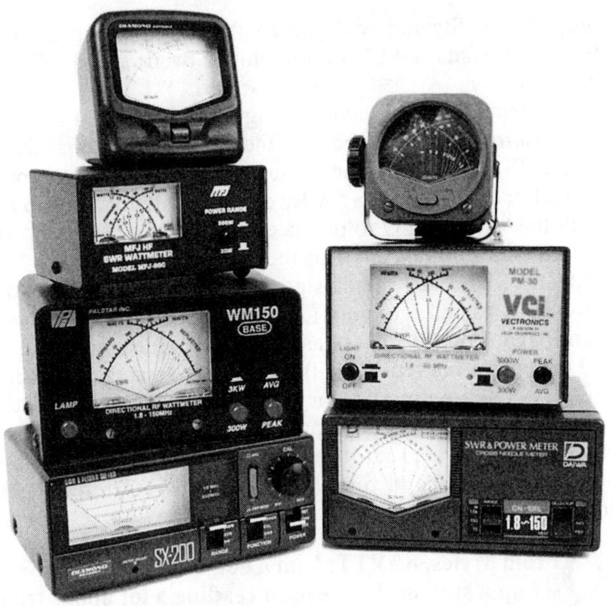

Figure 9.11—Hams have lots of wattmeters to choose from. These were reviewed in the July 2002 Product Review column.

popular line of wattmeters. These use plug-in measuring elements specific to different frequency ranges and power levels. Their specified accuracy is ±5% of full scale for CW signals and, for those models that have a peak-reading function, ±8% for PEP measurements. Given even that accuracy, the meter cost is still several hundred dollars. Achieving better accuracy would require a better wattmeter, perhaps built to laboratory standards. Accurate commercial or laboratory instrumentation could cost more than most amateur HF transceivers, so most hams are content with the accuracy of amateur test equipment.

See if you can get either transceiver to put out full rated power on CW or on SSB with a loud sound of constant level (such as a whistle, several seconds long). You can then be reasonably certain that it is also producing the same PEP on voice peaks (assuming they are equally loud), regardless of the meter reading.

Q From Adam, in Indiana, comes the following: I live in an apartment complex in Bloomington. Is there any possibility of operating a ham station from my apartment? I have one window, which faces more or less north.

A Operating the HF ham bands from an apartment (assuming you are on the first floor) represents quite a challenge and one many hams are familiar with. To be honest, nothing beats outdoor antennas. If you have trees or bushes you can hide them in, then, by all means, go that route. As Bruce, W6TOY, so aptly put it: "Antennas are outdoor creatures… they are much happier when they can live as nature intended." If your building is brick, you may be able to run a modest wire (of small gauge and dark insulation) in stealth fashion along the mortar seams such that it will be invisible for all practical purposes. If you have a patio or balcony that you can use to set up a temporary antenna after dark, then I would recommend that, too. If, like some locations, the rules of your lease prohibit putting *anything* outdoors at your apartment, you might consider going mobile; that is what many hams do.

Assuming that all of the above are out (or otherwise wouldn't work for you), indoor antennas can be used, but you must be aware of a few things—

● Indoor antennas will never do as well as outdoor antennas

(even at the same height) so adjust your expectations accordingly.

● When it comes to the HF bands, longer is generally better, given that most rooms are a fraction of a wavelength long on the bands below 10 meters. Consider a loop running around the ceiling of the largest room in your apartment, painted to match the walls or the ceiling so it doesn't stand out. Cup hooks make excellent "hidden" supports.

● The RF field intensity in close proximity to antennas is quite high, so indoor antennas carry greater risk of excessive RF exposure. They also tend to overload nearby consumer electronics equipment, so be mindful of this if you have upstairs neighbors. In any case, you should reduce your transmitter power—especially if you will be operating in the same room that the antenna is in. Twenty watts is a good ballpark figure for CW operation, with up to 50 W acceptable for SSB.

Q Austin, W9DKT, asks: For normal CW operation what are the advantages of using an iambic key over a vibrating type key?

A An iambic keyer is an electronic keyer that contains digital logic that allows the operator to squeeze the paddle levers to form a series of alternating dots or dashes. As an example, consider the letter "c," which in Morse code is *dah-di-dah-dit*. Simply holding both levers of the paddle together and releasing them after the proper interval produces that character. Depending upon which paddle is activated first, the element series can be started with either a dot or a dash. The advantage of iambic operation is that fewer paddle (key) strokes are required for alternate sequence characters like a period (*di-dah-di-dah-di-dah*) or the ending prosign AR (*di-dah-di-dah-dit*). It does take a bit of practice to master iambic sending and not all operators like it or use it. Those who do, however, agree that the fewer number of keystrokes (or "paddlestrokes") required makes for easier sending.

Iambic operation can usually be programmed in two modes, so-called Mode A or Mode B, and some iambic keyers offer that choice. Mode A operation will complete a dash or a dot after its appropriate paddle lever is released, exactly like most electronic keyers do (the character is said to be "self-completing"). Mode B operation results in the opposite code element being sent after a paddle lever is released. In other words, if I were sending the letter "c" in iambic Mode B, I would start by squeezing both levers *almost* simultaneously, but with slightly more delay given the dot side. The sequence would begin, therefore, with a dash, as that lever has been activated first. I would then *release* both paddles after the second dash started (*dah-di-dah…*) and then the final dot generation (*dah-di-dah-dit*) would be automatic. The amount of motion required to activate the paddle has thus been reduced considerably, instead of going back and forth 4 times for the character "c," the operator need only squeeze the paddle levers once and let go (providing his or her timing is correct!).

A non-iambic keyer does not have the "squeeze" feature. Some operators, including myself, don't use the iambic feature. It's a matter of personal preference—and one that, as I said, takes some practice to master. It also requires that the keyer have the necessary logic to accommodate iambic keying modes. Additionally, the paddle (key) must be a dual-lever design, one lever dedicated to dots and another to dashes.

A mechanical key, usually called a *bug*, uses one or several weights on the end of a spring arm to *vibrate* the arm (hence its commercial name) and forms dots with a set of contacts mounted to the arm. These are called *semi-automatic keys*—they send only dots automatically; dashes still need to be made manually. Characters are formed as if you were using a straight key, only the motion is sideways (horizontal) instead of up

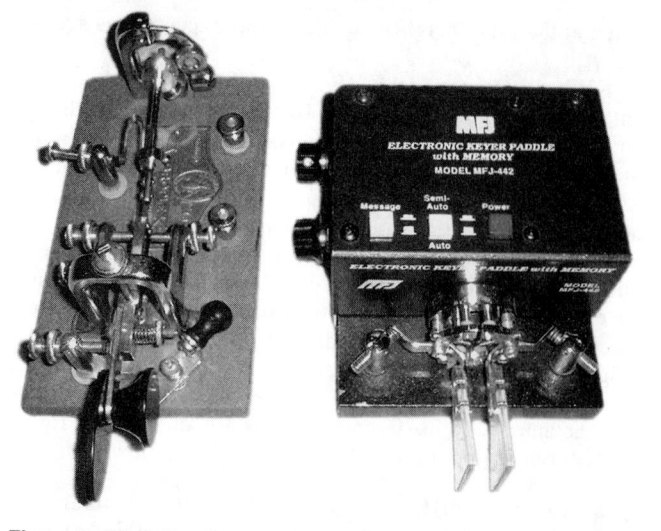

Figure 9.12—A "bug" or semi-automatic key (Vibroplex) is shown at the left. Note the long spring arm with weight and the arm contacts to the left of the arm. The vibrating arm makes automatic dots when the key knob is moved to the right by the operator's thumb. An electronic iambic keyer with a dual-lever paddle is shown to the right. Iambic operation is described in the text.

and down. In the case of a right-handed key, the operator's right thumb makes the dots and the index finger (usually) makes the dashes. There's considerably less effort in sending with a bug compared to a straight key, as the dots are made automatically. This, too, requires practice, although many operators prefer the sound of "machine code" sent from an electronic key. However, the bug does impart a certain style or "swing" to one's sending that can't be easily duplicated with an electronic key. Incidentally, the name "bug" derives from the term coined for an incompetent telegrapher. Poor landline operators of the early 1900s were known as "bugs," and when the semi-automatic key first appeared the keys were purchased and used by operators without practice (one can only imagine what that sounded like!). Hence, the key itself became known as a "bug."

The Vibroplex[6] is a good example of a commercial bug and one that has been in production since 1905. Bugs do not require any outboard electronics; the key itself takes care of all final contact closures in the character formation. A Vibroplex bug and an electronic keyer with dual-lever paddle are shown in **Figure 9.12**.

QRichard, K5RN, asks an interesting question: I have wondered for a long time why Amateur Radio operators use both upper and lower sidebands. Most commercial and military communications systems make use of only one sideband (usually USB). Hams seldom mix upper and lower SSB on a single band. Could the answer be that it has something to do with interference (QRM) reduction?

ARichard, the answer has much to do with history and it was a matter of economics. In the early days of SSB, the most cost effective way of generating and receiving an SSB signal was to use a 5 MHz (approximate) crystal filtered IF and a 9 MHz (also approximate) tunable VFO—you could then cover both the 75 and 20 meter bands relatively cheaply and easily. Back then, before phase locked oscillators and frequency synthesis, covering both sidebands meant you'd have to buy two crystals for carrier injection, a somewhat costly

proposition. Staying with the convention of using USB for the upper bands and LSB for the lower bands saved SSB pioneers money.

For receiving, the incoming signal (3.8 MHz or 14 MHz) was *heterodyned* or mixed with the 9 MHz VFO to produce a 5 MHz IF (using the mixer-produced sum and difference products). For transmitting, a 5 MHz carrier oscillator was *summed* with the 9 MHz VFO to produce the 20 meter (14 MHz) signal. It was *differenced* with the VFO to produce a 4 MHz (3.6-3.9 MHz), 80 meter signal. The result, after passage through a shared (common) crystal filter, was a lower sideband signal on 80 meters and an upper sideband signal on 20 meters—a convention still used today. In actuality, there's no reason not to use USB on 75 meters or LSB on 20 meters, provided the receiving operator knows you are doing this. In fact, by mutual consent, two stations might resort to "unconventional" sideband operation to avoid interference in a crowded band.

QFrom Myles, K3VTT: I am a new ham and am about to set up a station. I have been reading a lot about transmission lines and antennas. I keep reading that for 2 meter work and above, ladder line would be the best feed line for my antenna. I have not been able to find any articles about how to install the line, however. Some articles caution about running ladder line too near to metal. I would want to run it perpendicularly across a steel support beam in my house and across an aluminum grid in my drop ceiling. Do you think that path would be a problem and are there any good articles about the installation and care of ladder line?

ALadder line (it is also referred to as *window* or *open-wire* line) is generally not recommended for 144 MHz and above ("above" meaning higher in frequency but shorter in wavelength) due to the difficulty of obtaining good quality line for VHF/UHF use, its ineffectiveness at these frequencies and the difficulty in installing it properly. It's worthwhile to reprint a paragraph written by Dean Straw, N6BV, in *Simple and Fun Antennas for Hams*:[7] "For a fixed distance between the (ladder line) wires (say, 1 inch for 450 Ω window line) the spacing in terms of wavelengths goes up as the frequency is raised. Thus the phase difference between the currents flowing in each wire will be different from the 180° needed for complete cancellation for higher frequencies. For this reason open-wire line loses its effectiveness as the frequency goes into the low UHF range. You will rarely find open-wire line used above the 450 MHz band, while coax is still going strong at 1.2 GHz and beyond."

That said, ladder line *is* recommended for HF use and has such low loss at these lower frequencies that SWR almost ceases to be a problem. A "flat-top" or dipole as long as you can make it, fed in the center with ladder line and matched through an antenna tuner, makes an excellent multiband HF antenna. Ladder line is far superior to coax here because of its loss characteristics. Ladder line run perpendicular to a metal structure should be spaced several inches from it. Common TV standoff insulators will suffice, and one can be used on each conductor of the line, if you're careful to not change the line spacing. An excellent reference for the installation of ladder line at HF can also be found in the earlier mentioned reference, *Simple and Fun Antennas for Hams*, Chapter 11, where it is pointed out that the line should be spaced away from nearby conductors by a factor of three times the wire spacing. For 450 Ω ladder line, this works out to be about 3 inches.

The ceiling grid should not pose a problem if the line is

[6]The Vibroplex Co, Inc, 11 E Midtown Park, Mobile, AL 36606; tel 251-478-8873; **www.vibroplex.com**.

[7]Available from your local dealer or the ARRL Bookstore. Order no. 8624.

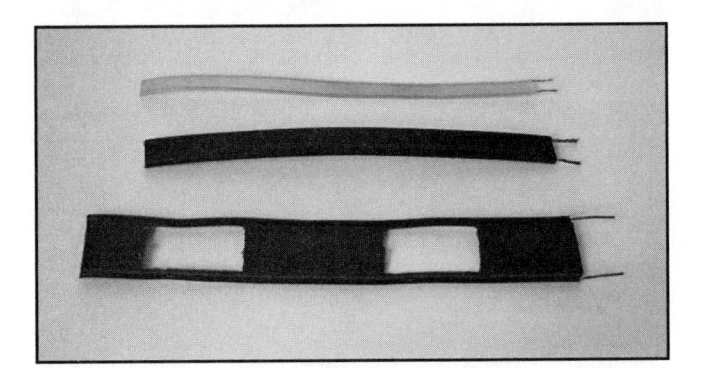

Figure 9.13—Three types of open-wire line. TV receiving line is at the top, heavy duty transmitting line is at the center, and 450 Ω window-type ladder line is at the bottom. Window line has characteristics that come closest to traditional open-wire bare conductor line.

**Table 9.1**
**Common Types of Open-Wire Transmission Line**

| Type | $Z_0$ Ω | Velocity Factor, % | Wire Gauge | Power Handling | Matched-Line Loss, 100 MHz |
|---|---|---|---|---|---|
| TV Twin Lead | 300 | 80 | #22 | Low | 1.4 dB/100' |
| Twin Lead | 300 | 80 | #20 | Med | 1.1 dB/100' |
| Generic Window | 405 | 91 | #18 | High | 0.3 dB/100' |
| High-Power Window | 450 | 91 | #16 | High | 0.3 dB/100' |
| Open-Wire | 600 | 92 | #12 | High | 0.2 dB/100' |

not coupled closely to it for any appreciable distance. Try to cross the grid perpendicularly; run the line equally between the grid supports and try to avoid close parallel coupling. The same arguments apply to outdoor use when the feed line comes close to any support structures. It's also a good idea to give the line a few twists while installing outdoors. This will keep the wind from grabbing the flat line and blowing it around—the objective being to minimize line motion with respect to surrounding structures. Examples of open-wire lines can be seen in **Figure 9.13**. **Table 9.1** lists some of their characteristics.

Additionally, a good reference on installing open-wire line at VHF/UHF can be found in an old edition of *The Radio Amateur's VHF Manual*, Third Edition, 1972, pages 162 and 165. (This is no longer available but it may be obtainable at your local library or a used book dealer.) The author claims that with a 100 foot run of 12 gauge conductors spaced ⅝ inch apart with Teflon spreaders every 6 feet, losses of 1.1, 1.35 and 1.56 dB were obtained on 144, 220 and 432 MHz. That represents the best that can be expected in a practical installation. By comparison, 1⅝ inch *Heliax* (**www.andrew.com**) coaxial cable has under 0.5 dB of loss on all of the bands 70 cm and below (here, "below" means lower in frequency; longer in wavelength). It is probably cheaper too—surplus large diameter coax is often free for the asking from commercial users—if you hunt around for someone who needs to get rid of it. Even ½ inch *Heliax* will beat ladder line at these frequencies. The difficulty is finding it inexpensively and finding suitable connectors for it. The connectors are apt to set you back as much as the cable itself! This smaller coax is much easier to handle than the heavier variety.

**Q** Charles, N2KR, writes: I'm having problems with "motor-boating" in my electronic keyers. After completing a character, the keyer continues to send a continuous string of dots or dashes—more common with some characters than others—using a non-iambic paddle. I originally thought is may be due to RF getting into the cables, but it also occurs with the keyer and paddle standing alone; away from, and not wired to, the radio equipment. I have four different keyers and paddles and it happens with all of them. Since I primarily operate CW, this is very frustrating—I don't want to go back to using a straight key, and I don't like "bugs" very much, but I may be forced to go to a mechanical bug. Any suggestions?

**A** Most keyers are designed to operate with very low power, in order to minimize battery drain. What this means is that the paddle sensing circuit is usually designed to operate at high impedance and there is very little current passing through the paddle contacts. In fact, water across the paddle contacts will short out most designs. This low current design sometimes results in "contact bluing," in which a microscopic oxide layer builds up on the contacts and requires more current than is available to "punch through" that layer. Try cleaning the contacts of the paddle with bond paper and set the contact spacing slightly farther apart. Also, a covering to enclose the paddle may help. **Figure 9.14** shows a typical example of a paddle cover. This will help prevent dirt buildup on the contacts, but it won't do much for the effect of environmental air conditions on the contacts. Periodic cleaning and slightly wider spacing is the answer here. By the way, it's one of the reasons that sensitive relays are often hermetically sealed.

Figure 9.14—A plastic cover over the paddle will help keep those contacts clean. It takes only a microscopic layer of dirt to insulate a high impedance paddle circuit.

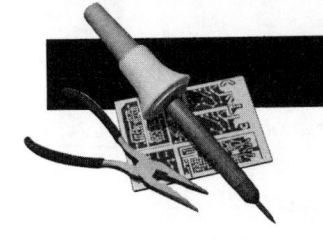

# Chapter 10

# Around the Shack

## YOU MAY ALREADY HAVE A 6-METER MOBILE ANTENNA!

◊ As an avid 6-meter operator and repeater owner, I am often informing owners of the new multiband HF/VHF multimode rigs about antennas. Common 2-meter $^5/_8$-λ base loaded (and other types) as well as 54-inch HF-mobile antenna masts (dependent on the attached resonators and such) are $^1/_4$-λ antennas for 6-meter operation. So, if you have a rig with 6 meters and no antenna in use, you may be all set. Depending on the make and model of the radio, a software menu selection of antenna port or the addition of a diplexer may be all that is needed to get in on the excitement of 6 meter SSB or FM while mobile.—*Steve Hajducek, N2CKH, PO Box 117, Howell, NJ 07731-0117; n2ckh@arrl.net*

## AN OLD-FASHIONED RF AMMETER FOR LADDER LINE

◊ Those amateurs who use open wire feed lines to feed wire antennas may desire to observe the RF current in the feeders. An SWR measuring device in the coaxial cable between the transmitter and the antenna tuner will indicate a match of the entire antenna system to the rig, but it leaves a lot to be desired if you are interested in what is going on in the open wire feeders themselves. "Hot wire" or thermocouple RF ammeters are available but expensive, so I use an old-time method.[1]

This device uses a 2-V incandescent lamp (such as #43, #48 or #49), wired in series with each feeder at some point a little ways away from the antenna coupler or tuner. Each lamp is shunted with a piece of #24 AWG copper wire about six

---

[1]A more sophisticated indicator was described by Zack Lau, W1VT, in "A Relative RF Ammeter for Open-Wire Lines," *QST*, Oct 1988, pp 15-17, 20.

---

inches long. Lay out the device such that the symmetry and spacing of the feed line is maintained as closely as possible. I soldered two short pieces of wire to each side of the lamp so that the total length of the leads with the lamp in the center is six inches. Then the #24 AWG shunt wire is laid adjacent to each lamp with its leads, and the lamps with their shunts are mounted on a piece of insulated material (dry wood, unplated perf-board or equivalent) with suitable terminals at each end for connecting the feed line. If desired, a DPST knife switch with blade spacing similar to that of the feed line can be incorporated to bypass the device when desired. Do not use it if the transmitter power level at full power exceeds the capabilities of the lamps (they're too bright).

In use, the lamps will illuminate when some amount of RF power is applied to the antenna system. If the antenna system is well balanced, the lamps will illuminate to equal brilliance. If there is imbalance, one lamp will illuminate less than the other, displaying a qualitative measure of current imbalance.

You cannot quantitatively determine feeder current in RF amperes with this device, but you can easily see any imbalance and the success of efforts to correct it. Then you can tune your system for maximum current in the feeders, which should coincide with maximum power transfer to the antenna's radiating elements. In my station, a 50 W CW transmitter lights the shunted 2 V lamps to nearly full brilliance when the antenna system is matched to the rig.

I tune the system with reduced power, then if more output power is necessary, I close the cutout switch to prevent burning the lamps out at higher power levels.—*L. E. "Ed" Trump, AL7N, 2950 S Kobuk Ave, Fairbanks, AK 99709; al7n@arrl.net*

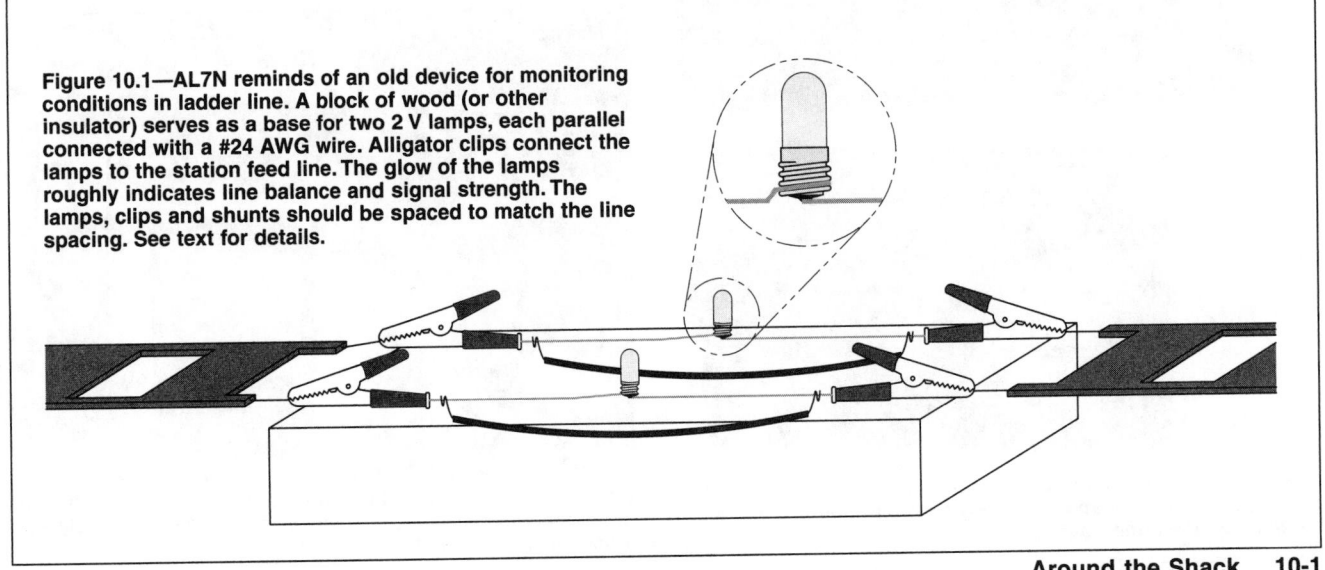

Figure 10.1—AL7N reminds of an old device for monitoring conditions in ladder line. A block of wood (or other insulator) serves as a base for two 2 V lamps, each parallel connected with a #24 AWG wire. Alligator clips connect the lamps to the station feed line. The glow of the lamps roughly indicates line balance and signal strength. The lamps, clips and shunts should be spaced to match the line spacing. See text for details.

## CW FREQUENCY MATCHING WITH MUSICAL INSTRUMENT TUNERS

◊ Many transceivers provide no means to help the operator match the transmitted frequency to that of the other station. Usually it's a case of matching the audio beat tone for the received CW signal by ear.

I've found that quick and accurate CW frequency matching—within a few hertz—is possible through use of a digital tuner meant for musical instruments. The better tuners are actually small audio frequency counters, complete with a crystal time base. They display frequency not in hertz, but as points on the musical scale: notes and hundredths of a note. Their circuitry allows them to "listen" only when a tone is present, ignoring background noise between CW dits and dahs, while displaying the average pitch continuously. I found these tuners to be effective and accurate with weak signals, almost to the point where the signals vanish in the noise. The input audio level is not critical.

The two tuners in **Figure 10.2**, a Seiko ST-747 and a Korg CA-30, work about equally well for this purpose. They cost about $20 to $30 from retailers or on-line suppliers. I didn't test other models, but I suspect some might not work for CW, particularly under noisy band conditions.

To use a tuner for CW frequency matching, you'll first need to determine exactly what pitch of a received CW signal corresponds to zero beat of your transmitter with that station. To determine this, find a reference signal and zero beat your transmitter to it by listening on a second, independent receiver. Then, switch to receive mode on your transceiver and note the pitch reading on the tuner for this reference signal. For any future station you wish to contact, adjust your receive frequency so the tuner shows this same pitch reading.

The tuners in Figure 10.2 have built-in microphones, but feeding an audio signal directly to the microphone-input jack of the tuner yields much better results. I found mine worked best with a series resistor of about 100 kΩ in the line between my transceiver headphone jack and the tuner input. I'd sug-

gest experimenting with different resistances. Find a value low enough to yield a pitch display on the tuner with a weak CW signal, yet high enough that no pitch displays if only noise is present.—*Dick Lamb, KØKK, 44 Post Rd, Iowa City, IA 52245-3622; k0kk@arrl.net*

## WHICH WAY DOES THE WIND BLOW?

◊ Thank you, N9PUG. Your article on the poor man's anemometer (see Dec 2001 *QST*) brought back many memories and a rekindled interest. Back in the early 1970s, I was instrumental in providing materials to members of our local radio club to homebrew anemometers for our work with the local weather service during periods of severe weather activity.

As mentioned by N9PUG, my version used the ubiquitous "Leggs eggs" to catch the wind. They were mounted on the ends of 6-inch-long rods attached to a central hub, which then turned the shaft of a small motor similar to that used by N9PUG. They worked great, but Leggs eggs are not very durable. Now, 25 years later I seriously doubt that any still exist.

Our good editor wondered if someone could add a remote wind-direction indicator, and that took me back an additional 25 years. In the late 1940s, I put up my first beam antenna: a 2-meter beam turned by a war surplus bomb-bay-door motor. It worked perfectly. For a direction indicator, I used two war-surplus selsyns: the big model 2J1H1 versions that measure about 2+ inches diameter by 4+ inches long. Much smaller versions are sometimes available.

Lo and behold, the Fair Radio Catalog[2] still listed both types. [At the time of printing, Fair Radio's site lists only the 2J1H1.—*Ed.*] The 2J1H1 and the smaller one (about $1{\times}^{11}/_{16}$ inches) both sell for about $10 apiece. They call the small one "wind-sel"; how appropriate. I ordered two of the small ones and used them to build a remote wind-direction indicator that that can't be beat. As shown in **Figure 10.3**, I made a small compass rose that I placed next to my wind-speed meter. The indicating hand for wind direction is a spare electric-clock second hand from my junk box; it is epoxied to the shaft of the selsyn. A visit to a clock repair shop might get you one free of charge.

Mounting the indicating selsyn can be a bit of a problem since it must be mounted horizontally. I used a acouple of **L** brackets fastened to a piece of PVC pipe holding the selsyn (see **Figure 10.4**). Fair Radio also sells a radio-compass indicator that would work equally well and mounts like a meter in

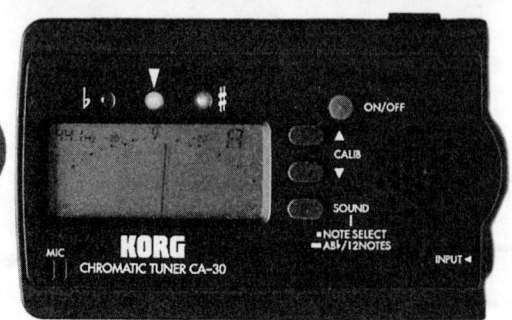

Figure 10.2—Musical instrument tuners like these can help the CW operator quickly and accurately tune a transmitter to the frequency of another station.

Figure 10.3—The finished unit installed in my shack. Notice the old homebrew receiver on its left. Circa late 1920s or early 30s, it uses a single UV199.

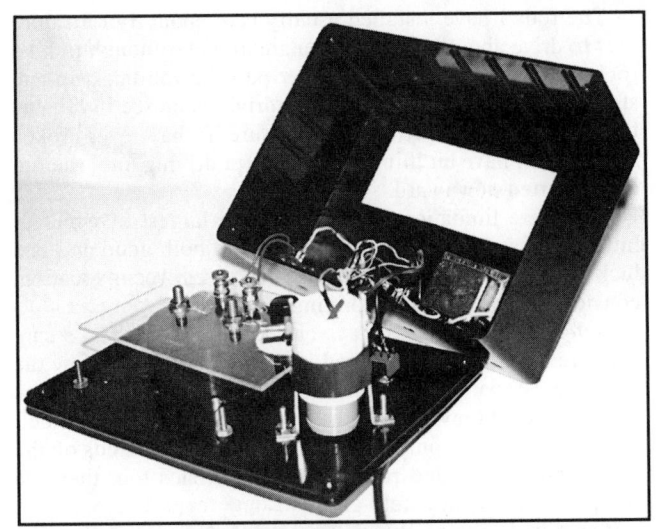

Figure 10.4—A view showing direction-indicating selsyn in the PVC with mounting brackets. The partly visible knob at the top left of the PVC is for the wind-speed calibration pot.

Figure 10.5—N9PUG anemometer, W8OZA remote wind-direction sensor. Direction-sensor rod is made from a piece of an old TV-antenna element. The grey PVC holding the direction selsyn is required to fit selsyn diameter to the PVC elbow fitting.

a single hole. With that approach, you would only need one selsyn. As an old sea dog, I prefer the compass rose. Ex-"flyboys" might prefer the radio-compass indicator. The rest of you take your choice.

A word on the selsyns: Both types were designed for use in aircraft and operated at 400-Hz. To use them on 60 Hz, it is necessary to reduce the voltage. If memory serves me correctly, I used 24 V on the 2J1H1. My tests show that the smaller version will operate as low as 4.7 V ac; 6.3 V is the obvious choice.

Your direction indicator can be accurately set on the ground. Just be sure the sensor that will be mounted in the air is in a known direction and the indicator in the shack corresponds before gluing the clock hand in place. When you erect your outdoor sensor, remember what you did on the ground.

To get accurate readings of wind speed and direction, I have mounted the collectors up on a leg of my antenna tower with two **U** bolts. A piece of eight-conductor cable from RadioShack (#278-1583, about 15¢ / foot) feeds the information to the indicators in my shack. Yes, I've a few bucks in it. About $40 for an assembly that I will put up against anything I've seen on the market, which costs about $400 and up.—*Russell F. Sievert, W8OZA, 1411 Lonsdale Rd, Columbus, OH 43232*

²Fair Radio, 2395 St Johns Rd, PO Box 1105, Lima, OH 45802; tel 419-227-6573, 419-223-2196, fax 419-227-1313; **www.fairradio.com**.

## GROUND-ROD INSTALLATION, INEXPENSIVE AND EASY

◊ After being more or less absent from ham radio for many years, I have returned. It is an outlet for work stress and helps me relearn my analog engineering skills. My first task in setting up a station was to install a ground rod and antenna system. Secondly, I reviewed *The Handbook*. I was a bit surprised to see a reference to flared end on a ground rod. Even 17 years ago, I installed ground rods with ease and without appreciably flaring the rod.

Having grown up around farms, I watched while steel fence posts were driven into the ground with a tool called a fence-post driver. A fence-post driver is actually some type of thin metal pipe with a weight on one end. This pipe was fitted over the post, lifted and then slammed downward. The weight acts as a hammer that is guided by the pipe assembly for a "perfect hit" every time.

With such a tool, it is possible for one person to install fence posts quickly and easily. A fence post has a T shape and is only driven a couple feet into the ground; otherwise, they are strikingly similar to ground rods in the way they need to be installed.

A weight attached to a pipe that fits over the ground rod can function as a driver for ground-rod installation. With a little effort and about $5 in materials, you can create your own ground-rod driver. The parts for my ground-rod driver are available from the local home-supply store and metal scrap yard.

My selection of materials started with a visit to the metal scrap yard. Look for a total of about 3 to 5 pounds of steel. The thickness of the metal is important because you will have to drill a hole through the metal weight for assembly. I chose two pieces of steel of a triangular shape. Both pieces were about ³/₈-inch thick and had a bump on one corner. I used a hacksaw to clean up the bump and then a grinder and file to remove any sharp edges.

The pipe for the project will likely be ¹/₂-inch (ID) galvanized water pipe. It should easily slide over the ground rod. You should get two pipes: one about 30 inches long, and the other about 18 inches long. Both should be threaded on at least one end. You will also need a pipe flange to secure the steel weights to the pipe.

While you are at the home supply store, select some bolts that fit the holes of the floor flange. They should be long enough to go through the flange and the weights and secure them. It is a good idea to buy two nuts for each bolt so that you can "lock" the nuts to prevent accidental disassembly.

Refer to **Figure 10.6**. First, find and label the center of gravity on each steel piece. You can easily find the center of gravity by balancing the weight on the point of a small sharp rock. We need to mark the center of gravity so that we can mount the pieces with their centers of gravity near the center of the floor flange. With the weight centered, it will generate little sideways force when the weight hits the rod. The weight needs to exert force downward to drive the rod into the ground.

After marking the center of gravity, mark the holes where you will attach the weights to the floor flange. Punch the hole centers and drill holes in the steel to accept the bolts. I used only two bolts to attach the flange. The bolts actually only hold the pipe to the steel weight during use. You don't want the pieces to come apart, but you don't need a lot of bolt strength either. Use some form of locking on the bolts and nuts so that the driver will not fly apart and hurt someone during use. Once the weight is secured, you can thread the weighted flange assembly onto the short or long pipe as needed.

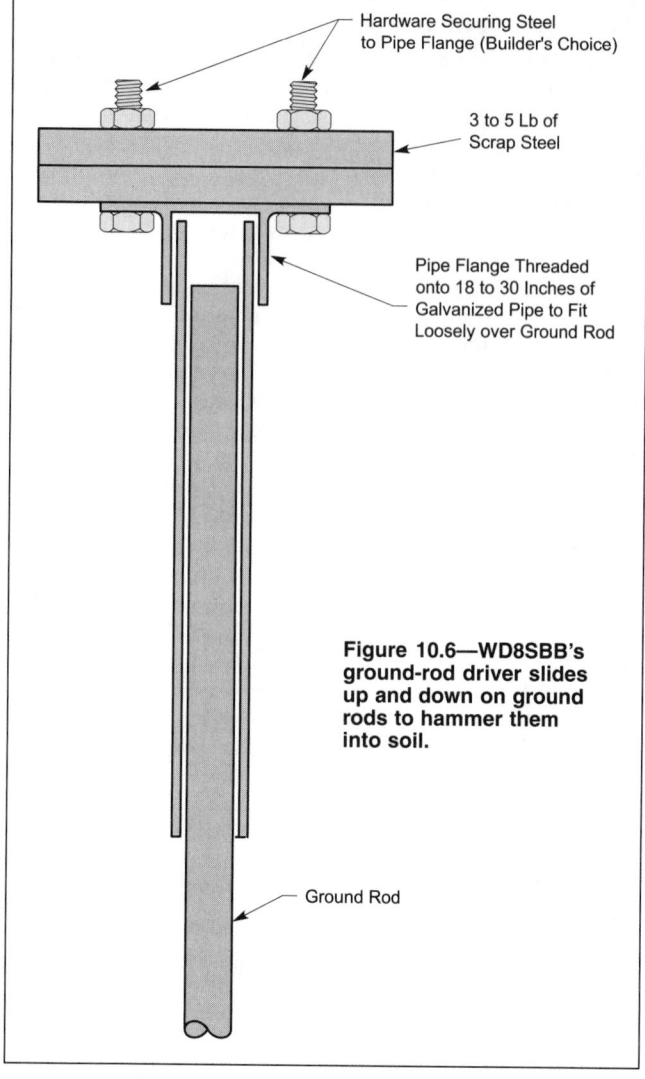

Hardware Securing Steel to Pipe Flange (Builder's Choice)

3 to 5 Lb of Scrap Steel

Pipe Flange Threaded onto 18 to 30 Inches of Galvanized Pipe to Fit Loosely over Ground Rod

**Figure 10.6—WD8SBB's ground-rod driver slides up and down on ground rods to hammer them into soil.**

Ground Rod

The rods I have installed usually take about 5 or 10 minutes to drive about 10 feet. If you are unlucky enough to hit a rock, you have two options: either pull the rod back up and start again in another hole, or keep driving and see if you can break or displace the rock. I am not sure if I have ever broken a rock, but I have hit things and just kept driving until the rod again started downward.

There are limitations to this tool, the largest of which is hitting rocks. As I mentioned, I have had both good and bad luck with "solid objects." If you live in a very rocky location, consider other methods of driving ground rods.[3-6]

*Safety first always.* Always check the bolts to make sure they are tight and not damaged in such a way as to allow the driver to fly apart. Wear leather gloves. I was never so glad as the day I caught my hand in the driver and my gloves got cut, while my hand was only in mild pain. Keep your hands on the driver, not the ground rod. Watch the threads too, they are sharp. Always wear safety glasses.

Good luck. I think this will provide a lot of "bang for the buck" around a well grounded ham shack.—*Ron Wagner, WD8SBB, 5065 S Kessler Frederick Rd, Troy, OH 45373-9205;* **wd8sbb@arrl.org**

### GROUND-ROD INSTALLATION—SAFETY FIRST!

◊ Be sure to find the location of buried electrical lines, water lines and gas lines before driving a ground rod as described in the May 2003 column! Many natural-gas utilities use polyethylene pipe for service lines. Using a driver as described, you would never know when you hit a gas line and cause a very dangerous situation.—*Larry L. Lehmann, KCØDA, 528 West Ave, Minden, NE 68959-1421;* **kc0da@arrl.net**

### INSTALLING GROUND RODS—THE EASY WAY

◊ In all of the instructions I've seen on how to "drive" a ground rod, usually the easiest way to get it in at least ³/₄ of the way is left out—you simply push or pump it in. Assuming that the ground is not rock or frozen, put some water on the spot that you want the ground rod to go into. Then start pumping the rod up and down like you are churning butter and continue to add water slowly to the spot. A trickling water hose is best. Keep pumping the rod up and down easily and slowly. You should be able to get it down almost ³/₄ of the way or more. What little you have left to drive in the conventional way (a sledge hammer) very seldom flattens the top of the rod. Fancy devices are not required. I spent a summer putting in ground rods for Memphis Light, Gas and Water and was quite successful. I just assumed everyone did it that way.—*Stewart Nelson, KD5LBE, 8 Deerwood Dr, Morrilton, AR 72110*

### NO ATTRACTIVE NUISANCE HERE (TOWER GUARD)

◊ Any ham using a tower must be careful, so as not to be sued for having an "attractive nuisance." That is anything that would draw the attention of a young child, who might then be injured as a result of their attraction. Because we do not want any child hurt by their attempt to emulate the ham they see climbing his radio tower and we do not want to be legally liable for an injury, we are obligated to prevent children from

*Safety first! Wear safety glasses and leather gloves while using the driver. Keep your hands on the pipe, not the ground rod!* Start the process of installing a ground rod by digging a hole about 10 inches deep. You may remember the fence posts only went in a few feet, but the ground rod goes into the ground "up to its neck." The shortness of the rod left above ground means that the rod driver will end up driving itself into the ground with the rod. The hole allows the rod to reach the ground while preventing the driver pipe from penetrating the ground too deeply.

Install the weights and flange onto the longer section of galvanized pipe. Slip the driver over the ground rod, and set the ground rod into the hole. Based on the height of the rod, you may require a stepladder. Put the drive over the end of the ground rod. Lift the driver up and "slam" the driver down on the rod, making sure that your hands and fingers are on the pipe and away from the end of the pipe as it comes down. Let the weight drive the rod. You should not use muscle to propel the driver downward. Weight and gravity should do the job; you need only raise the driver between blows.

After you get the ground rod almost installed, the long driver pipe will be hitting the ground. This is okay, but you may want to switch to the shorter pipe to continue driving the ground rod. Be careful when you change to the shorter pipe because it can more easily slide off the ground rod during the upward strokes.

[3]M. Goins, WB5YJX, "Another Way to Install Ground Rods," *QST*, May 1996, p 75.

[4]H. Brown, KC5EIY, "Installing Ground Rods in Heavy Clay," *QST*, Oct 1995, p 76.

[5]A.W. Edwards, K5CN, "Tips on Installing and Connecting to Ground Rods," *QST*, Jun 1994, p 76.

[6]R. Hinshaw, WD6L, "Water Makes Driving Ground Rods Easier," *QST*, Aug 1990, p 37.

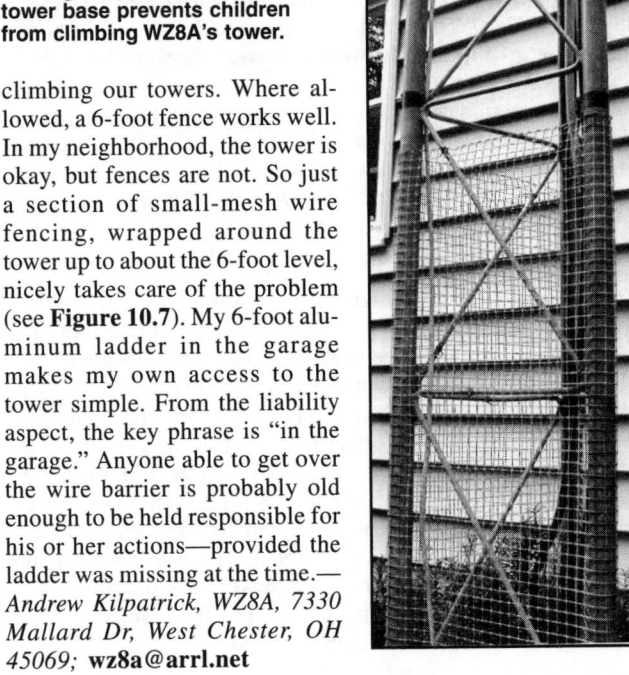

Figure 10.7—Small-mesh wire fencing wrapped around the tower base prevents children from climbing WZ8A's tower.

climbing our towers. Where allowed, a 6-foot fence works well. In my neighborhood, the tower is okay, but fences are not. So just a section of small-mesh wire fencing, wrapped around the tower up to about the 6-foot level, nicely takes care of the problem (see **Figure 10.7**). My 6-foot aluminum ladder in the garage makes my own access to the tower simple. From the liability aspect, the key phrase is "in the garage." Anyone able to get over the wire barrier is probably old enough to be held responsible for his or her actions—provided the ladder was missing at the time.—*Andrew Kilpatrick, WZ8A, 7330 Mallard Dr, West Chester, OH 45069;* **wz8a@arrl.net**

## A MIGHTY DUCK FOR EMERGENCIES

◊ Even if it hasn't yet happened to you, it still can. The rubber duck for your handheld goes AWOL, gets kinked or loses the lock on its BNC—right as you're getting ready for a big public-service event. It happened to me when the one for my 222-MHz radio disappeared the night before the Marine Corps Marathon here in Arlington, Virginia.

But help is at hand, right behind your VCR if not in your coax collection: a 4-foot RG-6 video patch cable. That, plus an F-female-to-BNC-male adapter and some heat-shrink tubing will put you back in business (The RadioShack part numbers are #15-1550 and #278-251, respectively.)

This example will use dimensions for 222 MHz, but adjusting the radiator portion will easily yield 2-meter and 440-MHz versions. (A 2-meter might take a different complement of shrink tube for the needed rigidity.)

First, cut the RG-6 at 13$^1$/$_2$ inches above the bulge for its F-connector. Strip off the outer cover by slitting it lengthwise down to 1 inch above the bulge. (That last inch is important for rigidity.) Then remove the silver shield down to the same point, being careful not to cut the foam dielectric beneath. That will yield 12$^1$/$_2$ inches of effective—but rather floppy—radiator.

Now gather three pieces of shrink tube. First, get a 13$^1$/$_2$-inch section small enough to fit snugly on the radiator portion and down to the remaining coax cover/shield braid. Second, get 2 inches of somewhat larger-diameter tube to fit over the first layer at the same point. Third, get 3 inches of some with a still larger-diameter that will fit over the 2-inch layer and down past the bottom of the white covering to where the F-connector's bulge begins.

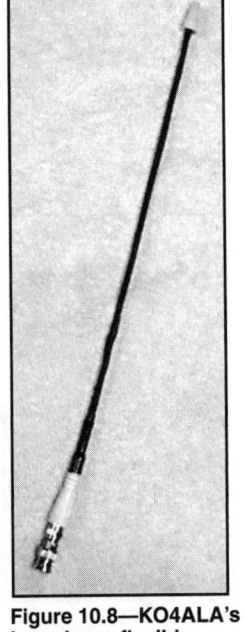

Figure 10.8—KO4ALA's homebrew flexible antenna for emergencies. See text for construction details.

For a finishing touch, screw a wire-nut onto the end of the radiator. Then attach the adapter and you're back on the air.

I did not have an SWR meter that could deal with 222 MHz, so I contented myself with the 12$^1$/$_2$-inch dimension from an antenna chart. [That's okay; handhelds must tolerate moderate SWR with the stock antenna.—*Ed.*] If you have the right meter, you could start with a 14$^1$/$_2$-inch piece of cable and have plenty to trim for tuning. But, from the "git-go," mine enabled me to hit all the repeaters that the original duck could.—*Alan Bosch, KO4ALA, 5832 20th St N, Arlington, VA 22205-3306;* **ko4ala@arrl.net**

## HISTORY OF HINTS & KINKS—A TIMELINE

◊ I was recently asked when "Hints and Kinks" began. The research illuminated a long history that began with readers. The "Hints and Kinks" column appeared in 1936, but it was based on an earlier "Experimenters' Section" column that started in 1923-24. The Experimenters' Section was a part of the ARRL organization with many registered members, who worked on technical tasks of concern to hams. The column "Experimenters' Section" reported on activities of those members, but continued well after the registry ceased in 1930. Here is a brief timeline:

*Jul 1923*: ARRL includes a reader survey (p 126) in *QST*.

*Jan 1924*: "The Growth of the Experimenters' Section" on p 35 indicates that headquarters is overwhelmed by survey results. There is great interest in experimentation and technical education. Result will be an Experimenter's Section of the ARRL organization.

*Feb 1924*: The first "Experimenter's Section Report" appears in *QST* (p 72). It solicits readers to register with headquarters to help with experimentation concerning technical problems of the day.

*May 1929*: The "Experimenter's Section" (p 41) states that results of the Technical Development Program will cover many technical problems previously considered by the Experimenters' Section. Those problems not addressed are stated, with bibliographic resources, in columns from May 1929 through May 1930.

*Jun 1930*: "Experimenters' Section" (p 33) headquarters activities associated with the Experimenters' Section cease, but the column continues. The space is used for "ideas and kinks which experimenters find useful." The column solicits technical ideas from readers.

*May 1933*: First Hints and Kinks book is published.

*Apr 1936*: "Hints and Kinks for Experimenters" first appears on p 59.

## RESEAL CORROGATED BOXES EASILY

◊ Here's a great way to keep larger corrugated cardboard radio and electronic parts storage boxes neatly closed, yet easily opened when needed. Just staple two (non-sticky) hook and loop strips, about 2$^1$/$_2$ inches long, to each side of one of the box's top flaps. Apply two-layers of packaging tape over the stapled part of the strips for extra strength. Next attach two self-stick 1 inch hook and loop mating strips (or glue the 1 inch mating non-stick variety) to the side of the box, so that the top hook and loop strip will mate with it when bent over. Leave a little open space at the bottom of the closure to grab onto, to facilitate disengaging the strip. Now do exactly the same thing to the other top flap and box sides.

The hook and loop strips keep the box tightly closed, yet it's easily opened when access is needed, without bending and wearing out the box flaps by over-and-under crossing them as is nor-

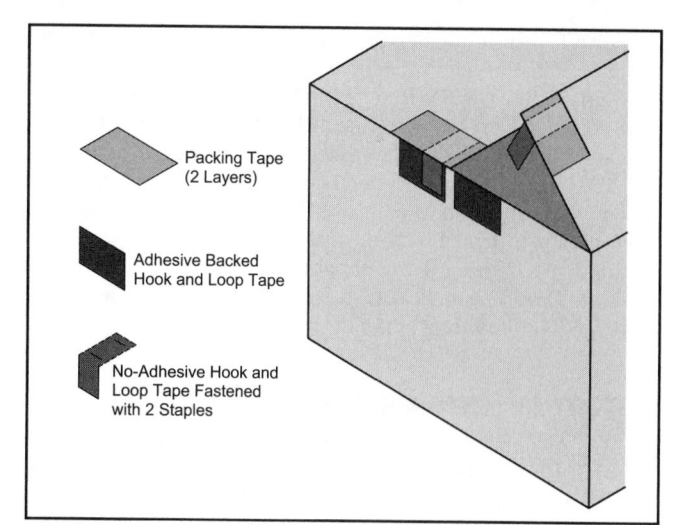

**Figure 10.9—NZ9E's solution for resealing equipment boxes with hook and loop tape.**

Packing Tape (2 Layers)

Adhesive Backed Hook and Loop Tape

No-Adhesive Hook and Loop Tape Fastened with 2 Staples

mally done with these boxes.—*Dave Miller, NZ9E, 1216 Terry Andrae Ave, Sheboygan, WI 53081;* **dmiller14@juno.com**

## A WINDOW-LINE SUPPORT

◊ A popular parallel-wire transmission line is a 450 Ω version encased in brown polyethylene with cutouts in the web, called "Ladder Line" or "Window Line." Because its fields are external to the wires, it works best when spaced away from metal masts, roofs, gutters, fascia, fences and the like. Any support needs to be low-loss, weatherproof, readily available, easily worked, versatile and inexpensive. Believe it or not, a single shape, a PVC plumbing pipe cap in 1¹/₂ inch size (actually 2¹/₄ OD 1¹/₂ inches deep) meets all these requirements. You can mount it horizontally or vertically, to any kind of structure, by its top or side, with screws, bolts, clamps or straps. You can notch it to accept the line, then drill two places to accept a nylon cable tie. By using two or more ties, you can change the line direction by wrapping it partway around the circumference. If you need more clearance, stack two caps side-by-side, end-to-end or side-to-end. Beware, however, that the hidden danger in using encased line is that it can develop invisible broken wires from constant flexing from the wind. So, to be safe, use more, not fewer, supports.— *W. A. "Spud" Monahan, K6KH, 817 Pacific Ave, Manhattan Beach, CA 90266-5849*

## CLEANING ANTENNA WIRE

◊ Regarding the cleaning of old antenna wire (see The Doctor is IN, Mar 2004 *QST*): An old-timer gave me this advice years ago, and it's proven invaluable over the years. Vinegar and salt cleans copper. Create a mixture of vinegar and salt and insert the section of wire to be soldered. After a few minutes it will be shiny and in like-new condition (even the individual strands will be clean)— and it will take solder like a new wire. —*Bill Arnold, WV8WVA, PO Box 1, Cabins, WV 26855-0001;* **wv8wva@arrl.net**

## N CONNECTOR FAILURE

◊ My 6 meter quad (4) Yagi antenna system uses nine common N connectors. About two years ago one of the connectors came apart. This last winter two more of these connectors also failed. These connectors have been in use about 10 years. There are no markings on these connectors, so I do not know who made them.

Just this spring, my former employer in the two-way business-radio business was installing a new FM broadcast antenna system and tower (88 to 108 MHz). There were eight N connectors on a factory-made matching harness. Of these eight, four of the new connectors failed—even when hand-tightened. Again, the connector maker was unknown. The construction crew was forced to secure the connectors with plastic tape until a new harness arrived.

*The Failure*

There is a snap ring in a groove in the body of the connector (see **Figure 10.11**). This snap ring is compressed and the coupling sleeve slipped over the snap ring. This snap ring then enters a matching groove in the coupling sleeve. All of the many connectors I have seen with coupling sleeves use this method of assembly.

On my failed connector, I measured the metal thickness of the coupling sleeve at about 0.040 inch. The snap-ring groove depth is around 0.025 inch deep. If the manufacturer is a little

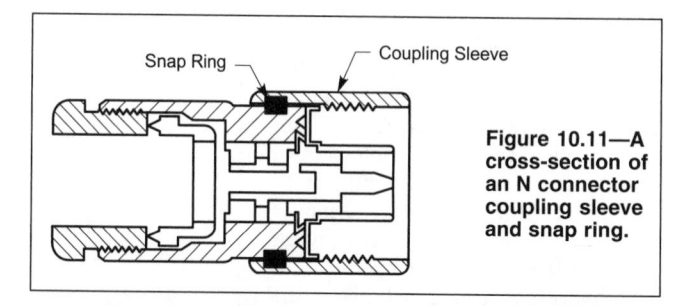

Snap Ring          Coupling Sleeve

**Figure 10.11—A cross-section of an N connector coupling sleeve and snap ring.**

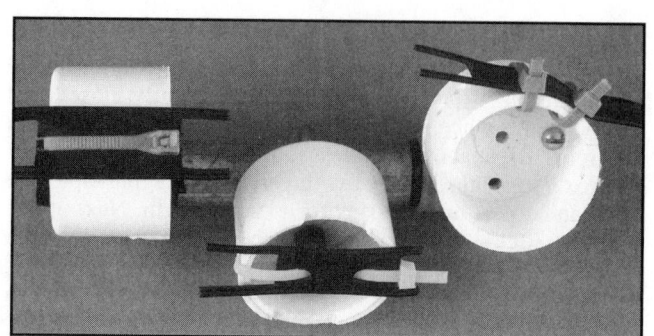

(A)

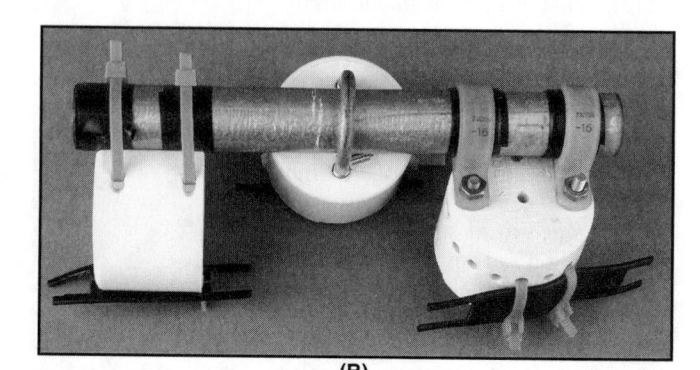

(B)

**Figure 10.10—A front view (A) shows several ways of securing window line to PVC caps used as standoffs. A rear view (B) shows several ways of securing PVC caps to a pipe. The caps could be secured to flat surfaces with appropriate screws through the cap and into the surface. Appropriate screws would be wood screws for a wood wall, sheet metal screws for thin metal or wood screws with plastic anchors for masonry.**

sloppy in machining this coupling-ring groove, there is maybe only 0.010 inch holding the ring together.

On the connector I checked, the snap ring inserted in the coupling sleeve was loose in the grove, and I could see visible movement. When I shook the coupling sleeve, I could hear it rattle in its 0.025-inch-deep groove. The locking of the snap ring is controlled by the release of the snap ring in the coupling sleeve's groove.

Another possible problem area is temperature. Here in western Colorado, we often see a day-to-night temperature change of 50°F or more, plus solar heating. Just yesterday (May 27, 2003), the night-to-day swing was 48°F. Today, it is 46° so far and increasing.—*William J. LeBaron, W0MTK, 1155 W Paradise Way, Fruita, CO 81521-2049;* **w0mtk@gvii.net**

## DEET INSECT REPELLENT WARNING

◊ As summer approaches, hams will be getting out into natural environments for events such as Field Day. We will be applying liberal amounts of DEET. As the Consumer Specialty Products Association says, "DEET is the common name for N, N-diethyl-m-toluamide, which is the active ingredient in the most widely used insect repellents applied to the skin." (**www.deet.com/deet_fact_sheet.htm**).

I want to make all amateurs aware of one problem with DEET. In strong as well as diluted concentrations, DEET will soften or dissolve many plastics. The battery compartment of my Alinco DJ-G5 softened in my hand, just after I used the hand to apply DEET. Some spilled into a Stearlite clear plastic container that held a 250 W soldering gun, and two Garmin GPS units. All had substantial damage to their cases from the DEET. So, be careful how you apply and use DEET-containing bug repellents this summer.—*David Pearce, AB0NG, 4571 Huntridge Dr, Roswell, GA 30075-6367;* **ab0ng@arrl.net**

## CUSTOM-FITTED HEADPHONES

◊ Many of you may be in the same situation as I was: endlessly searching for a set of headphones that feel right, block out enough ambient noise enough yet permit your spouse's voice to get your attention, remain cool in the summer and warm in the winter. My chosen headphones developed an intermittent connection and I found that repairing them was impossible: It required soldering a very small and easily melted foil tab under the speaker cone.

Rather than simply buying another pair, I found a set of small "ear buds" that came with a commercial receiver I bought a couple of years ago. The devices simply stick on your ear and have very good fidelity. Unfortunately, they readily dislodge if you move your head quickly. An ideal solution would be to place the devices into an appliance fitted to the exterior part of my ear, but I figured such a thing would cost much more that I was willing to pay.

I found the solution at a sporting goods store. A product called "Ear Putty" (Santa Barbara Medco, **www.sbmedco.com/ear_putty.asp**) is for swimmers' use. I took a finger full of the material and formed it around each ear bud, then placed the buds in a comfortable position on the exterior of my ear while conforming them to the contours of my ears. These are the perfect headphones for about $3 and a set of ear buds that were otherwise of no use. The material has a sticky consistency and is made from silicone. When they become dirty or too misshapen, I will

make new ones; the package contains enough to make three or four more pairs.—*Bob Cowan, WB6DAC, 2740 Canary Dr, Costa Mesa, CA 92626-4748;* **wb6dac@attbi.com**

## BATTERY LEAKAGE REMOVER

◊ At one time or another, most of us have left batteries in a device for too long—only to open the device and find a mess. This happened to me recently and I tried a product now widely available called "CLR" (an acronym for calcium, lime and rust). It comes as a liquid and a spray foam. I sprayed CLR on the battery holder section of the equipment case and the mess went away in less than five minutes. After a quick rinse and air dry the battery compartment was clean. I then attacked the battery-negative contact spring, which was covered with battery drainage and rust. Again, in five minutes it was clean. I lightly sanded the contact point and reassembled the device. It works fine. The repair was cheap, quick and effective! —*Dave Routzon, W5GT, 6917 Post Oak Dr, North Richland Hills, TX 76180-3418;* **w5gt@arrl.net**

## A NOVEL MICROPHONE HOLDER

◊ I recently installed a new dual-band rig in my truck. Not desiring to drill a series of holes to mount the microphone holder, I contented myself with simply laying the microphone in the vehicle's cup holder. This proved not totally satisfactory, and I began searching for a "no-holes" method to mount the microphone. The first thing I tried was commercial Velcro. This didn't stick and I was back to the cup holder. A few weeks later, I spotted a product in a local discount store called

Figure 10.12—The "Phone-On-Hold" magnetic holder. While designed for cell phone use, it's ideal for microphone stowage.

*Phone-On-Hold* (see **Figure 10.12**). This is simply a powerful magnet mounted to the dash with 3M foam tape. I installed this after cleaning the dash area with alcohol, as instructed. It appears to be very powerful and can easily hold a cellular telephone, as shown on its package.

In order to mount the microphone, I removed the holder button and replaced it with two ⁵/₈ inch fender washers. Unlike standard washers, these have very small holes. I countersunk the hole on the outside washer. After removing the standard holder button, I installed the two washers over the opening by using the same screw that originally held the holder. I placed the countersunk washer to the outside, so that the screw would draw up tight and flush with the washers.

This arrangement works well and might be of some benefit to others looking for a way to mount a microphone neatly and securely without drilling holes. Should the washer modification not be possible, the device does come with a small ferrous metal strip that could be mounted to the microphone.—*William D. Cleveland, WD5IBY, 501 E Adoue, Baytown, TX 77520*

# The Doctor is IN

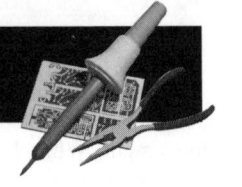

Q John Van Walleghen, NØUBQ, asks, "I am in charge of setting up a club station for the Wichita Amateur Radio Club. I have read your publication, *RF Exposure and You*, www.arrl.org/catalog/6621/, and have a question that appears to not be covered in the book. How do you calculate exposure for multi-transmitter stations? We plan to expand our station to three HF radios, VHF voice & packet and one or two VHF repeater inputs. Our station is on the third floor of an aviation museum, so there are few people about. There are no nearby structures, as we are on the edge of a runway.

A The actual calculations for multiple transmitters are a bit more complicated than for a single station, but nothing past some simple math is needed. This actually is covered in the book *RF Exposure and You*, on pages 5.22-5.24. What you have to do is to calculate the percentage of exposure from each transmitter and add them all up. This is done on a time-averaged value of the power densities involved, or the squares of the fields.

For example, let's assume that you are simultaneously operating a 1500 W SSB station on 10 meters and a 50 W VHF packet station on 2 meters. The 10 meter antenna has a gain of 7.5 dBi and is 50 feet, diagonally, from the operator. The 2 meter antenna has a gain of 5 dBi and is 40 feet from the operator. The permitted exposure levels are time averaged—using 30 minutes for uncontrolled (general public) exposure levels or 6 minutes for controlled exposure. This applies to single or multi-transmitter operation. (You can apply a controlled exposure calculation to the amateurs operating the station and their guests if they have been given information about RF exposure.)

The easiest way to time average the exposure is to time average the transmitter power and use that power level in subsequent calculations. This is done by taking your PEP transmit power, multiplying it first by the duty factor of the mode being used and then by the maximum percentage of time the transmitter *could* be on the air during the averaging period.

For example, an SSB transmission that doesn't use a speech processor would conservatively have a 20% duty factor—the average power while the transmission is occurring is 20% of the peak-envelope power. If your station uses a 1500 W PEP amplifier, 1500 W PEP SSB × 20% duty factor × 1.0 (100% on/off time) = 300 W average power in a 6 minute period. [The Doctor used a 100% (multiplicative factor of 1.0) on/off time because the station could be transmitting continuously for 6 minutes at a time.]

Next, determine the distance from the antenna to areas where people might be exposed. If the antenna were 55 feet in the air—directly over a first-floor station on a concrete slab, the distance from the operators or to people walking on the ground would be about 50 feet.

The calculation for exposure can be done using any method that the operator chooses, although one convenient way is to use the RF calculator at the University of Texas Web site, **n5xu.ae.utexas.edu/rfsafety/**.

The Doctor used that calculator and obtained:

300 W at 50 feet at 28.5 MHz = 23.6 V/m. On 28 MHz, the permitted controlled exposure is 64.7 V/m. Remember, we need to square the fields to compare the exposure limits, so this station is:

% Exposure = 100 [ $(23.6)^2$ / $(64.7)^2$ ] = 13.3%

This station is exposing the operators of the station (a controlled exposure) at 13.3% of the limit.

The 2 meter packet station is expected to be transmitting no more than half the time (a conservative estimate for most DX-cluster type operating) so its average power is:

50 W PEP FM × 0.5 (50% on/off time) = 25 W

Running this through the RF calculator, I got:

25 W at 40 feet at 146 mHz = 6.4 V/m

The % exposure is:

% exposure = 100 [$(6.4)^2$ / $(64.7)^2$] = 1%

To calculate the exposure from these multiple stations, all we do is add up the percentages of exposure. This is a handy way of taking into account the way RF exposure limits vary with frequency.

Adding up the percentages, this station is at 14.3% of the controlled exposure for the operators.

Repeating this for the 27.5 V/m uncontrolled exposure, if the same average power was assumed, this would be:

% Exposure (10 M) = 100 [ $(23.6)^2$ / $(27.5)^2$ ] = 73.5%
% Exposure (2 M) = 100 [ $(6.4)^2$ / $(27.5)^2$ ] = 5.4%

So, the total uncontrolled exposure in this case is at 78.9% of the limit.

See the ARRL RF Safety Committee Web site, **www.arrl.org/rfsafety/**, for links to the ARRL FAQ, the University of Texas site and other useful sites. One of those links is to a comprehensive article written by Greg Lapin, N9GL, the Chairman of the ARRL RF Safety Committee. His column, *N9GL's RF Safety Column: The Multiple Transmitter Question*, covers the subject in some detail. Another good article to read is "RF Safety at Field Day," *QST*, Jun 1999, pp 48-51; **www.arrl.org/tis/info/pdf/9906048.pdf/**.

MARVIN COLLINS, W6OQI

Figure 10.13—Hams aren't the only ones that have to do RF exposure evaluations. This broadcast installation on Mount Wilson in California is a *lot* more complicated than the ham station described in this answer.

Q Our club is putting a PL of 130.8 on the repeater. What are they talking about?

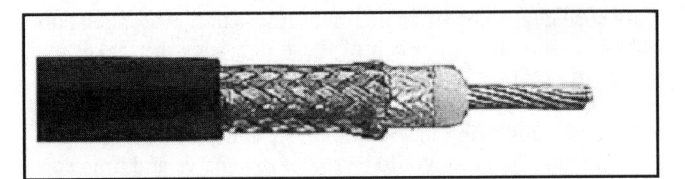

Figure 10.14—BURY-FLEX is a 50-Ω cable with double shield yielding 100% shield coverage, consisting of a 97% braid shield that is tinned for ease of soldering and corrosion protection, plus a bonded foil shield for added moisture protection.

A Many repeaters require the transmission of a continuous sub-audible tone or a short "burst" of tones for access. These are called CTCSS (continuous tone-coded squelch system) or PL (Private Line—PL—a Motorola trademark) tones. The reason for requiring access tones for "open" repeaters is to prevent interference from extraneous transmissions that might accidentally key the repeater. Sometimes a repeater receives interference from other nearby strong signals. For example, the repeater may be located at a commercial communications site. The repeater antenna may share tower space with many other antennas. If the repeater requires a certain CTCSS signal to activate the transmitter, then only the desired signals will be repeated.

Let us suppose your local repeater operates on the 146.67/ 146.07 MHz repeater frequency pair. There may be another repeater using this same frequency pair that is located 75 miles away. Normally, the operators using the two repeaters don't hear each other. Occasionally, however, some of the stations using the other repeater also key up your club's repeater. Operating through this interference can become more than a minor annoyance, especially if it occurs during a public service activity or some type of emergency. This is another example of why many repeaters use a CTCSS system. As long as the hams using the other repeater don't transmit the tone to access your club repeater, they won't key it up when they transmit. That PL your club is referring to is a 130.8 Hz CTCSS encoding-decoding access tone.

Q From Blair, K3YD, comes this: "Do you have any suggestions for bringing feed lines through modern Anderson-type windows for a short-term interval (2-3 months)? I recently moved into a new home and until I can construct a proper basement shack with a bulkhead for cable feedthrough, I plan to operate from a spare bedroom using modest power levels (20-50 W). My wife thought my solution to drill through the sash frames was a bit extreme."

A Since you have a basement, it may be more practical to bring the feed line in through the floor. I suspect your new home may have hot water radiators. There may be enough space around the radiator pipes to bring in RG-58 type coax, if you remove the decorative metal plates used to hide the holes. RG-142 type Teflon coax will easily take the heat of a typical home heating system. Also, see the *QST* article elsewhere in this issue by W6TOY, "My Antenna is a Compromise—and It Works!" The author has some excellent suggestions for bringing feed lines through sash windows.

Q Dan, W9CP, asks about burying coaxial cable: "I want to bury my coax using electrical PVC pipe and would like to know if there are any specific precautions that must be taken to ensure a good installation."

A If the cable is of the type designed for burial, no precautions are usually needed to place it directly in the ground. Such a product is BURY-FLEX, a 50-Ω cable with double shield yielding 100% shield coverage, consisting of a 97% braid shield which is tinned for ease of soldering and corrosion protection, plus a bonded foil shield for added moisture protection. The jacket is also designed to withstand the abrasiveness of living in the ground with sharp sand and small stones that can move around a bit with changes in the soil. If the cable will be subject to excessive soil moisture or heavily acid or alkaline soil, you may want to use coax with a "non-contaminating" jacket—chemicals or moisture don't leach materials from the jacket that damage the rest of the coax.

However, if you'd rather place the cable in a PVC pipe, you will have to prevent water condensation in the pipe. The Doctor asked our advisor in commercial and cell phone in-

stallation, John, K1TLV, for his input. John, who has also been a ham for 40 years, had this to offer:

> The easiest solution is to use the pipe available with perforations used for "drain tile" around the perimeter of dwellings. These perforations, or holes, are limited to one side of the pipe and so the pipe is buried with holes facing down. However, I would also use a sand and stone combination under the pipe (6 inches–1 foot) to allow any water accumulation to drain away.

Rainwater, soil or insects could get into the pipe, so the Doctor also recommends sealing the ends of the pipe well to minimize the entry of contaminants into the pipe. It is not recommended to bury coax in PVC or any other pipe below the water table.

Q As if he knew we were getting another coax/moisture question from W9CP above, Joe, N1KHB, follows up with: I have heard about the detrimental effects of moisture in coax, but no real explanation was ever offered. After thinking about it, I kind of thought that maybe the most damage might occur to foam filled or air cell types of cable, whereas solid dielectric might be minimally affected if at all.

Could I do a test of the characteristic impedance of the line to determine if moisture has affected the line? People also occasionally talk about "aged" coax and that they periodically change it as a precaution. Can you shed any light on any of these subjects? I have checked through many of my references including ARRL publications and so far have found nothing that addresses these points as presented here.

A You pose some interesting questions! Unfortunately, The Doctor is not aware of many studies in this area. One actual lab experiment was conducted in the ARRL Lab and published in our experimenter's magazine QEX. In the "RF" column of the March 1999 issue, Senior Lab Engineer Zack Lau, W1VT, published a study of the effect of soaking exposed N connectors (on RG-213) in a jar of water for various periods of time. At each time interval, he measured the resulting loss at a number of VHF, UHF and microwave frequencies. This was a good study of short-term moisture exposure. In this study, the losses ranged from a few hundredths of a dB for short soaking and VHF test frequencies to more than 10 dB for longer soaks and UHF.

However, long-term moisture exposure is also a major concern. The Doctor have yet to hear of a study on long-term exposure to moisture. But Doctor can offer anecdotal information from the examination of coax that was being replaced after years of exposure to the elements. The chief problem noted was that the braided shield was severely corroded for several inches along its length the end. It would seem that this corrosion would be due to a 'wicking' effect of the braided strands. It is possible that this could have been prevented by properly sealing the connection on the ends.

Of course, there are a number of weather related effects

that cause degrading of cable, including wind, prolonged sunlight exposure and ice. Each of these degrades the jacket and will in time allow moisture intrusion in places far removed from the connectors. It would be difficult to isolate each of these problems using an outdoor test, and performing a prolonged indoor lab test would be rather expensive and time consuming.

So what about coax kept for years in a dry basement or garage? Well, those conditions are much kinder to coax, but they still pose some problems over the long run. Again, the Doctor has not seen studies on this, but the soft plastics used for many dielectric and jacket materials in coax may harden over time in a dry environment. This may create small cracks in the jacket and if cable with a cracked jacket is used outdoors, moisture will take its toll quickly. In extreme cases, the changes in the dielectric materials could cause a change in characteristic impedance and line loss.

The bottom line here is that if one is ever in doubt, it is best to perform a test on the specific coax in question. A fairly simple way to do this is to connect the length between a dummy load and transmitter with a known power output and measure the loss directly by measuring the power going into the dummy load. Note that this technique is useful even if the original loss of the line is not known.

The loss in dB can be determined from the formula:

Loss dB = 10log(power at transmitter / power at load)

**Q** Chuck, NØEBN, has this question: I have an old Unadilla W2AU balun, but I can't remember if it is a 1:1 or a 4:1 ratio. Is there any way to tell? Or, should I just toss it and buy a new one? This would very much go against the grain.

**A** Heavens no… don't toss anything! "Real hams" have to have a basement or other room chock full of all sorts of fine "junque" to keep you amused for the rest of your life!

To check the ratio of a balun, connect coax to both ends, and run the antenna side coax to a 50 Ω dummy load. Feed a modest amount of power into the transceiver side (an antenna analyzer makes this a snap, but you can also use a transmitter with the output reduced to perhaps 5-10 W), and you should see an SWR indication. If the SWR is low—around 1:1—the balun is a 1:1 type, and if it is high, it should be a 4:1 type. A 4:1 balun should theoretically read 4:1, but your SWR meter may not be accurate at high SWR, so a "high" reading generally indicates that the ratio is 4:1.

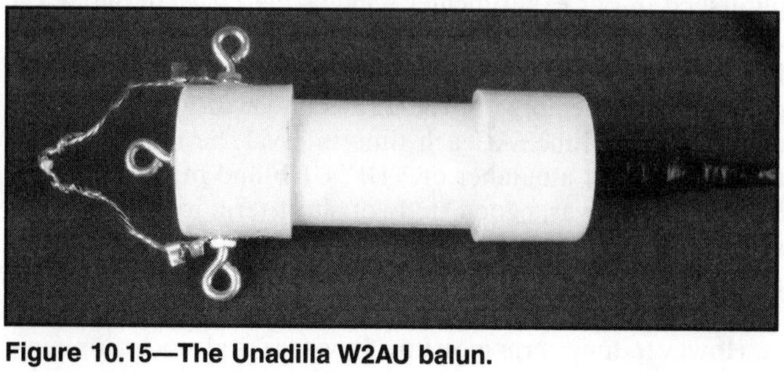

**Figure 10.15—The Unadilla W2AU balun.**

**Q** Brent, WB8TRL, has a very short question with a long answer: What is the formula to convert a power level specified in dBm to watts?

**A** The conversion formula for decibels to the equivalent power is: dB = 10 [ log $(P_1/P_2)$ ]
where $P_2$ is the "reference" power. Note that $P_1$ and $P_2$ must be expressed in the same units (W or mW or μW). To convert

from a dB figure to an actual power, you would solve the above formula for $P_1$ like so:

10 [log $(P_1/P_2)$] = dB or, dividing both sides by 10
log $(P_1/P_2)$ = dB/10 and $P_1/P_2$ = $log^{-1}$ dB/10 = $10^{(dB/10)}$
10 raised to a power is the "opposite" of a log (usually written as $log^{-1}$).

Now, keeping track of the different base units can be tricky, but you can take advantage of a log characteristic with a special trick—every "factor of 10" change in power level gives a corresponding addition or subtraction of 10 dB when working with decibels (only for power, not voltage). Since zero gain is equal to 0 dB, a power increase from 1 W to 10 W would be +10 dB. An increase from 10 W to 100 W would be another +10 dB and an increase from 100 W to 1000 W would be another +10 dB, for a total of 10 dB + 10 dB + 10 dB = 30 dB or a 1000 W increase.

So if you have a figure in dBm (decibels relative to a milliwatt) and you want to know watts, your best bet would be to first figure what the dBW (decibels relative to a watt) value would be. Since 1 mW is 1/1000th of a watt, you would subtract 30 dB. Thus, a level of −120 dBm would be −150 dBW. Plugging −150 into the above equation, we get:

$P_1/P_2 = 10^{(-150/10)}$

which gives $P_1/P_2 = 10^{-15}$ W and since $P_2$ is 1 W, $P_1$ is $10^{-15}$ W.

As a second example—if the power level is +50 dBm, subtracting 30 dB gives +20 dBW. Plugging +20 into the equation gives $P_1/P_2 = 10^{20/10}$ which gives 100 W.

**Q** Lou, KB6JLI, asks: The other day a ham asked me a question with regard to baluns and I could not give him a decent answer, so I thought I would ask you the question and relay it to him. What is the difference between a 1:1 and a 4:1 balun and what is the difference between current and voltage types. How much power can be applied to the voltage type? I have seen it advertised up to 300 W.

**A** The term "balun" means *bal*anced to *un*balanced. It is an impedance transformer that is designed to convert a balanced or unbalanced system to a balanced or unbalanced line. This question was covered in great detail in *The Antenna Compendium*, Volume 1, in an article by Roy Lewallen, W7EL.[7] In a post to the Usenet newsgroup **rec.radio.amateur.antenna**, Roy excerpted six points from his paper, saying:

1. The purpose of a balun used in feeding an antenna is to prevent common-mode feed line current, and therefore feed line radiation.

2. Common-mode feed line current is the vector sum of the two conductor currents (or half this value depending on your definition), so common-mode current is zero only when the conductor currents are equal and opposite.

3. The "current" balun (a term I coined in that article) is one that forces the conductor currents to be equal and opposite, which is what a balun needs to do when used with an antenna. A current balun can also be appropriately called a choke balun or common-mode choke.

4. A "voltage" balun (also coined in that article) is one that forces the conductor voltages to be equal and opposite relative to the "cold" side of the balun input.

5. If the antenna is entirely symmetrical with respect to ground, the third winding in a 1:1 voltage balun conducts no current. It can then be disconnected with no effect. The result is identical to a two-winding 1:1 current balun.

6. If the antenna isn't entirely symmetrical with respect to ground, a voltage balun will *cause* common mode current to flow by attempting to balance the conductor voltages. So at

best, a voltage balun will work as well as a current balun. At worst, it will increase feed line radiation. At the time that article was written, nearly all the commercial baluns were voltage baluns. I'm glad to report that this has changed. I'd like to note that there is a place for voltage baluns, in feeding voltage driven push-pull amplifiers, for example. But they're not the thing to use for feeding antennas. I highly recommend the analysis of balun operation at **fermi.la.asu.edu/w9cf/articles/balun/index.html**.

Another good reference on the topic of baluns and transmission line transform-

**Figure 10.16—Another reference for learning more about the theory and art of building and using baluns is this volume by Jerry Sevick, W2FMI. It is available from ARRL.**

ers, both balanced and unbalanced, of various ratios and impedances, is *Building and Using Baluns and Ununs* by Jerry Sevick, W2FMI.[8] Its cover is shown in **Figure 10.16**.

To answer your question about the differences between a 1:1 and 4:1 balun we've got to talk about impedance. The 1:1 balun is designed to transform an unbalanced coaxial line to a balanced line of the same impedance. Let's say we wanted to connect a 50 Ω or 75 Ω coaxial cable to a dipole antenna. That dipole ideally wants to see a balanced transmission line and the coax is unbalanced, so... enter the 1:1 balun. Placed right at the junction of the coax and the antenna, it will transform (remember, it's a transformer) the unbalanced impedance of the feed line to the balanced feed point of the dipole. A 4:1 balun simply transforms that impedance using a different ratio. In this case it will transform a 50 Ω or 75 Ω unbalanced coaxial line to either 200 Ω or 300 Ω balanced output, respectively.

If you're feeding a folded dipole antenna (made of 300 Ω line) with 75 Ω coaxial cable, you'd use a 4:1 balun to transform the balanced antenna impedance of 300 Ω to an unbalanced feed impedance of 75 Ω. The circuits that are interior to the balun are different and depend on the impedance transformation ratios. To be sure, baluns are not only used for antennas, they can be used anywhere RF signals need to be converted from balanced to unbalanced levels, as in interstage coupling or the driver to push-pull amplifier situation described above. Modern baluns are usually wound on ferrite cores in order to make it easier to achieve their required inductance while keeping them small. Choke baluns are also frequently used at antenna feed points and on transmission lines to keep unbalanced RF from traveling down the outside of a coaxial line and back toward the transmitter.

As far as the power handling capability of a balun is concerned, that depends on a number of factors. If they are ferrite wound, the core material and size will affect the core saturation level and hence the balun's power handling capability. The complex impedance and any reactance that the balun "sees" will also affect its ability to handle power. The

manufacturer will almost always state the power handling capability of the balun, but remember, that implies a matched transmission line/antenna system (essentially resistive) with an SWR of 1:1. Antenna systems that are reactive at certain frequencies will limit the balun's power capacity. A good example is the G5RV antenna, which uses a length of 300 Ω or 450 Ω balanced line as a matching section connected directly between the antenna and an unbalanced coaxial line. Because the matching section will frequently be reactive on various bands (except at 14 MHz, the antenna's design frequency) a balun is *not* recommended here as its power handling capability will be compromised due to the high SWR on bands other than 20 meters. Excessive power through a ferrite wound balun usually manifests itself as heating and eventual destruction of the core.

The best advice the Doctor can give is to remember that a balun is not a magic cure-all for all antenna problems. Use it wisely and understand what it does to transform balanced voltages or currents to unbalanced ones. Above all, if you do use it for an antenna, make sure that system is properly designed to present the proper impedances to the balun and the transmission line.

**Q** Ed, K4SB, asks: What is the formula for an LC constant? I can't seem to locate it in my collection of books, but I know I've seen it before. It is a "dream" for calculating L and C values for a resonant network. One of the best applications for this is in matching an end-fed half-wave vertical. Since a $\frac{1}{4}$ wave vertical with a feed point near the ground can suffer from ground losses, this technique allows the high current point to be moved up so as to reduce the losses greatly.

**A** It took The Doctor a while to dig this one up, but he discovered the answer in the 1970 *ARRL Handbook*. It's actually present, in rearranged form, in the current (2003) *Handbook*, p 6.35, equations 91 and 92. The formula is:

$L \times C = 25,330 / F^2$ (where F is in MHz C is in pF and L is in μH)

That formula is easily derivable with a little math, however, so you don't have to clutter up your brain with a bunch of numbers or constants. Remember that, at resonance, the capacitive reactance is equal to the inductive reactance in a series circuit. So,

$X_L = X_C$ or $2\pi fL = 1 / 2\pi fC$ and...multiplying both sides by $2\pi fC$,

$(2\pi)^2 f^2 LC = 1$, so $f^2 = 1 / (2\pi)^2 LC$. Now, take the square root of both sides,

$f = 1 / 2\pi\sqrt{LC}$ ...and, presto, we've derived the formula for resonance in a series circuit.

Now, rearranging and squaring, $LC = 10^6 / (2\pi)^2 f^2$. We added the $10^6$ term because we want our formula to reflect frequency (f) in MHz, not Hz. If you carry the mathematics through, you'll see that $LC = 10^6 / 39.478 f^2$ or...
$LC = 25330 / f^2$ and...there's our formula!

The Doctor recommends that you not memorize formulas, if possible....Try to remember what they really mean and you should be able to derive them with little work. That way, you'll understand where they came from.

The Doctor would also note that a quarter-wave vertical can be raised above ground and, with the addition of a few radials (3 or 4) as a counterpoise, the same result that Ed describes will be achieved.

**Q** A note from Bill Turini, KA4GAV, asks: How important is the impedance match between your radio and your headphones? I know that, with RF, impedance is very important for power transfer, but is a direct impedance match necessary for headphones? I noticed that when I use

[7]R. Lewallen, W7EL, "Baluns: What They Do and How They Do It," *The ARRL Antenna Compendium*, Vol 1 (Newington: ARRL), 1985, pp 157-164.

[8]Available from the ARRL Bookstore for $19.95 plus shipping. Order no. 7644, tel 888-277-5289 (toll-free in the US), 860-594-0355 (elsewhere); **www.arrl.org/shop/**.

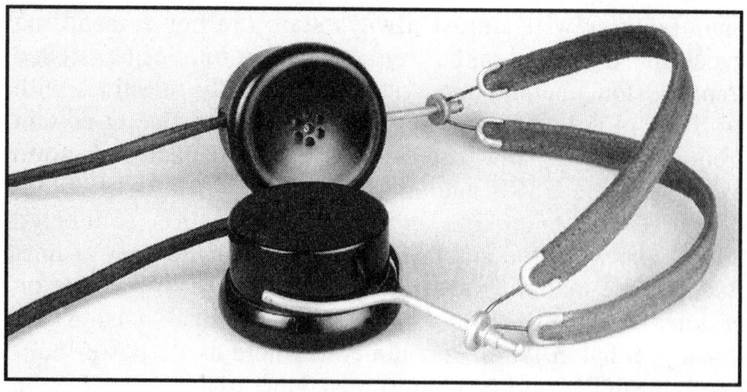

Figure 10.17—An older pair of high impedance headphones (Baldwin). These are also known as "high-sensitivity" types.

headphones of higher than 8 Ω impedance the only noticeable change is in volume. Can other changes occur, such as distortion, sensitivity and damage to the audio output circuitry?

A In conventional amateur equipment headphone, impedance matching is not normally of concern. There's enough audio output power available to drive any reasonable load impedance at ample volume levels and, as long as the level doesn't approach clipping, distortion won't be a problem. Most equipment includes a current limiting resistor in series with the headphone jack to preclude damage to both the audio output circuitry of the equipment and the attached output device.

Headphone impedance is important, however, if the output device can't source very much audio output current like an RF field strength meter, a grid-dip oscillator or a crystal set. In that situation, the higher the impedance the better, as you'd want to minimize the current drawn by the headphones. So-called "high-sensitivity" headphones with impedances in the range of 2000 to 10,000 Ω are typically used with the devices mentioned. They are called high-sensitivity because they require very little current to produce a given audio sound pressure level in dB. Recall that $P=I^2R$ (W), so the higher the R or Z, the greater the output power for a given current. Headphones in the low to mid impedance range (8 to 600 Ω) are commonly available for use with modern day amateur equipment, although high impedance headphones can be used, too. Notice that I said "modern day" equipment. Amateurs of the teens and early 1920s used crystal detectors and battery power for their receivers, and their headphones (Baldwin, Brandes and Trimm were some of those early manufacturers) had to be of the "high-sensitivity" and high impedance type. A pair of high impedance, high sensitivity headphones is shown in **Figure 10.17**.

There is another factor to be considered when using headphones. The impedance level is generally indicative of the frequency response of the headphones. Generally, low impedance headphones have a wide, "high-fidelity" type response whereas high impedance headphones tend to have a communications type, narrow response. That may be something to consider, especially if you're using them for CW, as the narrow response would be better suited to noise cancellation. Also, remember that a low impedance output circuit, as found on most modern amateur gear, will support both low and high impedance headphones, but the converse is not true. A high impedance output circuit will not be capable of driving low impedance headphones. As you can see (or hear), there's more to headphones than meets the ear!

Q Ralph, W6DV, poses the following: I know a lot of chips aren't made any more, but it amazes me that

they seem to have no history, either. I have searched the Web for the following:

    SN72747, Texas Instruments, 10 pin can

    SN75138, Texas Instruments, 18 pin DIP

    SD12386, National, 14 pin DIP

  I'm hoping you can find me a source of data on these. I have many of the 72747s and am hoping they are good for something. Can you direct me to something, hopefully on the Web, that I can read and copy?

A I'll try to answer your question as best as I can, Ralph, but information on older ICs is not easy to come by. I'd guess that the 747s are TI's equivalent of the Fairchild μA 747, a popular dual operational amplifier. If you have a lot of them, it might be worthwhile to put one in a test circuit and see if it works.

The SN75138 appears to be a quad TTL data transceiver, and you can find a data sheet at **www.scanti.ru/docs/datasheets/slls079b.pdf**. I typed SN75138 into my Web search engine and it came up with several sources.

I don't recognize the National chip. One possibility is that the number is a special proprietary house number. Semiconductor house numbers are fairly common and are not easily deciphered. They are often assigned to custom circuits made for a particular customer. *The Art of Electronics* by Horowitz and Hill, has a useful guide on deciphering part numbers. Look at Appendix J of the first edition and good luck!

Q Christopher B. Jones, G3RCU, writes: I am currently researching radio badges and I am particularly interested in the ARRL badge, which incorporates the symbols representing antenna, coil and earth, surrounded by a diamond. I will be obliged if you can reliably inform me as follows:

  a) The person who invented the design.

  b) The exact date that this badge was used in the magazine.

  c) The exact date when it was manufactured as a badge and sold to members.

A In January of 1920, *QST* ran an editorial soliciting design suggestions for a suitable emblem to represent the ARRL. Apparently the reponse was enthusiastic, for in July of that year, the final design was announced, and the new emblem appeared (for the first time) on the cover of that issue. The cover of that July 1920 issue of *QST* is shown in **Figure 10.18**. The designer was not named, but the wording of the

Figure 10.18—The first time the ARRL emblem appeared was in the July 1920 issue of *QST*. The cover emblem is shown alongside and it was also the first time the emblem appeared on the cover of *QST*.

July editorial suggested that it was created at headquarters based on the suggestions received over those last several months. We quote: "Several months ago we solicited an expression of opinion on the subject of an A.R.R.L. Emblem. The response was instantaneous, and solidly in favor of it. Many were the designs and suggestions received, and from them we arrived at the device shown, which was officially adopted by our Board of Directors at its last meeting."

The idea of manufacturing pins for members to wear is also mentioned in the July 1920 editorial, with a note stating that arrangements had already been made to manufacture them. The first advertisement for these pins appeared in the same month (July) and the ad stated that they would be available for distribution on July 15 of that year.

Perhaps the most compelling comment can be found at the end of that early 1920 *QST* editorial. "Let us never forget the purpose for which we adopted this Emblem—that we may have a device for recognizing True Amateur Radio when we see it. May it ever stand for the highest in amateur affairs!" To which the Doctor adds… Amen!

**Q** From K5GB comes the following: I found the recent *QST* article[9] about the maintenance of amplifiers both interesting and timely since I'm getting ready to reactivate an amplifier (pair of 3-500Zs) that hasn't been plugged in for at least 10 years. I seem to remember a suggestion I got a long time ago to bring the power up using a Variac variable ac transformer. I don't remember if this was to be used on the filaments (which I can't see any sense in) or just on the high voltage (which I can see great sense in). I would appreciate any comment you may have on this before I blow up a couple of tubes that have become quite expensive to replace.

**A** A Variac or Powerstat (a variable ac transformer) can be used effectively to bring life to an older piece of equipment, but be careful. Ever notice how ordinary light bulbs sometimes fail when they are turned on? The filament resistance of the bulb is measurably lower when the filament is cold; hence, the starting or "inrush" current will be much higher than normal. When a weak bulb filament fails, it will most likely fail during turn-on. As far as tube filaments are concerned, the same thing applies. A low start voltage limits the inrush current and it is, therefore, a "kinder, gentler" way to get the tube filaments up to temperature.

Along with the tube filaments, the power supply filter capacitors have also been idle on an older piece of equipment. Particularly in the case of an amplifier, those capacitors are generally high value electrolytics. The electrolyte (generally an aluminum oxide wet paste) of the capacitors may have dried out and full application of primary voltage could result in catastrophic failure of one or more capacitors. Many feel that a gradual application of voltage will "re-form" the electrolyte in the capacitor, extending its useful life. There's a useful editor's note about re-forming capacitors in the October 2003 issue of *QST*.[10]

There is a caveat to this technique, however. Many electromechanical components, such as relays or fans and blowers, do not take kindly to low voltage. They frequently draw excessive current when operated at low voltages—relays chatter and blowers hum. Also, circuit parameters are very different at low ac input voltages compared to the specified normal ac operating voltage. Bias voltages will not be proper and operating point characteristics will be all over the place. I would advise starting the equipment at its *minimum specified* ac line

voltage setting, generally 85-90 $V_{rms}$ ac, rather than at 0 V, then gradually bring the voltage up to the normal ac input voltage. By the way, many modern amplifiers have "inrush current protection" to limit the current drawn by the power transformer during the first second or so of power application.

**Q** Warren, W5KKW, asks: I am installing a pair of crank-up towers. *The ARRL Antenna Book* states that the tower base rebar should *not* be connected to the grounding system. Other articles indicate that the rebar *should* be connected to the grounding system. What to do?

**A** The myth about grounding rebar stems from a direct lightning strike heating the rebar as the charge travels through it. In a direct strike, the current density of that charge could be high enough to vaporize moisture close to the rebar. The thinking was that the intense localized heating, consequent steam generation and pressure could crack moisture-laden concrete, weakening the tower base. This suggested that it was best not to ground the rebar, although later studies have shown that significant lightning energy will flow through the rebar anyway. Whether or not the rebar is directly grounded, the concrete base itself is a good conductor at the potential levels of a direct strike. The tower mounting bolts are also embedded within the concrete and they, too, will pass some of the charge. So what is one supposed to do?

The answer is to reduce the localized heating within the concrete as much as possible by lowering the impedance and thus reducing the current density. A way to do that is to ensure that the bars are electrically connected to each other and to connect them (with heavy, wide, short conductors) to the lightning protection ground *outside* of the base. Making a low resistance connection to steel rebar isn't easy. A custom-made, welded rebar cage is a good way to go. Check with your local building code—some building codes may require wire bonding in addition to welding. Good references for lightning protection are the following Web pages: **www.polyphaser.com/ppc_PEN1016.asp** and **www.polyphaser.com/ppc_PEN1030.asp**.

**Q** Here's a question from Terry, W1QF: Like every wire-antenna freak, I have miles (well, yards, really) of old tarnished antenna wire, which I can't solder to. Any ideas how to get it shiny and tinable?

**A** A lot depends on whether or not the wire is stranded. Solid wire is easier to prepare. Stranded wire takes a little more effort, since most scraping techniques only clean the outermost exposed surfaces of the individual strands; the hidden strands remain oxidized. Here's where a good paste soldering flux comes in handy. Liberally apply the flux to the wire and then heat. A good flux will usually dissolve the oxide. Make sure to remove the remaining flux with a solvent after doing this.

I've also used steel wool with success. Pinch the steel wool around the wire and rotate slightly as you draw it across the wire you wish to clean. For stranded wire, try unraveling the strands a bit to clean around the circumference of each strand. Carefully retwist the strands when you are done. One extra point about stranded wire—it can be difficult to clean all the way around the circumference of the strand—even with steel wool. If possible, I use extra flux (rosin not acid) to help remove any residual oxide I can't reach with the steel wool. Another thing that works in place of steel wool is fine sandpaper. I hope this helps!

◊ Regarding the cleaning of old antenna wire: An old-timer gave me this advice years ago, and it's proven invaluable over the years. Vinegar and salt cleans copper. Create a

---

[9]H. Ward Silver, NØAX, "Amplifier Care and Maintenance," *QST*, Sep 2003, pp 33-37.
[10]Note 1 (Editor's Note), *QST*, Oct 2003, p 61.

mixture of vinegar and salt and insert the section of wire to be soldered. After a few minutes it will be shiny and in like-new condition (even the individual strands will be clean)—and it will take solder like a new wire.—*Bill Arnold, WV8WVA, PO Box 1, Cabins, WV 26855-0001;* **wv8wva@arrl.net**

**Q** Dwight, W9PFF, writes: I am slowly giving up ham radio because of loss of hearing. Electronic aids provide nearly normal hearing for conversation, but any room, house or people noises, especially kids and television, prevent me from hearing ham radio well enough to participate. I wear two behind-the-ear (BTE) aids that do not provide good telephone or television usage. Do you know of a company that has equipment for people like me with hearing difficulties? My hearing is spoiling a hobby I have always loved. My hearing aid dealer is not helpful.

**A** A company called Advanced Bionics does make a special microphone that you may be able to use with headphones or a small speaker—it apparently works well with cell phones and is designed for BTE type hearing aids.[11]

To address your other concerns, I might suggest something like the MFJ-616 Speech Intelligibility Enhancer.[12] It is basically a speech bandwidth (300 Hz-2.4 kHz) 4-band equalizer and amplifier with a L/R balance control. It can be used with most stereo headphones, so if you can find ones that will overlap your BTE hearing aid, it should help a great deal. The device will also feed a pair of small (4 inch), wide-range speakers and these might even be better for you. The MFJ-616 was reviewed in April 2001 (p 81) and is shown in **Figure 10.19**. Everyone's hearing situation is unique and the answer here probably lies in experimentation to find a combination of hardware and control settings that work best for you. I'd like to emphasize that these recommendations are not a substitute for a thorough clinical evaluation by a hearing professional. I hope this helps.

**Q** David, N1ZHE, asks: I recently moved my ham shack from the basement of my house to the second floor. My question has to do with the grounding of my station equipment. I've been told that I should ground my equipment. Other than a good ground at the electrical plug (I checked it and it is good), I can run a ground line to a stake (copper clad) driven into the ground. I was also told that the line running to the ground rod should not be resonant at any frequency that I plan to use. With my current rig, I operate from 70 cm to 80 meters and may add 160 meters, too. What would be the easiest way to calculate a safe length for my ground line or what would you suggest?

**A** I assume that when you say that you checked the ground at the electrical plug and that it was good, you're referring to the dc ground. Unfortunately, this has nothing to do with a good RF ground, except at very low frequencies. That plug ground will probably be useless as an RF ground on the HF bands. At the very least, however, it could be effective as an ac ground for the station and can be used for that purpose. It will not be a good lightning ground, however, and it shouldn't be relied upon for that purpose. For lightning (if that's a problem at your location), the shortest direct path to ground, outside the house, using an 8 to 10 foot ground rod with at least 10 gauge wire from either the coax shield or an arc arrester is to be preferred. This can also serve as an effective dc ground for the station. Keep the wire gauge large and the run short.

A good RF ground would require the lead to be short relative to a wavelength—generally less than $1/4$ wavelength at the highest frequency of interest. As a rule, it is best to keep ground leads as short as possible with a minimum of bends in the wire. It's also advisable to use a wide, flat braid for a ground wire, as the RF tends to travel on the outside of the conductor (the "skin effect").

As a practical matter, accomplishing a good RF ground is difficult at best, especially on the second floor. The good news, however, is that most installations do not necessarily require one. If you have a well balanced antenna/feed line system, you're probably okay. If you use a wire antenna and you do have a relatively poor RF counterpoise or ground system, you might look into an "artificial ground." One such device is shown in **Figure 10.20**. This can successfully resonate a random length ground wire and make the station "see" an effective counterpoise. These can work well, although every situation is unique, and it would have to be evaluated for your particular RF environment.

The bottom line: I suggest running the shortest ground lead that is practical for your station and keeping bends to a minimum. Make sure the station is at least at dc ground potential (ground all the equipment chassis to a common point and then to a good dc ground) and keep the lightning ground outside the house. If you're using a wire antenna and you're plagued with a poor RF counterpoise, try using the "artificial ground" device.

**Q** Here's an interesting question from Jack, W0NQ: I have acquired a black, US Navy, flameproof, type J-7-A, straight telegraph key, which was made by the L. S. Brack Manufacturing Company, Newark, New Jersey, per government order No. 141082, dated 1921. It has enclosed contacts as well as a removable dome-shaped metal hood, which encloses a large bayonet-base lamp socket. The hood has a large hole, through which, I believe, the lamp is

[11]**www.hearingexchange.com/articles/henews-090702.htm**.
[12]**www.mfjenterprises.com/products.php?prodid=MFJ-616**.

MFJ ENTERPRISES

Figure 10.19—One example of a commercially available intelligibility enhancer and equalizer, the MFJ-616. Devices such as this are useful for compensating for hearing loss in the speech range.

Figure 10.20—A commercial version of an "artificial ground" tuner.

viewed during operation. The lamp socket is permanently wired directly across the key contacts! The type of bulb used (I don't have it) and its purpose are mysteries that no one has yet been able to answer satisfactorily. Perhaps you can clear up the mystery.

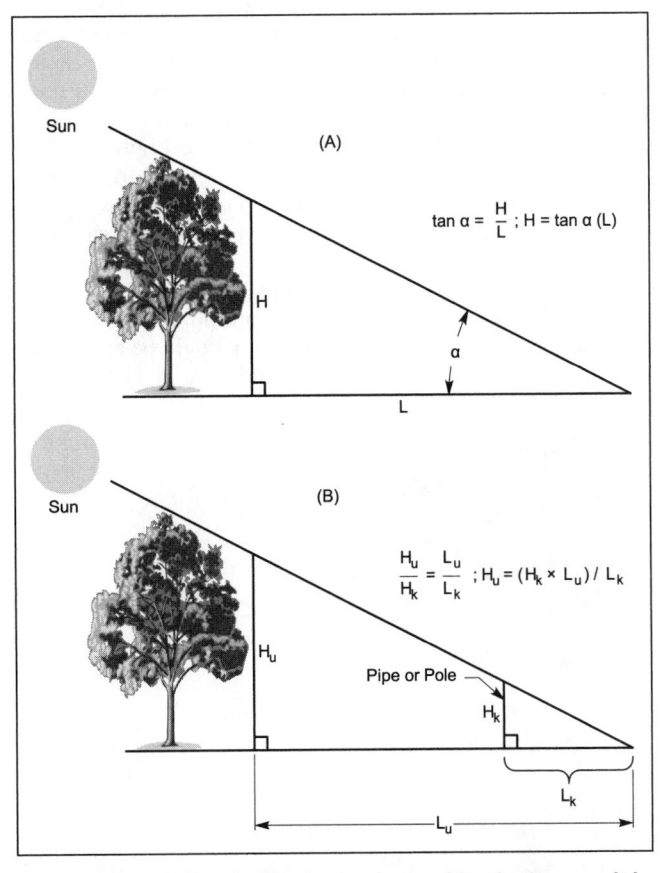

Figure 10.21—The J-7-A "winker" key.

**A** That key, shown in **Figure 10.21**, is uncommon. The bulb used in this key was called a "winker" light and it provided the operator with visual feedback in a noisy environment such as an aircraft. These keys were used with early synchronous spark-type transmitters, as part of the radio equipment on US Navy "flying boats." Interestingly, the wireless equipment was powered by a wind-driven generator mounted on the aircraft's wing. The usual complement was two keys—one for the pilot and one for the observer, who sat immediately behind the pilot. It is thought that the "winker" keys were wired so that the observer would have visual feedback of what the pilot was sending.

The original bulbs are not easy to come by these days and most keys are found missing their "winker" bulbs. You have a nice key and a part of early radio history—I hope this clears up the mystery.

**Q** Here's a practical question from Harry Woods, W2PAL: Standing on the ground, is there any way I can estimate the height of a tree or an antenna support structure?

**A** There are several methods for doing this; we'll present two. Both involve the application of a little trigonometry. Each method assumes flat and level terrain around the unknown structure and both involve sufficient sunlight such that a shadow is cast.

The first method requires the date and time at the location where the measurement is made. It further requires Internet access or some other convenient way to obtain solar position data. First, obtain the altitude of the Sun (in degrees) for the day and time that you wish to make the measurement. You can conveniently obtain this information from the US Naval Observatory Web site. Under *Positions of the Sun and Moon*, select *Altitude and Azimuth of the Sun or Moon During One Day* (**aa.usno.navy.mil/data/docs/AltAz.html**). You will need to enter the date and your location by city or town. The database currently contains about 22,000 locations, so if your town is not listed, choose the closest location.

The rest is easy. Simply measure the length of the shadow being cast by the unknown structure at a convenient time selected from the Sun's data. The height of the unknown structure can now be determined by looking at **Figure 10.22A**:

$$\tan \alpha = H / L$$

where:
   $\alpha$ = Sun's altitude (in degrees)
   $H$ = height of unknown structure
   $L$ = shadow length of unknown structure
then:
   $H$ = tangent of Sun's altitude in degrees ($\alpha$) × shadow of unknown structure ($L$).

As an example: The Sun's altitude is 53.38° at the time, date and location of the measurement. The shadow cast by the unknown structure is 70 feet, 9 inches or 70.75 feet. The height (of the unknown structure) = tan 53.38 × 70.75 = 94.9 feet, or 94 feet, 11 inches.

The second method requires a structure of known height such as a pipe or pole. Install (or have a helper hold) the pipe perpendicular to the Earth's surface. A level or a plumb bob should be used. Now simply measure the length of the shadows being cast by the known and unknown structures. Be sure to make both measurements as simultaneously as possible. The height of the unknown structure can now be determined by the trigonometry of similar triangles, as shown in Figure 10.22B:

$$H_u / H_k = L_u / L_k$$

where:
   $H_u$ = unknown structure height
   $H_k$ = known structure height
   $L_u$ = unknown structure shadow length
   $L_k$ = known structure shadow length
then:
   $H_u = (H_k \times L_u) / L_k$

As an example: The shadow of the unknown structure is 70.75 feet. The shadow of the known structure is 8.95 feet. The height of the known structure is 12 feet. Height of the unknown structure = (12 × 70.75) / 8.95 = 94.9 feet.

*The Doctor had quite a few comments to his reply to Harry Woods, W2PAL, relative to finding the unknown height of a tree (June 2004, p 56). Representative of the many replies was this one received from Larry, WR1B, and Dan Wolfgang, of ARRL HQ. Thanks go to Larry and Dan and to all the other readers who offered similar comments on the Doctor's tree*

Figure 10.22—Using the Sun's angular position in degrees, it is relatively easy to calculate the height of an unknown object, as in A. Similarly, in B, the height can be calculated by comparing the shadow length of a known object with one of an unknown. Note that the pipe shadow should *not* be in the tree's shadow; it is shown that way on the drawing for brevity. Both shadow measurements need to be done at the same time. Use this method when the Sun's angular position isn't immediately available.

*height solutions. The Doctor must confess—he was never a Boy Scout!*

With mild amusement, we read your June 2004 column in *QST*. The question from Harry Woods, W2PAL about how to estimate the height of a tree, tower or other structure is indeed a practical one. Obviously, neither W2PAL nor the good Doctor was ever a Boy Scout, or at least not a First Class Scout.

I would suggest that W2PAL contact a Boy Scout troop in his area and ask the Scoutmaster to bring the Troop to his location for some height-measuring practice. The Scouts will use one of two techniques to estimate the height of his tree. Once that contact is made, perhaps he would like to invite the Scouts back to his station during the third weekend in October for the Jamboree on the Air (JOTA), October 15 to 17, this year.

The first method the Scouts might use is called "The Stick Method." Start with someone of known height. (It is easiest if you can find someone who is 5 feet tall, although four footers or six footers will work equally well.) Have this person stand at the base of the tree. If you can't find anyone to help with the task, pick a board, post or other straight object of known length and stand it at the base of the tree.

Back up some reasonable distance (that does not have to be measured) and hold a short, straight stick at arm's length in front of you. Close one eye and sight along the top of the stick, moving your arm so the top of the stick is even with the top of your helper's head. Place your thumb at a spot on the stick that aligns with the base of the tree and your helper's feet. Now simply move your arm with the stick up until your thumb aligns with the top of the helper's head and note where the top of the stick seems to touch the tree. Move your arm up again until your thumb touches the new spot and again note where the top of the stick seems to touch. Continue this procedure until you reach the top of the tree. See **Figure 10.23**.

To estimate the height of the tree, simply multiply your helper's height by the number of times you moved the stick upward. For instance, if you started with a 5 foot helper and measured the tree to be 10 "stick lengths," you have a 50 foot tree.

The second method the Scouts may use is called the "Felling Method." This will probably result in a more accurate measurement than the stick method. In fact, it could be at least as accurate as the date, time, location and Sun angle from the

DAN WOLFGANG

**Figure 10.23—The "Stick Method" of estimating heights involves counting the number of times a known height will fit into the total height of the object. The "Felling Method" is described in the text.**

"Internet Method," as originally proposed by the Doctor.

You will still need a straight stick (probably a bit longer than that used with the other method) and a cooperative helper. Again, you will step back some reasonable (unmeasured) distance from the tree. Holding the stick at arm's length in front of you, close one eye again, and sight over the stick at the tree. Position the top of the stick so it appears to touch the top of the tree and then position your thumb along the stick so it appears to touch the ground at the base of the tree.

Now, rotate your wrist so the stick is horizontal, along the ground. Keeping your thumb at the base of the tree, have your helper move so he or she is standing where the top of the stick now touches the ground. Mark this spot. The most critical part of this measurement technique is ensuring that the line from you to the tree and then to your helper forms a 90° angle along the ground. The Scouts will now count their steps between the mark and the tree, multiply by the length of their stride, and give you the height of the tree with a fair degree of accuracy. (If your step is 2 feet and it takes 50 steps to cover the distance between the mark and the tree, you have a 100 foot tall tree.) If you need even better accuracy for your measurement, stretch a tape measure along the ground and measure that distance. Before the Doctor's computer can dial up the Internet and access the US Naval Observatory Web site, you will know the height of the tree at least as accurately as the Sun angle, shadow measurement and trigonometry calculation will provide!

We might point out that either of these methods works at any time, whether or not the sun is shining. You may need a powerful flashlight to make the measurements at night, but they will certainly work on rainy, snowy and cloudy days when there is no sunlight to cast a shadow. The methods also work well in a forest, where it may be difficult or impossible to find the entire shadow of that one tree you want to measure. There are similar methods for estimating distances, such as the width of a stream or river, although those become a bit more elaborate. Ask your friendly Scouts to demonstrate that technique.

Q Joe, WB2OSM, has a question about equipment cables and keeping them all neat and orderly. He writes: How do people keep all those power and RF cables straight and accessible at the back of their equipment? All of mine are interwoven and tangled and I have an impossible task determining what goes where. Troubleshooting becomes a mess and it's hazardous reaching around the back of that "rat's nest."

A There's no easy answer here, but there are several ways to make the task of wiring between equipment and power supplies easier. First of all, RF cables should be as short as possible—don't use a 20 foot length of coax when a 5 foot length will do. Secondly, minimize the interconnection length of both ac and dc power cables by using junction boxes. In the case of ac lines, use UL approved ac distribution strips; making sure that the current rating of the strips will accommodate the total current demand of the devices they feed. Use caution here; there are quite a few inexpensive ac power strips available and they are usually intended for low-current computer applications. Some amateur gear draws considerably more current than these strips can comfortably accommodate. Also, be careful about the so-called "surge protectors" used in some of these strips. Most are MOV devices designed as sacrificial components. If the surge voltage is high enough they will short and self-destruct, and they can't be used again.

As with ac distribution, a well-designed dc distribution system can pay off in the long run. Whether you chose to use commercially available dc junction/distribution boxes or de-

Figure 10.24—A platform caster useful for supporting and moving the operating table. One is required at each leg.

cide to build your own, it's a good idea to label each of the junctions or the cables so you know where that power is going. That will simplify troubleshooting later. Most modern dc distribution panels are fused—and there's another caveat: Make sure you've a supply of those fuses available. That holds for ac equipment fuses, as well. There's nothing like blowing a fuse in the middle of a contest and not having a replacement!

Cable labeling at both cable ends is a worthwhile consideration. A cable label can be as simple as a hand-written label covered with transparent tape. If you're really serious, there are cable labels available commercially.[13] There are even nylon cable ties available that have tags suitable for labeling. Properly labeled cables will make it a lot easier to remove or replace equipment during servicing, modification or just plain cleaning.

Speaking of servicing—I would hope that you disconnect all ac power from those power strips *before* doing anything blind behind the operating table. It's very easy to think you're safely unplugging a piece of gear behind a crowded operating bench; partially pull that ac plug with its blades exposed and, zap—unintentionally find yourself directly across the ac line! It's happened to me—but only once.

The best approach to operating table design is to allow a walk-around space behind the equipment. That way you can comfortably and safely get behind the gear to do what's necessary. Few of us have that luxury of space, so do the next best thing. Make it easy to move the operating table(s) by putting wheels under the table legs. I use this approach in my basement station and it's made a difficult job easy. Heavy-duty support (platform) casters are available that go under virtually any style table leg. These are even available for carpeted floors. A slight tug then moves the whole equipment table away from the wall, providing ready and easy access. A typical platform caster is shown in **Figure 10.24**.

And finally, consider making a wiring diagram of all those interconnections. Broadcasters call these "single-line" drawings and they rely on them for power distribution as well as RF, audio, pulse and video interconnections at their stations.

[13]**www.eiminc.com/pagepanduit.htm; www.hubbell-premise.com/HubbellCableLabel.asp; www.globalvideoconf.com/Cable% 20Labels.htm.**

Engineering personnel at these facilities wouldn't think of doing anything behind an equipment rack without them. There's good reason to consider doing the same for your station.

**Q** Ken, KE6ZWN, writes: Can you please give me a definition of *ground potential* and how it differs from real ground?

**A** *Ground potential*: *The zero reference level used to apply and measure voltages in a system. Note: A potential difference may exist between this reference level and the ground potential of the Earth, which varies with locality, soil conditions, and meteorological phenomena.* In other words, ground potential is the voltage at the negative terminal of your voltmeter, which is often different from the voltage present at "real ground." The zero reference level referred to above might be a considerable distance from the real ground reference level. The impedance of the path multiplied by the current in that path will equal the voltage difference between "real" ground and the system ground potential level.

**Q** Jorge, K4KB, asks: I live on the second floor of a house and the closest earth ground is about 13 feet down. Most of the pipes are PVC and I'm trying to find a viable solution to bring a ground into this room. My only alternatives would be to run a heavy wire or ground strap down the 13 feet and attach it to a ground rod. The other one is to use the ground of an electrical outlet. What would you advise in my case?

**A** The Doctor has covered this topic before (Mar 2004, p 57), but some of it bears repeating as the topic comes up repeatedly. A good dc ground is achievable (with some effort) but it's difficult, if not impossible in some situations, to ensure an effective RF ground. The good news is that it may not be necessary. If you design your station to minimize the need for a good RF ground you may be able to solve the problem easily. Use balanced antennas, such as dipoles, instead of verticals, which are hard to decouple from their transmission line. Feed them with a balanced feed line (like ladder line). You can also decouple with RF chokes, so that RF is prevented from flowing on wires and shields. Approximately 16 turns on an FT-240-43 ferrite core works well from 1.8 through 54 MHz.

A reasonably effective RF ground from a second story ham shack can be a pair of copper wires, one 13 feet long, the other 26 feet in length; each terminated at 8-10 foot ground rods. The junction at the two wires will provide an effective RF ground. This system may, however, cause problems with lightning protection, as it doesn't provide a good dc ground. For lightning protection, wiring should be grounded at a single point, and that should be fed outside the house with heavy wire (at least 10 gauge). A good article about installing a single point ground can be found at this ARRL site: **www.arrl.org/tis/info/lightning.html**.

While it may be difficult to find a good dc ground inside second story ham shack, try to make an effort to provide an easy path to ground for lightning *outside* the house. Lastly, don't depend on the ac ground at an electrical outlet for RF use. The ground path is typically long, generally more than a quarter wavelength from the outlet, and the ground tends to be noisy. It's okay for ac equipment grounding but not for RF, and definitely not for lightning protection.

A good place to look for grounding tips is the following ARRLWeb page: **www.arrl.org/tis/info/grounding.html**. In particular, in "Lab Notes: Different Grounds for Different Shacks," the reasons for grounding, the considerations for different types of grounds and the solutions to try for an above-first-floor installation are discussed.

**Q** Here's a question from Jim, W7QIS: I would like to have the instructions (and pictures, if possible) on exactly how to put a PL-259 type connector on the end of 9913 coaxial cable. The problem is the aluminum shield that seems to be bonded to the dielectric. I've tried scraping the bonded shield back from the center connection that enters the connector, but I wonder if there is a better way. In my copies of *The ARRL Operating Manual* and *The ARRL Handbook*, this cable/connector installation isn't mentioned.

I've a new ham station going in at our new home so would like this info ASAP so I can get the cable ordered and get on the air. I hesitate to proceed because of past problems. I will run a 1000 W on the HF bands (160-80) and 2-300 W on 2 meters and 440 MHz for now and I presume that the 9913 cable will be satisfactory.

**A** While 9913 has impressive low-loss specifications at VHF, I'd advise against its casual use because of its partial gas-filled center dielectric. This tends to be a magnet for water intrusion and unless the center dielectric is well sealed (no easy task), it will tend to "wick" water through the cable. Belden has addressed some of these problems with the manufacture of a new version of this cable, 9913F7.[14] This uses a gas-injected FHDPE (foam high density polyethylene) center dielectric, rather than the partial gas-filled dielectric. The solid dielectric comes at an increased loss of 0.1 dB/100 feet at 100 MHz (9913 has a loss of 1.40 dB; 9913F7 1.50 dB—both per 100 feet at 100 MHz). The increased loss is not consequential and I'd advise going with 9913F7 if you must go with 9913-type cable.

I would also urge you to consider 8214-type cable. The Belden variety has a loss of 1.70 dB/100 feet at 100 MHz. The advantage is that this cable uses a stranded center conductor (9913 is solid copper) with 97% copper braid shield coverage, giving a lot more flexibility than 9913. Of course, your choice of cable would also be dictated by the total cable length and the highest frequency of operation (you said that was 440 MHz). You might consider using different types of cable for each run. Use 8214 for the HF run, and, if the UHF run is excessive, 9913F7 for the 440 MHz run.

[14]**bwccat.belden.com/ecat/pdf/9913F7.pdf**.

Now, on to your original question: While I can't give you pictures or an exact description of the 9913/PL-259 installation, *The ARRL Handbook* (2004 edition, p 22.7) details should be a good start (also, read the article in this issue by S. Ford, WB8IMY, "The Ubiquitous PL-259").

My own recommendation differs slightly from that presented in *The Handbook*, in one respect. It advises you to tin the shield braid before insertion into the connector body. I've found that the increased shield thickness caused by tinning makes it more difficult to force the shield of a large diameter cable into the connector. In this case, I'd advise against pre-tinning the shield. Position the shield flatly against the center dielectric (or the first shield, if you have a cable with multiple shields) then carefully insert it into the connector body so it doesn't push back. In any case, if you do elect to pre-tin, do it quickly or the center dielectric will melt, particularly in a cable with a core like the FHDPE type.

I believe the problem that you're having has to do with the Beldfoil Duobond shield. This aluminum foil shield is bonded to the center dielectric and there should be a 97% plated copper shield over the foil. The trick is to make a very clean and sharp cut through *both* the copper and the foil shields, so you don't disturb the lay of the shields or push back the tinned copper shield. Both foil and tinned copper shields should lie flat. Make sure both shields are inserted into the PL-259 connector so that the copper shield is visible through the shield solder holes. This will take a bit of skill. If the copper shield pushes back upon insertion into the connector, you'll have to start again. There should be just enough clearance for passage of both shields if the copper shield is lying flat, and it is as close as possible to the foil shield. Use a hot iron and solder the shield holes without imparting too much heat to the connector body, as this will melt the center dielectric. This will take some practice. The trade-off is in knowing how much heat is required for proper solder-wetting and flow, as opposed to excessive heating of the connector body. That knowledge will come with experience. The advantage of a hot iron is that you're concentrating on localized, quick heating of the solder holes, rather than prolonged heating of the entire connector body. Take your time with cable preparation, use a proper temperature iron and good luck!

# Interference (RFI/EMI)

## SMART WALL-WART + CO DETECTOR = RFI

◊ This nasty combination (**Figure 11.1**) is sure to get your attention! Mixing a carbon-monoxide (CO) detector and an "intelligent" wall-wart style charger on the same ac outlet, surely got noticed in my home at about 2 AM. As the transformer cycles through various levels of its charge cycle, it generates electrical noise that triggers the CO detector. In particular, this charger, for a pair of Motorola FRS radios, won't find itself anywhere near a CO detector while in use. It's best to let safety devices monopolize their outlet and find other locations for all those radio chargers. Unless of course you want to wake up in the middle of the night with your heart beating faster than the little LED on the face of the charger! —*Chris Brady, N3CB, 5 Yale Rd, Plymouth Meeting, PA 19462;* **n3cb@arrl.net**

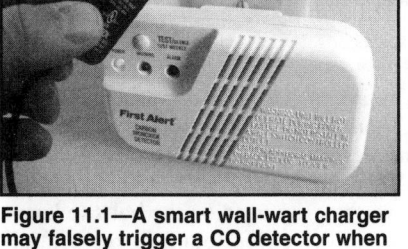

**Figure 11.1—A smart wall-wart charger may falsely trigger a CO detector when they're on the same outlet.**

## CO DETECTOR RFI

◊ Some amateurs are plagued with carbon monoxide (CO) and smoke detectors that are affected by RFI. In my case, if I pushed the memory button on my Kidde CO detector after transmitting at high power, it would display 800-1000 ppm of CO, after alarming.

My unit is a Kidde Nighthawk detector that plugs directly into an ac outlet. I opened the unit up, which is easy to do, and soldered a 0.01 µF, 1000 V disc ceramic capacitor across the ac line at the back of the plug. This was my first attempt at RF suppression. That did not completely cure the problem, but it reduced the displayed CO reading to 85 ppm. Next, I located the filter capacitor, in my case a 330 µF unit, positioned next to the 12 V transformer and rectifier diodes. Leaving the capacitor in place, I soldered an additional 0.01 µF, 100 V capacitor across the bottom of the existing 330 µF capacitor. That completely cured the problem. Pushing the memory button, the detector now displays 0 ppm and doesn't alarm. The problem could possibly have been solved with ferrite beads on the dc supply leads, but bypassing the dc for RF seemed like a good idea and no circuitry cuts or modifications were required. Since the changes are confined to the power supply, it seems unlikely that any normal performance parameters are affected.—*T. Tammaru, WB2TT, 58 Fish Hawk Dr, Middletown, NJ 07748;* **wb2tt@arrl.net**

## CURING ELUSIVE TVI

◊ For a very long time I was plagued with daily TVI that ranged from annoying to very severe. In the attempt to find the source, I checked with neighbors and noted the periods when the interference occurred. (Unfortunately, most nonprofessionals aren't very critical of television picture quality and, therefore, aren't reliable when answering questions about whether or not they are experiencing interference.)

After long suffering the cursed interference, I was finally led to the culprit, which was the RadioShack TV signal amplifier I was using to boost the signals for my several TV sets. I therefore purchased a new one and the problem seemed to be solved. The cure, however, was short-lived, and the interference soon returned. I then decided to try an RCA signal amplifier and the cure was permanent!

Although RadioShack still sells TV signal amplifiers, they no longer carry the model that caused me so much grief. For readers who might own this devil, it is a four-way distribution amplifier, catalog No. 15-1119.—*Dick Shongut, W2QFR, 25 Cameron Pl, New Rochelle, NY 10804;* **W2QFR2@aol.com**

## TAMING COMPUTER POWER SUPPLY NOISE

◊ Recently, I purchased a new computer. Soon after plugging it in, I observed with dismay that, when the computer was in operation, every HF band filled up with very strong spurious signals. The computer completely spoiled HF operation—it even created objectionable interference on 144 MHz.

I intended to use the computer for the digital modes, using its sound card, so I clearly needed to find the cause and cure the problem.

Grounding the computer case didn't work; neither did shielding the exiting cables, or placing ferrite chokes on them. I tried everything short of exorcism! Just as I was ready to toss the computer, I realized that the kind of interference I experienced was far too strong to be originating from its main board logic circuits. Also, the noise had a raspy quality that changed when the floppy drive or the CD drive started spinning. I reasoned that the interference was coming from the computer's switching power supply.

But how? My older computer was extremely "quiet"—what was different in the new machine? I proceeded to open the case of the computer's power supply to do some troubleshooting.

I observed that the supply was without many of the ancillary circuits found in most older computer power supplies. This "new" supply had very small capacitors, small heat sinks, messy construction and, most importantly, *no input ac line filtering at all*! The ac leads went directly from the plastic power connector to the printed circuit board and connected to the bridge rectifier. The PCB had space for the filter components, but they had been omitted and jumpered! That's why it "transmitted" its switching noise and power oscillator harmonics so well—the power cable was serving as an antenna.

There were two solutions: Either dump the low-quality supply in the junk box and get a better one, or correct the shortcomings of the design. Being a ham, you can guess the route I took.

I constructed an ac mains line filter, following the schematic shown in "A 13.8 V, 40 A Switching Power Supply" in *The ARRL Handbook* (1999-2004 editions). It's a very simple but effective filter, used in all good quality supplies. The parts can be easily found in a junked, older computer power supply—those seem to be much better built. The part values are not very critical. Also, I replaced the cheap, plastic power input receptacle with a CEE-22 ac connector that has a built-in ac line EMI filter and fuse. After completing and checking the wiring (I used the empty area on the PCB to mount the new parts), I replaced the supply in the computer and screwed the covers in place. I then turned on my HF radio to 40 meters (the most troublesome band) and powered up the computer.

*No noise at all*! The problem had vanished. I checked all bands and confirmed that everything was okay. Now, I enjoy using my computer on the air…on every band. Furthermore, the power supply circuits have more protection now—the filter eliminates harmful line voltage spikes.

This information could also be applied to the switching power supplies used in some low-cost video monitors. *A word of caution*: When working on a computer power supply, apply all safety measures. These are dangerous, high-voltage circuits—the primary side of the supply is usually *not isolated* from the ac mains! Make sure the filter capacitors are completely discharged before working on the circuit and unplug the supply before working on it. If you feel you're not up to the task, have someone who is more experienced help you out.—*Anastasios Thomaidis, SV8YM, 9-11 Therianou Str, Zakynthos GR 291 00, Greece;* **sv8ym@hotmail.com**

# The Doctor is IN

**Q** Phil, K6EID, writes: "Our utility is planning to install new 230 kV tap lines on 130 foot poles less than a quarter mile from my location. They have put out an Environmental Assessment that says the lines will have no impact on radio reception. Is there any study that I can refer to that would show the effect of these lines on noise impacting ham radio reception? I would like all the ammo I can get to refute their claim. The folks out here are pushing to get them to bury the lines but the utility is against this because of cost. Our county has put a moratorium on this for other reasons but we expect that they will take the county to court to break this. If we can refute the EA, we stand a chance in getting them to be more receptive to burying the lines."

**A** The truth of the matter is, while these lines may be big and ugly, if they are properly designed and built they are not normally the source of significant RFI from arcing. Unless you live almost directly under the lines where you might be affected by corona noise, a new line is not necessarily going to be a problem. There are several reasons for this. The hardware is massive and designed specifically to reduce corona and arcing noise. (There are no sharp edges, the bolts are recessed, helical spring washers are used on the bolts to keep them tight.) Unlike most utility poles found in residential neighborhoods, the high-voltage towers are made of steel, and hence they do not swell and shrink over time as wood does as weather conditions change. Most of the power-line noise we deal with here comes not from transmission lines, but from distribution lines mounted on wood poles that may be quite old.

Although burying the lines may reduce the interference potential slightly, if there is a problem it may be a lot harder for the power company to fix. Buried lines would have to be cooled with oil, a difficult and expensive undertaking.

If you do have a problem with power-line or electrical interference, first read the ARRL "RFI-Electrical" information at **www.arrl.org/tis/info/rfi-elec.html**. If necessary, then contact the ARRL RFI desk at **rfi@arrl.org** for advice and help.

**Q** Warren, WU3Y and Tim Gruber, KB3IYJ have an RFI problem. "I recently installed a 2 meter/440 radio for my son in his room. We have installed an outside vertical antenna. This antenna is on one side of the house and the TV antenna is on the other side of the house, about 50 feet away. When my son transmits on 2 meters he totally blocks out the lower VHF channels. My belief is that the TV set is getting overloaded by the power radiated from the 2 meter transmitter. All of the other TV channels are okay. How can I fix this? Does anyone make a notch filter I can put on our TV?"

**A** The Doctor handed this one over to Mike Gruber, W1MG, ARRL HQ's RFI expert. "A 2 meter notch filter might help. I would first suggest disconnecting the antenna from the TV receiver. If the interference is substantially reduced, it might be coming in through the ac power cord. If so, use a "brute-force" ac line filter. Next, try touching only the shield of the cable to the shield of the TV connector, without screwing it on. If the

Figure 11.2—The power lines found in most residential neighborhoods are a more likely source of RF noise than properly constructed high voltage lines.

Figure 11.3—This common-mode choke can be made by wrapping about 10 turns of the TV coaxial cable onto a FT-240-43 ferrite core.

interference to the snow on the raster is increased, you may be picking up the RF on the outside of the TV coax. Try installing a common mode choke directly at the receiver end of the coax, as shown in **Figure 11.3**.

If the TV receiver draws less than 300 W, try using a RadioShack catalog #15-1111 ac line filter. Industrial Communications Engineers, **www.arraysolutions.com/Products/ice/**, also sells ac line filters that operate at higher power.

The ARRL RFI Web site, **www.arrl.org/tis/info/rfigen.html**, contains a list of EMI/RFI materials suppliers for ferrite chokes.

If the common mode choke doesn't work, the strong 2 meter signal is probably overloading the front end of the TV set. Notch filters may help, as TV tuners typically do not have good adjacent channel rejection. Tunable notch filters will reject the amateur signal, allowing the TV receiver to function normally. Note, however, that these filters will not help when an amateur signal is interfering with cable channel 18, as cable channel 18 and the amateur 2 meter band occupy the same frequencies.

Here are two companies that sell notch filters. They can be expensive, so check the prices before ordering:

Microwave Filter Co, Inc, 6743 Kinne St, East Syracuse NY 13057; tel 800-448-1666; **www.microwavefilter.com**.

Winegard Company, 3000 Kirkwood St, Burlington, IA 52601; tel 800-247-8221; **www.winegard.com**.

**Q** Debbie, N1YYB, asks: I am plagued by interference from an unknown source. I suspect it's possible the noise is generated by something in our house but I'm not sure. Any suggestions on how to locate the noise source—or at least determine whether or not it's internal to our home?

**A** Certainly—and here is an easy approach. You'll need a battery-powered AM radio capable of hearing the interference and possibly a flashlight. Proceed as follows:

1. Go to the main breaker panel or fuse box in your home. Verify the presence of the noise with the battery-powered radio. Be sure to have your flashlight ready if electric lighting illuminates the panel or the area in which it is located.

*Caution*—you must take any and all precautions before proceeding to the next step if there is any possibility of physical contact with any live or hot circuit component within the breaker panel. Solicit professional help if you are uncertain or unsure of proper and safe operation. Do not, under any circumstances, remove the breaker panel sub-cover unless you are qualified to work on live ac mains-level circuitry. Even so, there should be no reason to work within the panel sub-cover unless you can confirm that a faulty or arcing breaker is the cause of the RFI (a rare occurrence). If that is confirmed, seek qualified help.

2. Set the main breaker to off. The noise will stop if its source is located within your house. If the noise continues, you can assume it is coming from a point external to your home.

Note that, if this is the case, the noise is originating from a source that is beyond your control. Radio Direction Finding techniques may then be used to isolate the noise to a particular residence or an area of your utility's power line system. This is obviously not a repair you can make yourself. In the case of power line noise, start by filing a complaint with your utility's customer service department. Never attempt to climb or bang on utility poles.

3. Assuming that the noise stops, return the main breaker to the on position.

4. Isolate the offending noise source to a particular circuit by turning off each circuit breaker, individually. Once you open the breaker associated with the offending source, the noise will disappear. Be sure to return all breakers to the normal on position once the circuit has been located.

5. Finally, isolate the noise to its actual source by unplugging each device on that circuit. You will have found the offending device when the noise again disappears. Don't forget potential RFI sources such as doorbell transformers and furnace controls. These devices are causal to common interference problems and can be overlooked by the novice RFI investigator. Good luck on your hunt!

**Q** From Christopher, N3QXX, comes the following: I'm experiencing interference and wondered whether BPL could possibly sound like a digital carrier. I live in Baltimore and have power lines parallel to my home, and for about a month and a half now I have had horrible interference on HF. It is typically on 20 meters and sometimes, but rarely, on 40. The sound starts low, fades in and then hits S9 while completely wiping out stations on the air. The signal hangs for about five minutes or so, and just stops. I can then hear it on other parts of 20 meters. It seems to move around and is on multiple frequencies at any given time.

**A** The problem you describe is not BPL. Switch mode power supplies are notorious for creating discrete bands of noise on HF. The noise tends to drift, as it is non-synchronous, and that can be a clue. Switch mode supplies are in wide use as computer power supplies and many of these do not have adequate line filtering, so the noise tends to be conductive, to the power lines, and then radiated from them. The noise usually repeats every 30 to 50 kHz or so. Television receiver cathode ray tube (CRT) high voltage supplies, which operate at the CRT horizontal sweep rate (15,750 Hz) will also tend to repeat at that frequency spacing. Newer television receivers appear to have less shielding than earlier sets and are actually worse offenders in this regard. This could also

Figure 11.4—Two noise-canceling devices.

be an arcing thermostat from a heating or cooling system. That could account for its cyclic nature. Try to determine a frequency interval; it could give a valuable clue as to its origin. Some wireless telephones use a frequency-hopping, spread spectrum technique, and while their RF frequencies are out of the HF radio spectrum, the gating switches could cause noise.

Unfortunately, conductive interference can become radiated interference if it reaches the power lines, and there's not much you can do about this short of antenna positioning. If the cause can't be discovered, there is one more approach you can try. There are a few "noise cancellers" available from several manufacturers. These are essentially noise receivers that detect and amplify the noise and inject it out of phase into the receiver, canceling or greatly diminishing the offending signal. They are most effective on a synchronous (stable in frequency and phase) noise source, but have to be evaluated in each case. Two such commercial devices are shown in **Figure 11.4**. Some transceiver noise blankers have adjustable gate times and these might also be effective. Once again, the repetitive nature of the noise could be a valuable clue as to its source. Good luck!

**Q** From Dave, KCØLTD, comes this: I just put my radio in my semi (a 2000 model year Freightliner with a Cummins engine). Now I have noise that sounds like flowing water. I have a ground from the antenna to the frame, a ground from the radio to the frame and a separate ground from an amplifier to the frame. Does this sound like fuel pump or engine management computer noise and do you have any suggestions for reducing it?

Additionally, and along the same vein, Donald, AA2ZS, asks the following: I have RFI coming from my 1988 Ford Bronco. It appears to be the fuel pump. When it is disconnected, the noise goes away. I tried using a toroid suppression choke but it didn't work. Dropping the fuel tank and putting in a Ford EMI filter, which may or may not work, is expensive. The same noise is coming from a large cable going through the firewall. Any suggestions?

**A** Dave and Don, first, I would suggest using a separate shielded cable all the way to the battery for both the positive and negative dc connections. Heavy coaxial cable of RG-8/U-type is suitable for this. Just make sure the center conductor is adequate for the current required and take the cable length into consideration. Ground the shield on both the positive and negative cables. Put a fuse in both halves of this cable, too. In general, I suggest you seek help from your dealer in these situations. I'd also be concerned about all those ground cables. If they're excessively long they could be causing a problem rather than solving it. Long ground connections can actually pick up radiated engine noise. Dave, if the shielded battery cables don't cure your problem, I wonder whether you are hearing alternator whine. One way to tell is to disconnect the belt from the alternator temporarily to see if the noise quits. Check with your dealer to see if there are EMI/RFI filters to help, too.

Another common source of noise in vehicles are fuel injectors. Does the noise change at all with engine speed? If yes, and it sounds like ignition noise but you've eliminated ignition as a cause, you could have fuel injector noise. Again I suggest you consult with the dealer.

Don, if you've narrowed your problem down to the fuel pump, I would ask the dealer whether there are any service notes regarding fuel pump electrical noise. If Ford has a filter for correction, this may be an ongoing problem with the vehicle and the dealer may be able to guarantee corrective results. Bypassing and filtering should be done directly at

the pump. If you don't do it there, you run the risk of the noise becoming radiated rather than conducted and that makes elimination more difficult.

The ARRL Web site has a page on automotive RFI that might be of interest to you both. Here's the link: **www.arrl.org/tis/info/rficar.html**. Good luck!

**Q** Jim, AC7PO, writes: I have two problems I need assistance with, one relating to an RFI problem and the other about commenting on a proposed power line. The first is with regard to a battery charger in my motor home. When hooked up to the 120 V ac line and charging the batteries, there is interference from the charger. It is a sharp buzzing noise that interferes with the AM broadcast radio and my HF band radio. It also causes interference with AM radios in the house while hooked up to the house wiring and in the car radios when I drive past the motor home. The charger is a Heart 2000. Is it my responsibility to resolve the problem or is it the manufacturer's responsibility?

The second question has to do with a proposed power line. North Western Energy is proposing a new 161 kV high voltage line that will run about 200 feet from my house and about 80 to 100 feet from the end of one of my antennas.

I need some advice as to how to comment on this proposal. The only avenue open to me is to comment on an environmental impact basis under Montana law. The property owners on the right of way have the ability to refuse the right of way but I cannot count on this.

**A** Let's tackle your charger question first. According to the FCC Rules, it is the responsibility of the "operator" or user to correct "harmful interference" caused by a Part 15 device. In your case, the battery charger is considered a Part 15 device, so you would be responsible for correction, as you are the operator or user. In practice, many manufacturers do assume some of that responsibility as a service to their customers. That responsibility also speaks to the manufacturer's integrity and credibility, so it wouldn't hurt to check with the equipment maker. Many modern high current tri-state (so-called *bulk*, *absorption* and *float* mode) battery chargers use digital circuitry to pulse the battery under charge and some are prone to cause RFI. I'd suggest contacting the manufacturer first. He may have an RFI filtering technique already designed for the charger. You might also try using a "brute force" toroidal filter at the ac input and at both output lines. They are easy to make and they have been shown to be effective.[1]

Regarding the second question: As a rule, most high voltage transmission lines do not cause RFI. Utilities are usually careful about avoiding arcing in high-tension lines, as arcing equates to losses and losses mean money. They use special anti-corona insulators and supports just to avoid the problem. Usually, it's the low voltage distribution lines that are the culprits as they, generally, are older, and they tend to receive less maintenance attention. There is one caveat, however, that might be of interest to you.

In a case in California, the FCC ruled that an antenna located in close proximity to high-tension lines could receive interference as a result of "corona discharge." The FCC further said that corona was a normal and expected phenomenon with regard to high voltage lines and the Commission failed to take action in that case.

Note that corona discharge is rarely a source of RFI and the reality is that it may not be a problem, but if it is—the FCC may decline to intervene. Especially in the case of a newly

---

[1]J. Hallas, W1ZR, "Emergency Power at W1ZR," *QST*, Dec 2003. See note 6, p 44.

constructed high voltage line, using modern corona suppression devices, the power company will usually be receptive to resolving problems, if there should be any. The bottom line is that a modern, well-constructed, high voltage transmission system, designed to minimize losses, may not pose a threat to amateur operations at all. Good luck!

**Q** Here's a question from Peter, W1EHY: It appears that at least some of us are going to have to contend with BPL. To the best of your knowledge, will a digital radio system (like the AOR ARD9800) eliminate the problem of noise?

**A** Digital radio can certainly enhance the system signal to noise (S/N) ratio by suppressing the noise at moderate S/N ratios (see Product Review, Feb 2004 *QST*, pp 80-81) but it can't recover a signal from below the noise floor. Unfortunately, BPL can raise the local noise floor dramatically (by tens of dBs) and effectively "bury" weak signals that are below that noise. There aren't too many communications systems that can recover signals from below the noise floor. Those that do rely on sophisticated signal summing algorithms and they use very narrow bandwidths with phase lock techniques. These systems are used principally for deep space communications. For more specific information on how BPL works and its effects, please see the ARRL Web pages on the topic at: **www.arrl.org/tis/info/HTML/plc/**.

**Q** Gary, N7GK, writes that he needs help with the prevention of RFI to a cable modem that he uses for Internet access.

**A** I would try a common mode choke on the cable feeding the modem. While the *ARRL RFI Book*[2] contains a detailed explanation of the common-mode choke, you'll find making one is a pretty simple matter. Wrap 10 to 15 turns of the cable through an Amidon (**www.amidoncorp.com**) FT-140-77 ferrite core. (Use an FT-240-77 core if the connectors or cable are large. For interference from 80 or 160 meter signals, use type J (75) material. Use type 43 ferrite material for VHF signals.) The common-mode chokes should be installed right at the affected device. In your case, that would be directly at the modem. The ARRL RFI Web site (**www.arrl.org/tis/info/rfigen.html**) contains a list of EMI/RFI materials suppliers for ferrite chokes. You can also refer to the advertisements in *QST*—there are usually several advertisers offering ferrite materials and chokes.

**Q** From Will, KC6NCF, comes this: I have recently signed up for DirectTV satellite TV service. It occurred to me that the coax cable run from my VHF/UHF amateur antenna might interfere with the coax from the satellite dish while I am transmitting. The most suitable location for the dish would place both coax runs together for about 50 feet. Other dish locations may have some tree shadows to deal with but would allow coax separation. Is this a critical consideration? Would the proximity cause interference to the TV? What would be the optimum separation of the coax?

**A** In an ideal situation, the coax cable should not radiate but, if you were using an HF antenna, I'd be more concerned. If the load is balanced (like an HF dipole) and you feed it directly with coax, there will be some current on the outside of the coax shield braid. That could result in some radiation from the feed line. One way to reduce or eliminate that unwanted radiation would be to use a 1:1 balun transformer or a choke balun on the coax, near the antenna. 1:1 baluns are available commercially or you can make your own

[2]Available from your local dealer or the ARRL Bookstore. Order no. 6834. Telephone toll-free in the US 888-277-5289 or 860-594-0355, fax 860-594-0203; **www.arrl.org/shop/**; **pubsales@arrl.org**.

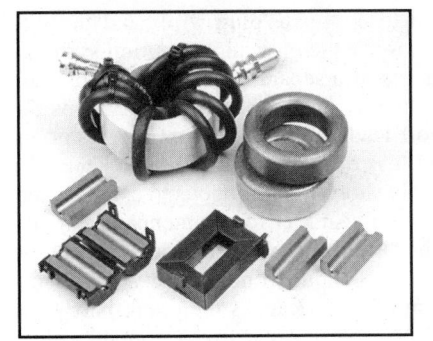

Figure 11.5—A selection of common-mode chokes. The rear toroid cable section with F-type connectors would be suitable for a satellite downlink cable. Make sure the connectors are waterproofed.

(see the current *ARRL Handbook* or *The ARRL Antenna Book*).

You mentioned, however, that your antenna is a VHF/UHF antenna and that your transmitter power is moderate. Normally, the directionality of both antennas will work to your advantage, as will the moderate power. The satellite dish has fairly high gain at its design frequency and its acceptance cone will probably not see the VHF/UHF radiation. Likewise, the VHF/UHF antenna will generally be well matched to its feed line and there will be minimal or no feed line radiation.

Whether or not these effects will mitigate an overload or interference problem is difficult to say. My guess is that it will be okay, but it could still be problematic. The first thing to try if there is a problem is a common-mode RFI choke on the dish coax feed line. Some of these are illustrated in **Figure 11.5**. Particularly note the coaxial choke with F-type fittings, to the rear. Chokes can consist of several ferrite beads or a toroid on the feed line, as shown. A good information reference for common-mode ferrite chokes is *The ARRL RFI Book*.[3]

The next approach would be a high or low-pass filter on the satellite feed line. The filter characteristics would depend on the downlink IF frequency and the frequency of your amateur operation. This would probably have to pass dc, as there is likely a dc signal on the satellite feed line to supply power to the dish preamp/converter. The satellite service people could probably recommend a suitable filter. Coax separation would also help, but only to the extent that there is coax leakage or radiation. The only way to tell is by trying to separate the two cables. There's no optimum distance…if there's leakage—the farther apart, the better—subject to diminishing returns, of course. Good luck!

**Q** Here's a question from Ford, NØFP: I have what appears to be ignition noise on the lower HF bands in my pickup truck. It's a 2001 Toyota Tundra V8. The same engine is also used in various models of the Lexus. The noise has been isolated to the 8 "coil on plug" pods located on the top of each spark plug. The plugs were replaced with no change in noise. There's no distributor, no common coil and no high voltage plug wires. The identical noise heard on the radio can be heard using a small loop at the end of a piece of coax and "sniffing" around under the hood. All the common-mode grounding locations have been tested using jumpers and none were located. The noise sounds identical to that found when sniffing around the pods, so I'm convinced that that's where it's coming from. Traditional logic indicates that a shield needs to be constructed to contain the noise. But the wiring harness is huge—it's the size of my wrist with dozens of wires going in and out. Any advice for me?

**A** Internal combustion engine ignition systems are certainly changing! First, a little background information. The coil-on-plug (COP) systems came about for a variety of reasons.

[3]See Note 2.

Manufacturers wanted to eliminate plug wires and the distributor, both a source of trouble on vehicle ignition systems. The COP system consists of a separate ignition coil for each spark plug, mounted directly above the plug. This keeps the high voltage (HV) coil leads as short as possible, avoiding wire deterioration and loss of spark energy. It also keeps the spark rise time extremely short. It's analogous to using a short transmission line from a transmitter to an antenna. Each coil is individually switched from a power train control module (PCM). The PCM takes its input from a variety of sensors but, in this case, the most significant is the crankshaft position or angle sensor (CAS). The CAS is driven from the crankshaft and determines the timing for the spark sequence. The PCM then outputs a low voltage primary pulse for each coil. Typical coil HV rise times are 12 µS, with a dwell time of about 0.85 mS at a coil voltage of about 35-40 kV.

The really neat thing about these systems is the short dwell time and the very short rise time. This ensures that the spark fires quickly and accurately for each cylinder. It also makes possible *multiple* coil firings in each firing sequence, especially at low rpm and idle. Consider that, in a 6-cylinder engine turning at 3600 rpm, the dwell time per cylinder is about 2.8 mS. That means that, with this system, there's enough time for the spark *phase* to be varied over that interval and also for programmed multiple strikes, thus ensuring clean fuel burning and maximum power from the fuel mixture. The firing characteristics are also dependent on other inputs that the PCM receives. It's easy to see why they're popular on newer vehicles.

You need to determine conclusively whether your noise is solely *radiated* or partially *conducted*. Conducted noise will be present with the antenna disconnected, but with dc power coming from the vehicle's electrical system, not a secondary battery (like a handheld transceiver). If you hear the noise with the engine running and the antenna disconnected, a major portion of that noise is conducted. Because the coil wires are very short (or practically non-existent) and there is no distributor with these systems, the opportunity for radiated HV noise is considerably less and these systems should have lower radiated noise than conventional ignition systems.

On the surface, that seems not to be the case with your experience. The location of the COP modules in relation to other engine wiring could be a factor here, as well as possible suppression capacitor failure used at the coil primaries. Also, don't rule out the possibility of a defective COP module. Some of the COP module radiation could be coupling to other wiring and radiating or conducting it to the vehicle's electrical system. Some systems use one primary suppression capacitor for each bank of COP modules or, in the case of an 8-cylinder engine, 2 capacitors. It may be possible for you to put a capacitor at the input to each coil, rather than have one capacitor per coil bank. And, shielding may be easier than you think. Use some heavy-duty aluminum foil over the COP modules and try to ground these to the engine block. You can then determine whether shielding will be effective.

Check with your dealer—the service department may be aware of a service note addressing the EMI issue, if it turns out to be generic and not unique to your vehicle. This may take considerable research on your part and/or the dealer's part. Next, contact Toyota directly. Many manufacturers take ignition noise suppression seriously, as they must, in many cases, satisfy the demands of public safety radio agencies. I would not make hardware modifications (suppression capacitors) to the ignition system until I had exhausted all the other options. Finally, make sure you visit the ARRL Web sites pertaining to automotive interference: **www.arrl.org/tis/info/rficar.html** and **www.arrl.org/tis/info/rfiignit.html**.

**Q**Tom, KC2GEP, writes: I have a short question regarding outdoor portable operation. I have a Kenwood TS-520 that we would like to operate outdoors at a weekend campout. There is a grounded three-pronged electrical outlet available that furnishes 120 V, 60 Hz ac. What safety precautions do we need to take for safe operation when used outdoors? We also plan to use a 20 meter dipole, suspended from trees, for an antenna. The site of operation will be 2 or 3 miles from a very large electric power generation plant. Could interference be a problem?

**A**As long as you use three-wire power cords for everything and observe all safety precautions in the generator owner's manual (if you use a generator), you should be fine. Installing a temporary ground rod would be advisable and run all of your equipment grounds to it. For general safety considerations, refer to the safety chapter in either *The ARRL Handbook* and/or *The ARRL Antenna Book*.

I do suggest that you use an ac outlet tester, such as the ones shown in **Figure 11.6**. These are useful and worthwhile devices for determining open grounds, crossed neutral-ground connections and the myriad of other possible failure modes with ac outlets. If you consider that there are three connections available in a standard ac outlet, there are six paths to failure (plus the chance that any one or more of the three is open). I routinely use one before embarking on any field operation that's powered by an ac source; be it portable or fixed, and it should be a standard part of your field toolkit. You don't want to be around outlets with missing grounds or crossed neutrals, especially in the field! These problems are more common than you think, especially when homebrew three-wire ac extension cables are used. Also, I would check all ac equipment grounds and make sure the ground (green) lead (the long center pin of the plug) is connected to the equipment chassis or case. This can be easily and quickly done with an ohmmeter.

Whether or not there is a problem with the electric plant or the local power grid depends on the utility's power system maintenance program. Distributed power systems typically only generate interference when there is a problem with the hardware in the system like arcing line splices, defective insulators, poor pole transformer connections, etc. Many of these problems are detailed in the *AC Power Interference Handbook* that is available from the ARRL.[4] Stay safe and have fun!

[4]Available from the ARRL Bookstore. Order no. 9055. Telephone toll-free in the US 888-277-5289, or 860-594-0355, fax 860-594-0303; **www.arrl.org/shop/; pubsales@arrl.org**.

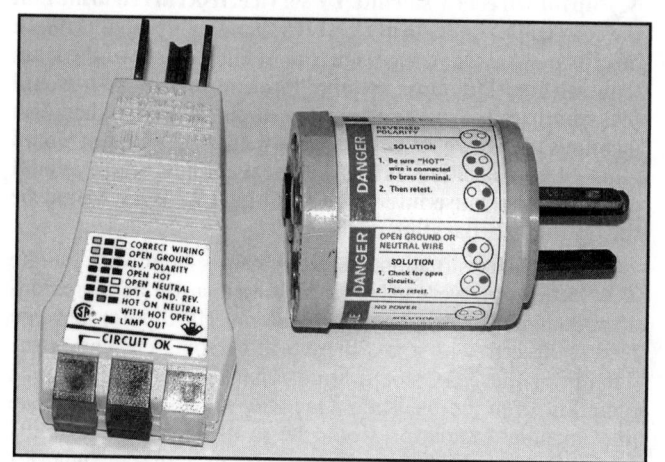

Figure 11.6—A pair of utility ac testers. These come in various package styles. The three lights indicate crossed or missing connections and can check more than six possible failure modes. They should be part of every amateur's field/emergency kit.

# Hands-On Radio

## Let's get Started

Welcome to "Hands-On Radio"—a series of simple bench-top experiments for the ham. Every month, this column will present a simple electronics or radio experiment for you to try at home with basic equipment. You'll learn a few simple design rules and equations that you can use on your own when you design your own circuits. We'll cover transistors, op amps, voltage regulators and all sorts of useful circuits. This will be a low-cost, interesting and fun way to get your feet wet building real, functional electronics.

### Equipment

To perform the experiments, you'll need to have some basic electronics test equipment, of course. Let's start with the minimum that will enable you to perform the dc portions of the experiments:

*12 V at 0.5 A power supply.* These are widely available from all of the sources listed below. In a pinch, you could use your rig's power supply. Don't use a wall-transformer supply—they're too poorly regulated.

*Volt-ohmmeter (VOM), digital or analog, with test probes.* Use a name-brand meter, such as a Fluke, B&K, or those available from RadioShack. Don't rely on a "mystery meter" from a hamfest—these are often inaccurate, have too great an effect on the circuit being tested, or have been damaged. An example can be seen in **Figure 12.1**.

*A prototyping board or breadboard.* Because you will be making a lot of circuits and adjusting the values of the components frequently, a plug-in style base for construction is invaluable. You'll need one with at least 30 rows of contacts and dual power busses on each side. RadioShack #276-169 (p 256 in the 2002 catalog) is a good example of what's needed.

*Clip leads.* Buy or make a dozen 10 to 18 inch leads of stranded hookup wire with small, insulated alligator clips on each end. These will be used for connecting the power supplies and meters. While you're at it, obtain a few feet of solid #20 AWG or #22 AWG wire for the prototype board. Used telephone twisted-pair cable is a good source.

*Tools.* Have a small pair of needle-nosed pliers, wire clippers and wire strippers

The circuits are most useful when used with ac signals, so you will get an awful lot more out of the experiments if you can obtain the following:

*20 MHz oscilloscope with two probes.* Good deals abound

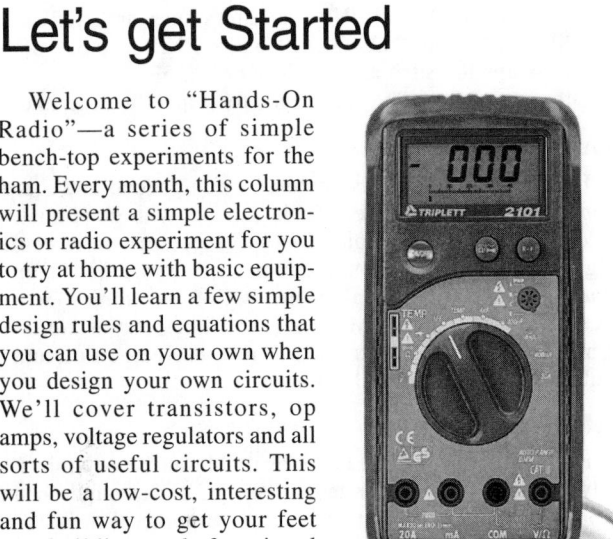

Figure 12.1—A typical digital volt-ohmmeter.

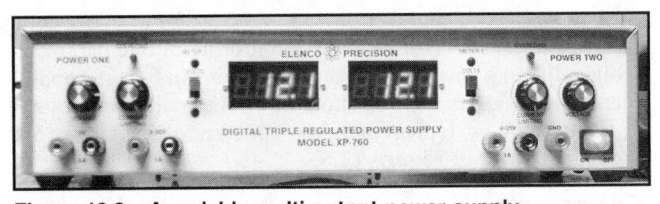

Figure 12.2—A wide-band oscilloscope with internal triggering.

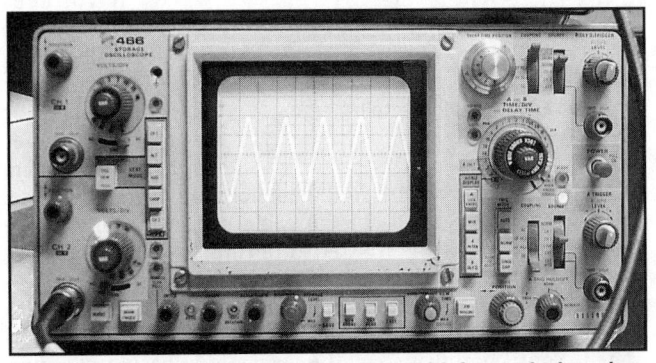

Figure 12.3—A variable multi-output power supply.

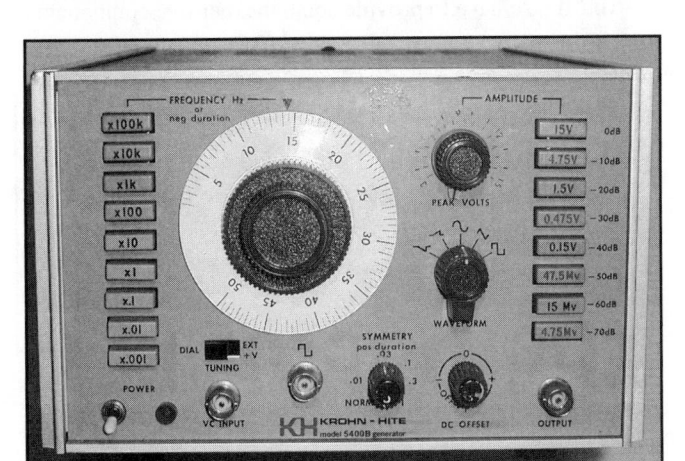

Figure 12.4—A basic function generator.

for oscilloscopes with excellent specifications. A typical oscilloscope is shown in **Figure 12.2**. Internet auction sites, hamfests and ham swap Web sites regularly show excellent 'scopes selling for less than $200. Make sure it has internal triggering and be sure to get probes (they'll cost from $20-50 separately) and an operating manual.

*Adjustable, dual power supply, 0-20 V at 0.5 A.* A dual supply will allow you to have a source of adjustable dc voltage, as well as power your circuit. Dual supplies will be needed

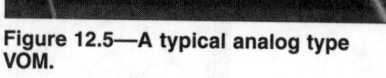

Figure 12.5—A typical analog type VOM.

for our op-amp experiments, as well. **Figure 12.3** shows an example of a multi-output power supply.

*Function generator, 0-1 MHz.* As with the 'scopes, excellent equipment is widely available for under $100. The generator should be able to supply both sine and square waves at voltages from 0.1 Vp-p to 5 Vp-p. Other features such as dc offset, triangle or asymmetric waveforms and sweep are not required, but you will find them helpful for your own use. If your generator has a coaxial cable output (usually BNC) you'll need either a BNC-to-binding post adapter (for connecting the clip leads) or a BNC cable with test clips. **Figure 12.4** shows a function generator. The figures show some examples of commonly used test equipment. Don't be intimidated. You'll find that a small investment in basic test equipment now will be valuable for learning and troubleshooting later.

*A second VOM and test probes.* Very useful to allow comparisons in real-time or to allow monitoring of one parameter while adjusting another. The second meter can be less capable than the primary meter and should be able to measure voltage at a minimum. A typical analog VOM, useful for the second meter, is shown in **Figure 12.5**.

## Components

You'll also have to provide some inexpensive components,

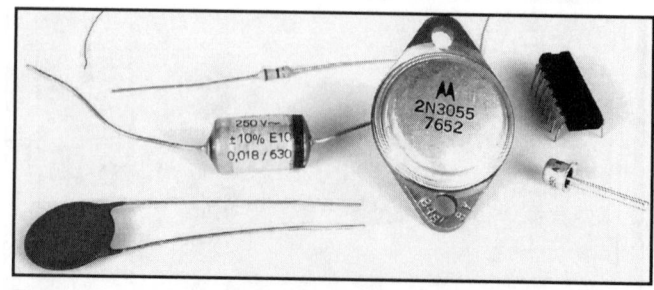

Figure 12.6—Some of the components you'll use.

such as resistors, transistors, capacitors, integrated circuits, and the like. Some of these can be seen in **Figure 12.6**. A shopping list of components and equipment will be provided in the column preceding the experiment. In this way, you will be able to have them on hand when *QST* arrives. Generally speaking, if you have the following selection of components, you'll be ready to go!

• ¼-W resistors from 10 Ω to 1 MΩ and adjustable resistors or "pots" of 1 kΩ, 10 kΩ, and 100 kΩ
• capacitors from 100 pF to 10 µF of various types
• signal diodes such as 1N4148 and low-voltage rectifiers such as the 1N4001
• common NPN and PNP transistors such as 2N2222 or 2N3904 (NPN) and 2N2907 or 2N3906 (PNP)
• op-amps ICs such as types 741 or LF353

Other components may be needed for a specific experiment.

## Sources

Here are a few of the distributors for components and equipment that I've found to be reliable vendors with good quality products: Future Electronics (**www.futureelectronics.com**); Digi-Key (**www.digikey.com**); Jameco (**www.jameco.com**); Marlin P. Jones (**www.mpja.com**); MCM Electronics (**www.mcmelectronics.com**); Mouser Electronics (**www.mouser.com**); Ocean State Electronics (**www. oselectronics.com**); RadioShack (**www.radioshack.com**).

## References

Because of the limited space available in the column, I'll only be able to give a limited amount of background on the experiment and the circuit. Having one or more of these texts on your shelf as a backup is highly recommended: *The ARRL Handbook for Radio Amateurs*—I will use the 2002 edition as my primary reference for all of the experiments; *Solid State Design for the Radio Amateur*, by Wes Hayward, W7ZOI, and Doug DeMaw, W1FB, published by the ARRL; *Understanding Basic Electronics*—by Larry Wolfgang WR1B, published by the ARRL; *The Art of Electronics*—by Paul Horowitz and Winfield Hill, published by Cambridge University Press.

### Experiment #1—Common-Emitter Amplifier

Our first experiment will feature the most common single-transistor amplifier—the common emitter. You'll need the following components:

• 2—100 kΩ adjustable resistors
• ¼-W resistors of the following values (Ω): 100, 470, 1000, 2.7 k, 3.9 k, 4.7 k, 10 k, 27 k, 39k, 47 k, 68 k, 100 k
• 2—1 µF capacitors with a voltage rating of 25 V dc or more (electrolytic or tantalum are fine)
• 2N3904 transistor (have two or more on hand).

If you can, read "Transistor Amplifier Design—A Practical Approach" in *The ARRL Handbook*.

# Experiment #1—The Common-Emitter Amplifier

Our first experiment will feature the *common emitter* (CE) *amplifier*. Why the CE amplifier? It is the most common amplifier configuration of all—it is found in analog and digital circuits, from dc through microwaves and it is made of discrete components and fabricated in integrated circuits (ICs). If you understand the CE amplifier, you've made a good start in electronics.

## Background

The CE amplifier (**Figure 12.7**) is used when modest voltage gain is required along with an input impedance (the impedance seen by the circuit supplying the signal to be amplified) of a few kΩ or more. The output of the CE amplifier is inverted from its input. (We call this 180° of phase shift.) As the input signal swings positive, more current flows into the transistor's base, which also causes more current to flow from the collector to the emitter. This causes more voltage drop across Rc and so the voltage at the collector also drops. The reverse is true when the input signal swings negative.

In order for the circuit to amplify both positive and negative swings of the input signal, its collector current ($I_c$) must be offset from zero so that it can both increase and decrease. An amplifier that has a continuous output current, even with no input signal, is called a Class A amplifier. The method of controlling this continuous current is called biasing. Resistors in the voltage divider R1 and R2 cause a small amount bias current to flow into the base and thus keep the collector current flowing at all times. The amplifier is then said to be operating in its "active" region. The resulting continuous collector current equals the base bias current multiplied by the transistor's current gain, $\beta$. Using Ohm's Law to find the voltages across $R_c$ and $R_e$, the transistor's collector-to-emitter voltage ($V_{ce}$) is also determined by the bias current. The combination of continuous $I_c$ and $V_{ce}$ is called the Q-point of the circuit, where Q stands for "quiescent." When an input signal is applied, output voltage and current changes are centered around the Q-point.

As the collector current changes in response to an input signal, the circuit's output voltage is developed across the collector resistor, $R_c$. For a given input signal, a larger $R_c$ means a larger output voltage change—a higher voltage gain ($A_v$). The function of $R_e$ is to set the transistor's Q-point such that the collector voltage can make wide swings without running up to the power supply voltage ($V_{cc}$) or down to ground. By being in the collector current's path, along with $R_c$, larger values of $R_e$ work against $R_c$ to reduce voltage gain. In fact, the voltage gain is approximately the ratio of $R_c$ to $R_e$.

Figure 12.7 shows capacitors at the input ($C_{in}$) and output ($C_{out}$). This is called an "ac coupled" design. The capacitors block the flow of dc current to the load or to the circuit driving the amplifier. These capacitors also cause the gain at very low frequencies to be reduced, as the impedance of a capacitor increases at low frequencies—hence the gain at dc is zero. For this experiment, all capacitors will be 10 µF—a value large enough to act as a short-circuit for most audio signals. If polarized capacitors are used, the positive side should be connected to the circuit.

## Terms to Learn

$A_v$—Voltage gain, the ratio of output to input voltage.

Beta ($\beta$)—DC current gain, the ratio of collector current to base current.

Cutoff—Collector current reduced to zero.

$I_b$, $I_c$—Base and collector current, respectively.

Q-Point—Quiescent or resting values of collector current ($I_{cq}$) and voltage ($V_{ceq}$) with no applied input signal.

$V_{ce}$, $V_{be}$—Voltage from collector-to-emitter and base-to-emitter, respectively.

## Key Equations

$$I_c \approx I_e,\ I_c = I_b \times \text{Beta } (\beta) \tag{1}$$
$$V_{cc} = (I_c \times R_c) + V_{ce} + (I_e \times R_e) \approx I_e \times (R_c + R_e) + V_{cc} \tag{2}$$
$$A_v \approx R_c / R_e \tag{3}$$
$$V_{R2} = V_{be} + (I_e \times R_e) \tag{4}$$

## Designing the Amplifier

1. Choose the circuit's operating requirements:

$V_{cc} = 12$ V *(our power supply voltage)*.

$A_v = 5$ *(a medium value of gain)*.

Q-point of $I_{cc} = 4$ mA *(a value to keep power dissipation low)* and $V_{ceq} = 5$ V *(rule of thumb—about one-half of $V_{cc}$)*.

Assume the transistor's $\beta$ is 150 and base-to-emitter voltage, $V_{be} = 0.7$ V. *(The actual range of $\beta$ can be read from the transistor's data sheet and $V_{be}$ is typically 0.7 V for silicon transistors.)*

2. *From equation 2*, $V_{cc} = I_c (R_c + R_e) + V_{ce}$

$(V_{cc} - V_{ce}) / I_c = R_c + R_e$, so $R_c + R_e = (12\ V - 5\ V) / 4$ mA $= 1.75$ kΩ

3. *From the above*, $R_c = 1750\ \Omega - R_e$ and with $A_v = 5$, $R_c / R_e = 5$ *(equation 3)* so

$R_c = 5\ R_e$ and $(1750\ \Omega - R_e) = 5\ R_e$, so $6\ R_e = 1750\ \Omega$ and $R_e = 1750\ \Omega / 6 = 292\ \Omega$ *(use 270 Ω, a standard value)*.

4. *From equation 1*, base current, $I_b = I_{cq} / \beta = 4$ mA / 150 $= 26.67$ µA (27 µA). Set the current through R1 and R2 equal to 10 times $I_b$ or 270 µA. *(This is a rule of thumb simplifying calculations and keeping $I_b$ stable with a "stiff" bias supply.)*

The voltage across R2 = $V_{be} + I_c (R_e) = 0.7$ V + 4 mA (270 Ω) = 1.8 V *($I_c \approx I_e$ and equation 4)*.

By Ohm's Law, R2 = 1.8 V / 270 µA = 6.7 kΩ *(use 6.8 kΩ, a standard value)*.

The voltage across R1 = $V_{cc}$ − 1.8 V = 10.2 V *(voltage divider)*

By Ohm's Law, R1 = 10.2 V / 270 µA = 37.8 kΩ *(use 39 kΩ, a standard value)*.

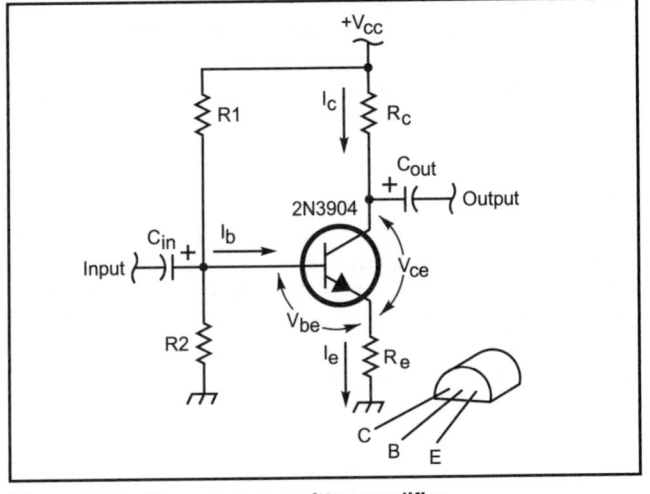

Figure 12.7—The common-emitter amplifier.

## Testing the Amplifier

1. Connect the power supply only after double-checking all connections, especially the transistor leads.

2. Use a VOM to measure the dc voltage from collector to emitter (it should be about 5 V), from base to emitter (0.6-0.7 V), and from collector and emitter to ground (7 V and 2 V, respectively).

3. Replace R1 with the 100 kΩ potentiometer, set to about 39 kΩ. Confirm that all the dc voltages remain about the same. Connect the VOM between collector and ground and observe what happens as R1 is decreased and increased (raising and lowering base current). Use Ohm's Law to determine what is happening to the collector current as you adjust R1. Reset the pot to 39 kΩ.

4. Set the signal (function) generator to output a 1 kHz sine wave of 200 mV$_{p-p}$, then connect it to C$_{in}$. If you are using an oscilloscope, you should see a sine wave at the output of C$_{out}$ with an amplitude of about 1 V$_{p-p}$ and inverted (180° of phase shift) with respect to the input. (A VOM measuring ac RMS voltage will show values of about 70 mV RMS at the input and 350 mV RMS at the output—a gain of 5.)

5. Adjust R1 in each direction and observe the output signal with the oscilloscope. As you lower the collector current, you will begin to see the output waveform clip on positive peaks as the collector current is cut off. Raising collector current will eventually result in distortion on negative peaks as the transistor enters the saturation region.

6. Return R1 to 39 kΩ and increase the input signal to observe distortion on the output. If you are using a VOM, note that the RMS output increases more slowly as the signal is clipped.

7. Turn down the input signal as far as possible. Connect the third 10 µF capacitor across R$_e$. (Connect the negative side of a polarized capacitor to ground.) Slowly increase the input signal and observe the new gain of the circuit. By bypassing R$_e$, the dc operation of the circuit is unaffected, but now the emitter circuit is effectively grounded for ac signals. The gain is now limited only by the internal impedance of the transistor emitter.

8. Now that you have a working circuit—experiment with it!

• Rework the math for a Q-point with 10 times more and 10 times less collector current.

• Raise and lower the input frequency to see where the gain drops to 70% of the peak value. These are the −3 dB frequencies that determine the amplifier's bandwidth. (These frequencies may be out of range, depending on your instruments.)

• Depending on your generator's capabilities, try different waveforms, such as square or triangle waves, at different frequencies. Does the amplifier faithfully reproduce them?

• Substitute other transistors of the same type and of different types to see what happens to the dc and ac performance.

### Suggested Reading

"Transistor Amplifier Design—A Practical Approach" in *The ARRL Handbook.* For a more complete discussion of the common emitter amplifier, check out Chapter 2 of *The Art of Electronics.*

### Shopping List

You'll need the following components:

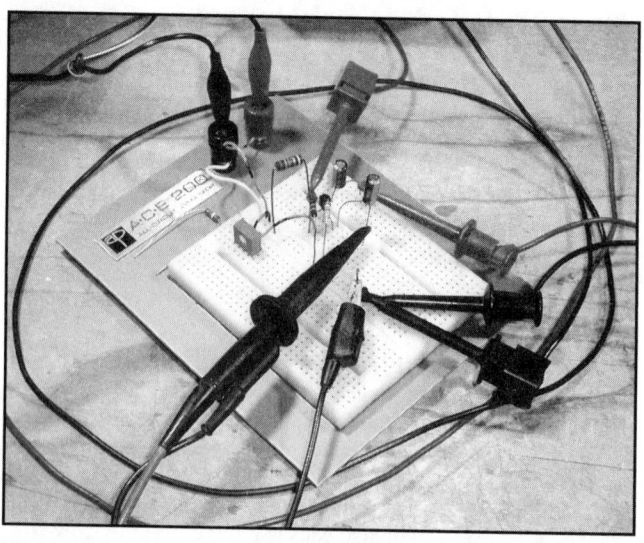

Figure 12.8—The experimental setup, showing the prototype board and connections to the power supply, oscilloscope and voltmeter. Note that the signal instrument grounds are all connected to a single point—this helps to prevent noise pickup and ground loops.

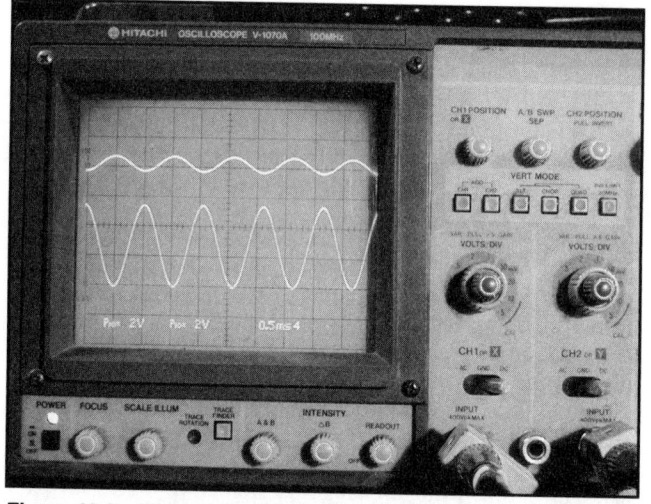

Figure 12.9—The oscilloscope shows the input (top trace) and output (bottom trace) waveforms. The output is inverted with respect to the input and the voltage gain is approximately 5.

• 100 kΩ potentiometer.
• ¼ W resistors of the following values: 270 Ω, 1.5 kΩ, 6.8 kΩ, 39 kΩ.
• 3—10 µF capacitors with a voltage rating of 25 V dc or more (electrolytic or tantalum are fine).
• 2N3904 transistor.

### Next Month

The common collector amplifier, also known as the emitter follower, will be the subject of next month's experiment. With the exception of a few more resistor values, you'll be able to reuse the components from this month's exercise. See you then!

# Experiment #2—The Emitter-Follower Amplifier

Our second experiment will again focus on a transistor amplifier—the emitter-follower. This handy amplifier doesn't offer much in the way of voltage gain (it has none), but it provides buffering or isolation for sensitive amplifiers and muscle to output circuits for driving loads like headphones or coaxial cables. It has relatively high input impedance with low output impedance and good *power* gain, as we'll see later.

## Background

The emitter-follower (EF) amplifier configuration, also called the common collector, is found in applications where an amplifier must have both high input impedance (to avoid loading a sensitive or low-power circuit) and low output impedance (to drive a heavy load).

The EF provides no voltage gain; in fact, its voltage gain is always less than 1. The collector of the transistor is connected directly to the power supply, without a resistor and the output is taken across the emitter resistor. There is no 180° phase shift as seen in the common-emitter configuration of experiment #1—the output signal follows the input signal with 0° phase shift. This is the origin of the name—the emitter voltage "follows" the input signal voltage.

Why does the EF configuration have a high input impedance? Let's start by looking directly into the base of the transistor at base voltage, $V_b$ and base current, $I_b$. Remember that $\beta$ is the transistor current gain, or the ratio of collector to base current.

$\beta = I_c / I_b$ so $I_c = \beta I_b$

$I_e = I_b + I_c$

Therefore, $I_e = I_b + \beta I_b = I_b (\beta + 1)$

$V_b = V_{be} + I_e R_e = V_{be} + [I_b (\beta + 1)] R_e$    [1]

The base impedance, $Z_b$, is the ratio of the change ($\Delta$) in $V_b$ to the resulting change in $I_b$. Biasing will keep the transistor current "turned on" so $V_{be}$ doesn't change much and can be treated as constant. So, small changes in $V_b$ due to the input signal will cause a corresponding change in $I_b$.

$\Delta V_b \approx \Delta I_b (\beta + 1) R_e$ and...    [2]

$Z_b = \Delta V_b / \Delta I_b \approx (\beta + 1) R_e$    [3]

This equation shows that the small changes in $I_b$ amplified by $\beta$ effectively also multiplies $R_e$ by the same amount. The base impedance (not counting the biasing network R1 and R2) is essentially the current gain, $\beta$, multiplied by the emitter resistor, $R_e$.

The input source doesn't just drive the base, of course; it also has to drive the combination of R1 and R2, the biasing resistors. From an ac point of view, both R1 and R2 can be considered as connected to "ac ground" (the power supply supplies a constant dc voltage; it should present a low impedance, which is effectively an ac short) and they can be treated as if they were connected in parallel. When R1 // R2 are considered along with the transistor base impedance, $Z_b$, the impedance the input signal source "sees" is:

$Z_{in} = R1 // R2 // Z_b = 1 / [1/R1 + 1/R2 + 1/R_e (\beta + 1)]$    [4]

Let's figure the output impedance, $Z_{out}$, too. Looking back into the connection between the transistor emitter and $R_e$, $Z_{out}$ is made up of three components. The first is $R_e$, which is connected to ground. The second, $Z_e$, is the series combination of the transistor's internal emitter impedance, $r_e$, (note the lower-case "r" which distinguishes it from the external resistance, $R_e$) and the combined impedance of the signal source, $R_s$, and the biasing resistors R1 and R2. Using the same explanation of current gain's effect on input impedance—in reverse this time—the impedance presented at the emitter, $Z_e$, is:

$Z_e = (R_s // R1 // R2) / (\beta + 1) + r_e$    [5]

From the physics of silicon transistors, at room temperature, $r_e$

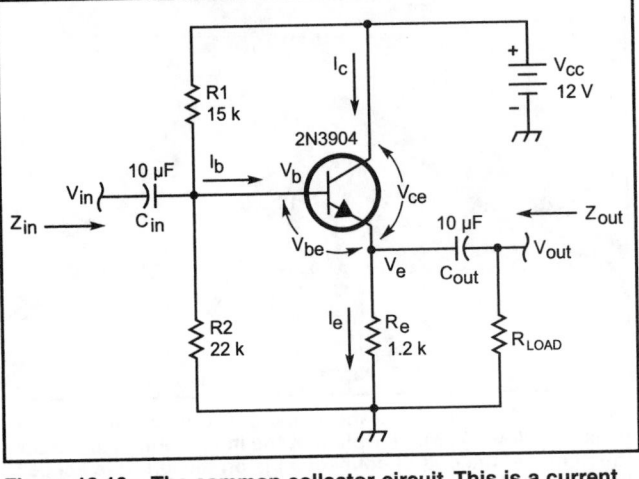

**Figure 12.10—The common collector circuit. This is a current or power amplifier, offering high input impedance and low output impedance. It is useful for driving low impedance loads, buffering and isolation.**

$= 25$ mV $/ I_{eq}$, where $I_{eq} \approx I_{cq}$ in mA, so, for most designs, $r_e$ will be much less than 50 $\Omega$. Similarly, in our experiment, R1 and R2 are likely to be much higher than $R_s$, the signal source impedance—which is usually less than 1 k$\Omega$. When $R_e$ and $Z_e$ are combined, the output impedance of the circuit becomes:

$Z_{out} = Z_e // R_e$    [6]

We see, therefore, that our emitter follower has a relatively high input impedance and a low output impedance, making it ideal for driving low-impedance loads.

## Terms to Learn

Input (Output) Impedance—the equivalent ac impedance looking into the input (output) of a circuit.

Cascade—two circuits connected such that the output of the first is connected to the input of the second.

Power Gain—the ratio of output power to input power.

Buffer—an amplifier used to provide isolation between two circuits.

//—in parallel with.

## Key Equations

$I_c \approx I_e$, $I_c = I_b \beta$    [7]

$V_{cc} \approx V_{ce} + I_c R_e$    [8]

$V_b \approx V_{be} + I_c R_e$    [9]

## Designing the Amplifier

Choose the circuit's operating requirements:

$V_{cc} = 12$ V *(our power supply voltage)*

Q-point of $I_{cq} = 5$ mA and $V_{ceq} = 6$ V *(rule of thumb, ½ $V_{cc}$ allows the maximum output voltage swing)*

Assume the transistor's $\beta$ is 150 and base-to-emitter voltage, $V_{be} = 0.7$ V

1. $R_e = (V_{cc} - V_{ceq}) / I_{cq} = 1.2$ k$\Omega$ *(Eq 8)*

2. Base current, $I_b = I_{cq} / \beta = 33$ µA *(Eq 7)*

3. Current through R1 and R2 = 10 $I_b$ = 330 µA *(a rule of thumb simplifying calculations and keeping $I_b$ stable with a "stiff" bias supply).*

4. Voltage across R2 = $V_{be} + I_c R_e = 0.7 + 5$ mA (1.2 k$\Omega$) = 6.7 V *(Eq 9)*

R2 = 6.7 V / 330 µA = 20.3 k$\Omega$ (use 22 k$\Omega$). *(Ohm's Law)*

5. Voltage across R1 = $V_{cc} - 6.7$ V = 5.3 V. *(Voltage divider)*

R1 = 5.3 V / 330 µA = 16.06 k$\Omega$ (use 15 k$\Omega$). *(Ohm's Law)*

$Z_{in} = 1 / [1/R1 + 1/R2 + 1/R_e (\beta + 1)] \approx 8.5$ k$\Omega$ *(Eq 4)*

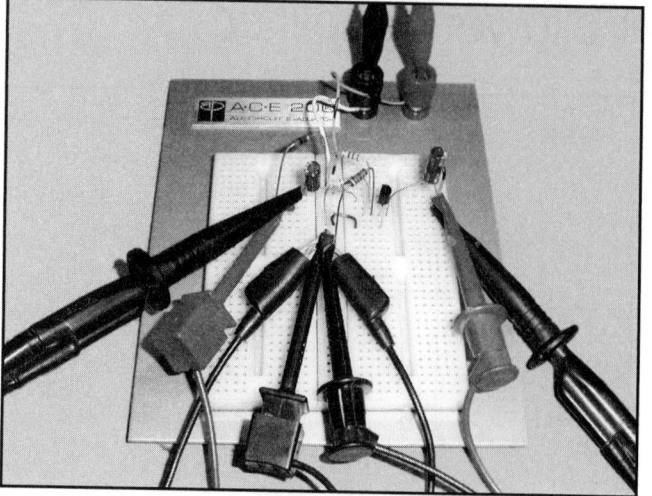

Figure 12.11—This photo shows the construction of the EF (emitter follower) circuit. Note that the input connection is on the right and the output connection is on the left. This keeps the input and output leads away from each other and helps prevent oscillation. All ground leads (black clips) are connected together at a single point.

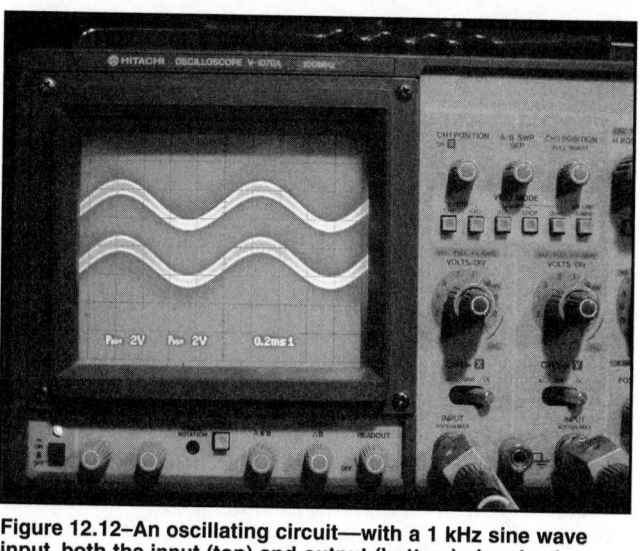

Figure 12.12–An oscillating circuit—with a 1 kHz sine wave input, both the input (top) and output (bottom) signals show significant oscillation at more than 1 MHz. Experiment with lead placement and circuit component placement to learn what causes and prevents oscillation.

Assuming $R_s = 50 \ \Omega$, $Z_{out} \approx r_e \ // \ R_e = 5 \ \Omega \ // \ 1.2 \ k\Omega \approx 4.99 \ \Omega$ *(Eq 5 and 6)*

That's where our emitter follower shines!

## Testing the Amplifier

Connect the power supply after double-checking all connections, especially the transistor leads. **Figure 12.11** shows the breadboard circuit.

1. Use a VOM to measure the dc voltage from collector to emitter (it should be about 6 V), from base to emitter (0.6 – 0.7 V) and from emitter to ground (6 V). Replace R1 with a 100 kΩ potentiometer, set to 15 kΩ. Start with a value of 10 kΩ for $R_{load}$.

2. Set the signal generator to output a 1 kHz sine wave at 1 $V_{p-p}$, then connect it to $C_{in}$. You should see a sine wave at the output of $C_{out}$ with an amplitude of about 1 $V_{p-p}$ and in phase with the input. (A VOM measuring ac voltage will show 350 mV rms at the input and output.)

3. You will find later that the emitter follower has a very high bandwidth. This can lead to oscillation at several hundred kHz or higher, if you're not careful. This instability is visible as the "fuzzy" oscilloscope trace shown in **Figure 12.12**. Those of you using voltmeters only might see intermittent or jumpy ac signal voltages. It's important to keep input leads away from output leads and use the single-point ground as shown in the breadboard circuit of Figure 12.11. Sometimes, just moving the leads around will cause the oscillation to start and stop, so don't be afraid to experiment.

4. Increase the input signal to 5 $V_{p-p}$. Adjust R1 in each direction and observe the output signal with the oscilloscope. As you lower the collector current ($V_b$ decreasing), you will see the output waveform clip on negative peaks as the collector current is cut off. Raising collector current will eventually result in distortion on positive peaks as the transistor enters saturation.

5. Substitute 1 kΩ, 100 Ω, and 10 Ω resistors for $R_{load}$, reducing the input voltage at each value, so that the output waveform remains undistorted. Lower resistance loads can only be driven at lower voltages because the ac currents in the transistor are much higher at lower values of load resistance. You can read about ac load lines in the reference texts for a detailed explanation. You'll also see the output signal begin to "lag" behind the input signal at these low load values. Why? The impedance of the output coupling capacitor at 1 kHz becomes significant for loads below 100 Ω, introducing phase shift in a series RC circuit.

6. If the input power is $(V_{in})^2 / Z_{in}$ and the output power is $(V_{out})^2 / R_{load}$, compute the power gain of the amplifier for the maximum undistorted values of input and output voltage at the different loads.

$$\text{Power Gain} = P_{out} / P_{in} = [(V_{out})^2/R_{load}]/[(V_{in})^2/Z_{in})] \qquad [10]$$

If $V_{in} \approx V_{out}$, then power gain = $Z_{in} / R_{load}$ ! See how closely this approximation agrees with your measurements.

7. Now that you have a working circuit—experiment with it!

• Rework the math for a Q-point with 5 times more and 10 times less collector current. Calculate $Z_{in}$ and $Z_{out}$ for those currents.

• Raise the input frequency to see if you can find where the gain drops to 70% of the peak value; this is the upper –3 dB frequency of the amplifier.

• Drive both the CE and EF amplifiers with a square-wave at the highest frequency your generator can reach, using a 1 kΩ load resistor. Use the 'scope to determine which circuit will follow the input more accurately thus indicating wider bandwidth.

## Suggested Reading

• "Transistor Amplifier Design—A Practical Approach" in *The ARRL Handbook*.

• "Low-Frequency Transistor Models" in *The ARRL Handbook*.

• For a more complete discussion of the Emitter-Follower amplifier, check out Chapter 2 of *The Art of Electronics*, by Horowitz and Hill.

## Shopping List

You'll need the following components:
• 100 kΩ potentiometer.
• ¼ W resistors of the following values: 10 Ω, 100 Ω, 1 kΩ, 1.2 kΩ, 10 kΩ,15 kΩ, 22 kΩ.
• 2-10 µF capacitors with a voltage rating of 25 V dc or more (electrolytic or tantalum are fine).
• 2N3904 transistor.

## Next Month

We shift gears next month to operational amplifiers—usually known by their nickname "op amps." Be prepared to buffer, invert, add and subtract!

# Experiment #3—Basic Operational Amplifiers

Let's give transistors a rest this month and take a look at one of the most popular components in electronics—the op-amp. The most widely used circuits are two simple amplifiers and an adder circuit.

## Background

Op-amp is an abbreviation for *operational amplifier*, a term coined 70 years ago. Complicated mathematical equations were then solved by analog computers. Amplifiers were used to add, multiply, integrate, or perform other "operations" on signals. Originally made with vacuum tubes, integrated circuit op amps—such as the 741—started a revolution in electronics.

Op-amps generally have a high voltage gain, a high input impedance and a low output impedance. These properties make designing op-amp circuits easy because they simplify the design equations, as we'll see.

## Terms to Learn

Inverting (–) and non-inverting (+)—signals at the inverting input cause the op-amp output to respond in the opposite "direction" and, for signals at the non-inverting input, in the same direction.

Negative feedback—routing some of a circuit's output back to the input in such a way as to oppose the effect of the input signal.

## The Operational Amplifier

**Figure 12.13** shows the basic op-amp symbol, including the inverting and non-inverting inputs. *The 2003 ARRL Handbook* incorrectly shows the pin-outs for several popular op-amps on page 24.27—the inverting and non-inverting input connections are *reversed*. The industry standard for single op-amp ICs is that pin 2 is the inverting input (–) and pin 3 the non-inverting input (+).

The bypass or decoupling capacitors (C1, C2) shown in Figure 12.13 keep the power bus clean and help prevent feedback paths that might cause the op-amp circuit to oscillate. They bypass the power connections to ground, hence "decoupling" ac signals from the circuit.

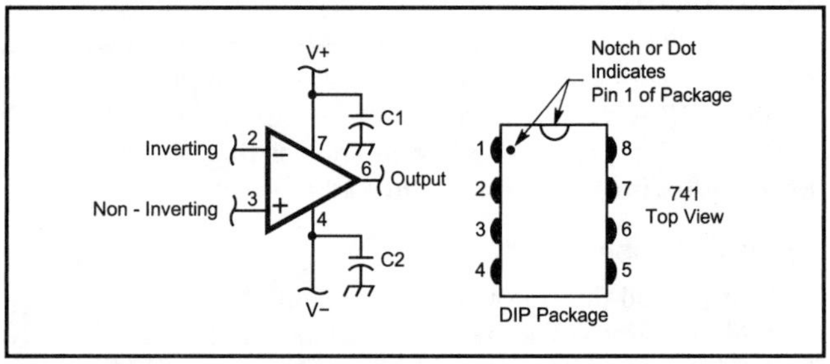

An op-amp has a huge capacity to amplify—80 dB or more of voltage gain at dc! Most of the time that's far too much gain, but so-called "negative feedback" can control that gain, creating useful behavior. Consider that the op-amp's gain is acting solely on the voltage differential between its two inputs. The trick is to connect components from the output to the inputs so that when the output is doing what we want, the voltages at both input pins are balanced. This is a "correction" or "feedback" signal. It stabilizes the op-amp output by correcting its input. If the input changes—even a little bit—the high gain immediately causes the op-amp to react, changing its output and the feedback signal until its inputs are balanced once again. When feedback is used we refer to the circuit being "closed-loop."

## The Non-Inverting Amplifier

**Figure 12.14A** shows a non-inverting amplifier. The input signal, $V_I$, is connected directly to the non-inverting (+) input, while resistors $R_f$ and R form a feedback network. Remember that the op-amp has a very high input impedance, so we can treat the series combination of R and $R_f$ as a voltage divider connected between the output pin and ground. The voltage at the inverting (–) input of the op-amp, $V_i$, must be:

$$V_i = V_{out} R / (R + R_f)$$

Since the op-amp's inputs must balance, $V_i = V_I$ and the circuit's gain, $A_v$ must be:

$$A_v = V_{out} / V_I = (R + R_f) / R = 1 + R_f / R$$
$$[1]$$

The non-inverting amplifier's gain is always greater than 1 and is determined only by the ratio of $R_f$ and R. There's no magic—the op-amp is just connected so that when its output is the correct amount larger than the input signal, both inputs balance.

## Testing the Non-Inverting Amplifier

• Design the amplifier to have a gain of 2. That requires $R_f$ = R. Use a value of 1 kΩ for this first circuit. Your power supply should be set to at least ±12 V (+12 V if you are using a single-polarity supply). Caution—do not apply signals above or below the power supply to the op-amp inputs or you may damage the IC.

• Build the circuit as shown in Figure 12.14A, including a 10 μF bypass capacitor to ground at each power supply pin. The 1 kΩ potentiometer will serve as an adjustable voltage source for $V_I$. Set the potentiometer so that the resistance from the wiper to ground is about 100 Ω. After checking all your connections, apply power and measure $V_I$ and $V_{out}$. $V_I$ should be approximately 1.2 V (one-tenth of V+) and $V_{out}$ should be close to twice the value of $V_I$.

• The voltage at the inverting input, $V_i$ should follow $V_I$ very closely.

**Figure 12.13—The operational-amplifier schematic symbol and typical package details.**

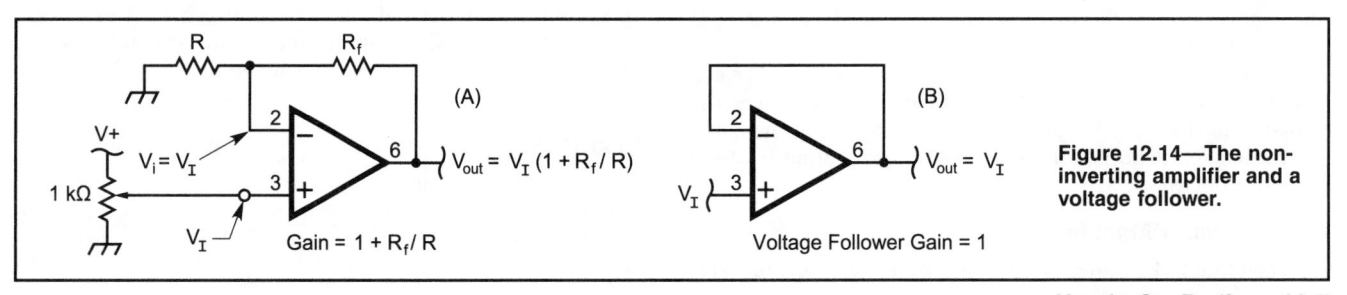

Figure 12.14—The non-inverting amplifier and a voltage follower.

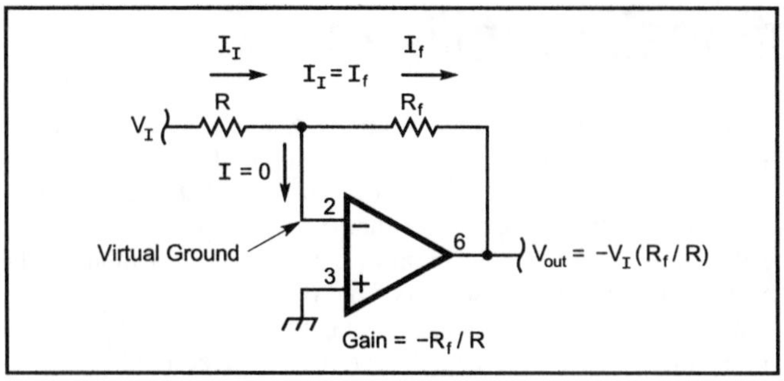

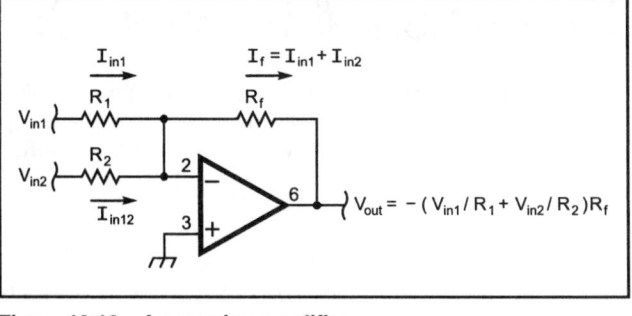

**Figure 12.15—The inverting amplifier.**

**Figure 12.16—A summing amplifier.**

• Adjust the potentiometer output voltage up and down while measuring both $V_1$ and $V_{out}$.

• You need a ±12 V power supply for this step. Replace the potentiometer with a function generator supplying a 1 $V_{p-p}$, 1 kHz sine wave. Use the oscilloscope to measure the output—it should be just like the input, but with twice the voltage.

• Experiment by changing the ratio of R and $R_f$ to obtain different gains. (Keep resistor values above 100Ω.)

• Make a unity-gain voltage follower by removing R and replacing $R_f$ with a direct connection as shown in Figure 12.14B. This circuit is frequently used to isolate a sensitive input or drive a heavy load.

### The Inverting Amplifier

The high-impedance of the op-amp input can be used to create an inverting amplifier whose gain is also set by the ratio of two resistors. In **Figure 12.15**, R and $R_f$ are again connected to the inverting input, but the input signal is connected to the free end of R and the non-inverting input is grounded. How does this work? Remember that the op-amp inputs are balanced, so the inverting input must also be at ground potential. It's not grounded, it's just at ground potential. This is called a "virtual ground."

With the inverting input at 0 V, the current through R must be $I_1 = V_1 / R$. Remember, too, that the op-amp input impedance is very high, so the input current must be balanced by the op-amp's output removing just as much current through Rf as flows through R. By Ohm's Law, the output voltage is then:

$$V_{out} = 0 - (I_1)\,R_f = - (V_1 / R)\,R_f = -V_1\,R_f / R$$

and the gain must be:

$$A_v = V_{out} / V_1 = -(V_1 R_f / R)/V_1 = - R_f / R \quad [2]$$

### Testing the Inverting Amplifier

• Design the amplifier to have a gain of –4. Select a value for R of 1 kΩ. This requires $R_f$ to be 4 kΩ. The closest standard value is 3.9 kΩ. You will need a ±12 V power supply to test this amplifier configuration.

• Build the amplifier as shown in Figure 12.15 and connect a 1 $V_{p-p}$, 1 kHz sine wave to the input. You should see a 3.9 $V_{p-p}$ sine wave at the output, but inverted with respect to the input. Look at the inverting input to verify that it is at ground potential.

• Use different resistor ratios to change the gain. (Keep resistor values above 100 Ω to limit how much power the op-amp must supply.) Input a dc voltage by using the 1 kΩ potentiometer as before and see if the circuit output is of the opposite polarity.

### The Summing Amplifier

The circuit of **Figure 12.16** shows how more than one sig-

nal can be combined and amplified by a summing amplifier. As for the inverting amplifier, the op-amp must balance all of the currents at the inverting input—even if current comes from more than one source!

The current from each input signal equals $V_{in}$ / R, so the total current in $R_f$ must be their sum:

$$I_f = V_{in1} / R_1 + V_{in2} / R_2$$

Using the same reasoning as before, the output voltage must be:

$$V_{out} = - (V_{in1} / R_1 + V_{in2} / R_2)R_f \quad [3]$$

The gain for either input signal is still the ratio, $- R_f / R$.

### Testing the Summing Amplifier

• Design the amplifier to have a gain of –1 for each input by setting all three resistors ($R_1$, $R_2$ and $R_f$) to 10 kΩ. You will need a ±12 V power supply to test this amplifier configuration.

• Build the circuit and input the 1 $V_{p-p}$, 1 kHz sine wave to input 1. Use the 1 kΩ potentiometer as before to supply input 2.

• Vary the potentiometer while watching the output on your oscilloscope. You will see the inverted sine wave from input 1 shifted up and down as the dc level at input 2 changes.

• Experiment by altering the ratio of either input resistor and $R_f$ to observe the effect on the addition of signals. Replace $R_1$ or $R_2$ (or both) with a 10 kΩ potentiometer and vary the channel ratios independently. Congratulations—you've just built a 2-channel mixer!

### Suggested Reading

*The 2003 ARRL Handbook*, pp 8.32-8.35; Horowitz and Hill, *The Art of Electronics*, chapter 4, sections 4.01-4.08; Ian Poole, G3YWX, "An Introduction to Op Amps," *QST*, Feb 1999, pp 55-56. The ARRL Web site for this series is **www.arrl.org/tis/info/html/hands-on-radio/**. Use it!

### Shopping List

You'll need the following components:

• 741 op-amp—The part may be labeled as an LM741CN, MC1741CP1, µA741C, etc. The prefixes and suffixes identify the manufacturer, package style and temperature grade. RadioShack part number 276-007 will fill the bill.

• ¼ W resistors of the following values: 1 kΩ (2 ea), 3.9 kΩ, 10 kΩ (4 ea) and miscellaneous values between 1 kΩ and 10 kΩ.

• 1 kΩ and 10 kΩ potentiometer (single or multi-turn).

• 2—10 µF capacitors with a voltage rating of 25 V dc or more.

### Next Month

Op-amps are frequently used as the engine driving an active filter. Sprinkle on a few capacitors and resistors and next month we'll see just how easy creating an audio filter can be.

# Experiment #4—Active Filters

Amplifiers are great, but where op-amps really prove their worth is in more advanced circuits that are difficult to execute with discrete transistors. A ham's radio shack is full of filters, many of which are based on the op-amp. This month, we'll take a look at two of the simplest filters and one that's a little more complex.

## Terms to Learn

• *Cutoff Frequency*—The frequency, $f_c$, at which the filter output voltage falls to $1/\sqrt{2}$ or 70.7% of its peak output. At this frequency, the power of the output signal has been cut in half.

• *Low, High and Band-Pass Filters*—Low-pass filters attenuate signals with frequencies *above* the cutoff frequency. High-pass filters do the opposite (attenuate *below* cutoff). Band-pass filters pass a range of signal frequencies, but attenuate signals *outside* that range, called the passband.

• *Q*—The ratio of a filter's center frequency to the bandwidth of its passband. Higher-Q means a narrower passband for a given center frequency.

• *Roll-off*—The gradual reduction in signal amplitude beyond a filter's cutoff frequency.

## The Low-Pass Filter

The amplifier circuits we built last month can amplify signals all the way from dc to the limits of the op-amp, more than 1 MHz. But what if we don't want to amplify all those frequencies—perhaps just those in the communication audio range below 3 kHz? That requires an amplifier whose gain changes with frequency, or a low-pass filter.

We'll start with the unity-gain amplifier (refer to Figure 12.15 on the previous page). Remember that the op-amp output must balance the input current ($V_{in}$ / $R_i$) with an equal current through the feedback component, $R_f$. What if $R_f$ was replaced with components whose impedance changed with frequency? Then the op-amp's output voltage would also have to change with frequency to keep the currents balanced.

That's just what is happening in **Figure 12.17**, where capacitor $C_f$ has been placed across $R_f$. The reactance of $C_f$ ($X = 1/2\pi f_c$) gets smaller with frequency. That means the impedance of the feedback path between the op-amp's inverting terminal and output also gets smaller with frequency. The lower impedance means that less output voltage is required to balance the input current and the circuit's output will decrease for high-frequency signals. This is a low-pass filter.

We only want to amplify communications audio, so the

cutoff frequency, $f_c$, should be about 3 kHz. In this circuit, $f_c$ is reached when the impedance in the feedback path (the parallel combination of $R_f$ and $C_f$) is one-half of the input resistance, $R_i$. This occurs when the reactance of $C_f$ equals $R_f$. The design equations for our low-pass filter are:

$$C_f = 1/2\pi f_c R_f \text{ and } f_c = 1/2\pi C_f R_f \qquad [1]$$

Let's try it!

## Testing the Low-Pass Filter

• Design the amplifier to have a passband gain of 1, so $R_f = R_{in}$. Use a value of 10 kΩ. For an $f_c$ of 3 kHz, $C_f = 1/2\pi$ (3 kHz)(10 kΩ) = 5.3 nF. Use the closest standard value of 5.6 nF, which will result in an $f_c$ of 2.8 kHz. (Don't forget the power supply bypass capacitors when building the circuit.)

• Confirm that the filter has unity-gain at dc by using a 1 kΩ potentiometer to apply a variable dc voltage as in the previous experiment. Use a ±12 V power supply across the potentiometer.

• Use the function generator to apply a 1 $V_{p-p}$ sine wave at 10 Hz to the filter input. If you are using a DMM to measure signal voltage, this is 0.35 $V_{RMS}$. Measure the input and output voltage at 10, 20, 50, 100, 200, 500, 1000, 2000 and 5000 Hz.

• Find $f_c$ by varying the signal frequency until output voltage is 0.7 $V_{p-p}$ (or 0.25 $V_{RMS}$). It's unlikely that $f_c$ will be exactly 2.8 kHz because the actual values of $R_f$ and $C_f$ are somewhat different than their labeled values.

• Change the filter's passband gain to 2.2 by increasing $R_f$ to 22 kΩ. Measure the output voltage from 1000 to 5000 Hz. What happened to $f_c$? As $R_f$ increases, the frequency at which the reactance of $C_f$ balances $R_c$ decreases. To restore $f_c$, $C_f$ will have to be decreased by the same amount as $R_f$ increased—to 5.6 nF / 2.2 = 2.5 nF. Replace $C_f$ with the closest standard value of 2.7 nF and see if $f_c$ is back where it belongs.

## High-Pass Filters

You can also make gain "roll off" at low frequencies with components that cause the balancing function of the op-amp to reduce its output voltage below the cutoff frequency as shown in **Figure 12.18**. As frequency decreases, the reactance of Ci increases, reducing input current. Balancing current thus takes less output voltage and the filter's output will decrease along with input frequency. Following similar reasoning, the design equations for the high-pass filter are:

$$C_i = 1/2\pi f_c R_i \text{ and } f_c = 1/2\pi C_i R_i \qquad [2]$$

Gain in the passband is still the same, $-R_f/R_i$.

## Creating a Band-Pass Filter

Continuing with the communications audio theme, it's usually desired to attenuate frequencies below 300 Hz. We can combine high-pass and low-pass functions as in **Figure 12.19**.

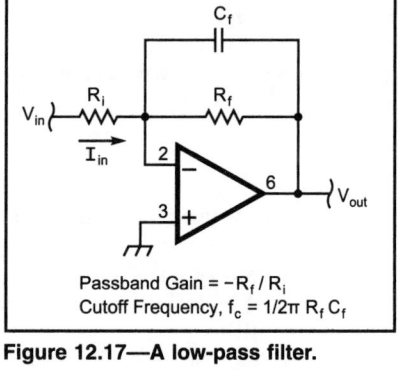

**Figure 12.17—A low-pass filter.**

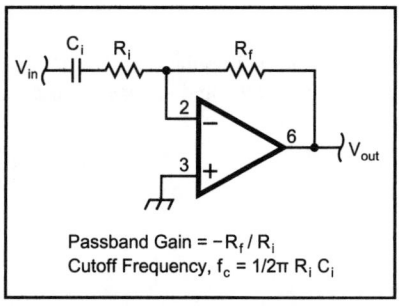

**Figure 12.18—A high-pass filter.**

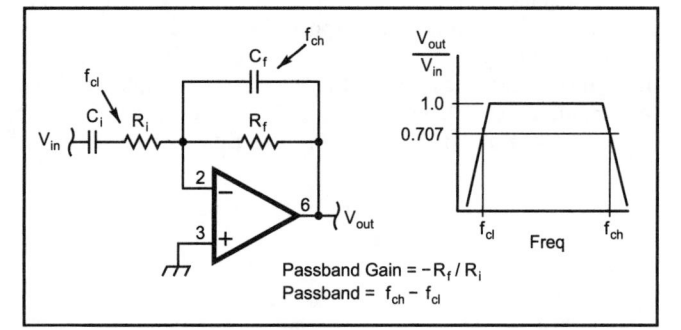

**Figure 12.19—A band-pass filter.**

This circuit has a cutoff frequency, $f_{cl}$ and $f_{ch}$, at each end of the passband. We already have $f_{ch}$ from our low-pass filter. For an $f_{cl}$ of 300 Hz:

$$C_l = \frac{1}{2\pi(300\ Hz)(10\ k\Omega)} = 53\ nF$$

We'll use the closest standard value of 56 nF. Let's build it!

## Testing Band-Pass Filter #1

• Restore the low-pass filter circuit to its original configuration with two 10 kΩ resistors. Add the 56 nF capacitor in series with $R_{in}$.

• Measure input and output voltage between 10 and 5000 Hz. Determine the lower cutoff frequency as before.

## A Better Band-Pass Filter

More advanced designs have a much steeper rolloff above and below the cutoff frequencies. The passband can be narrowed, amplification can be combined with filtering functions. There are a number of filter types that achieve these goals.

Band-pass filters have two additional parameters that define how the filter affects the input signals. The first is the filter's frequency of peak response, also called the "center frequency," and abbreviated $f_o$. The second is a measure, called "Q" of the filter's passband relative to $f_o$. (The symbol Q is also used in other related measurements, but it only refers to the shape of the filter passband here.)

$$Q = f_o / (f_{ch} - f_{cl}) \qquad [3]$$

Higher values of Q mean that the filter's response is getting narrower or sharper. The quantity $f_{ch} - f_{cl}$ is the filter's bandwidth.

**Figure 12.20** shows a "multiple feedback" band-pass filter, so-called because there are two feedback paths from the output through $R_f$ and $C_f$. Although there are many methods of designing this circuit, we'll use the "Equal-C" method in which both $C_i$ and $C_f$ are given equal values. After $f_o$ and Q are chosen, the resistor values are then calculated. The filter's gain is equal to $-2Q^2$. The circuit values shown set $f_o$ to 500 Hz, Q to 2.3, and gain to −10.4.

## Testing Band-Pass Filter #2

• Build the circuit and find $f_o$, $f_{ch}$ and $f_{cl}$ by measuring the input and output voltage of sine waves at frequencies from 50 to 5000 Hz. Calculate the filter's peak gain ($V_{out}/V_{in}$), bandwidth ($f_{ch} - f_{cl}$) and Q.

• Most filter responses are measured in decibels, or dB. Gain in dB = 20 log ($V_{out}/V_{in}$). Recalculate gain in dB. Gain at the upper and lower cutoff frequencies should be close to 3 dB below the gain of the filter at $f_o$.

• To change $f_o$, increase or decrease both capacitors, keeping their values the same. To increase $f_o$, decrease capacitance, and vice versa. $f_o$ is directly proportional to the value of the capacitors.

## Listening to Your Filters

All this measuring is fine, but it's more fun to actually use your circuits for a practical purpose. **Figure 12.21** shows how to route your rig's received audio through the filter circuit so that you can hear the effect of the filter using headphones from a portable music player. Set your rig to use its widest filter (usually "AM") and then listen to the filter output. The op-

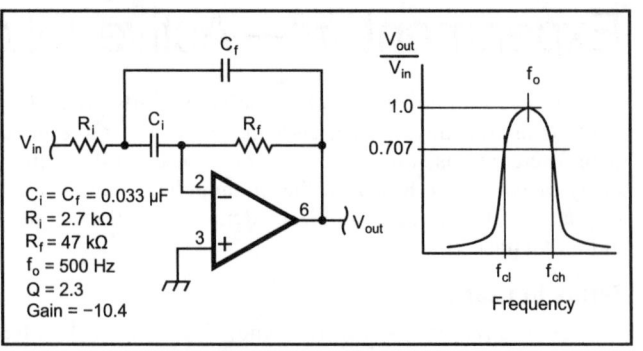

Figure 12.20—A multiple-feedback band-pass filter.

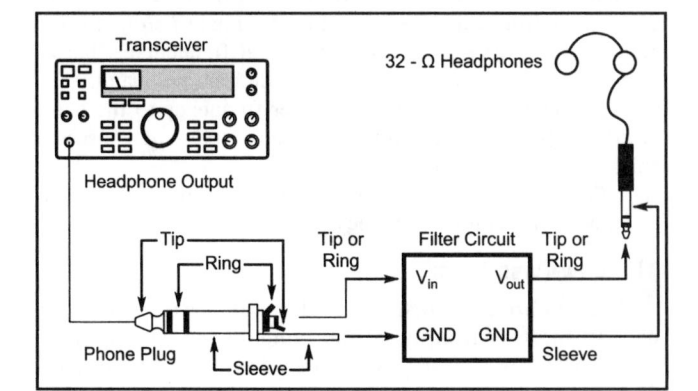

Figure 12.21—Listening to your filter circuit.

amp can't drive a very big load, so keep the audio output level low to avoid distortion.

## Suggested Reading

*The 2003 ARRL Handbook*, pp 16.1-16.2, 16.28-16.29; Horowitz and Hill, *The Art of Electronics*, chapter 5, sections 5.01-5.05. One of the best books for hobbyists on active filters is Don Lancaster's *Active Filter Cookbook*.

The ARRL Web site for this series is **www.arrl.org/tis/info/html/hands-on-radio/**.

## Shopping List

• 741 op-amp
• ¼-W resistors of the following values: 2.2 kΩ, 10 kΩ (2 ea), 22 kΩ, 47 kΩ
• 1 kΩ potentiometer (single or multi-turn)
• 56 nF, 33 nF (2 ea), 5.6 nF, and 2.7 nF film or ceramic capacitors (1 nF = 1000 pF = 0.001 μF)
• 2—10 μF capacitors with a voltage rating of 25 V dc or higher

## Next Month

Next month, we'll take a look at the popular "555" timer and use it as an oscillator, a pulse generator and maybe even as a timer!

# Experiment #5—The Integrated Timer

## Background

Timer circuits based on the 555 chip and its many relatives are found everywhere. Although not complex, it can be used to create many different circuits. This month we'll take a look at two popular applications of the legendary 555.

## Terms to Learn

• *Astable*—not stable; a circuit that cannot stay in one state.
• *Comparator*—a circuit whose output is indicative of the greater of two of its inputs.
• *Flip-flop*—a digital circuit that "flips" or "toggles" between two states.
• *Monostable*—stable in one state, these circuits stay there until perturbed, then attempt to return to the stable state.

## The Integrated Circuit Timer

The 555 integrated circuit timer has proved to be incredibly popular. Inexpensive and versatile, the 555 is used in myriads of circuits. What's inside that makes it so useful?

**Figure 12.22** shows the basic components of a 555. While it is the most complex circuit we've looked at so far, the 555 is easy to break into bite-size pieces. Let's start with the three resistors labeled "R" at the top left of Figure 12.22. Connected between power input ($V_{cc}$) and ground, they form a *voltage divider* that divides $V_{cc}$ into two equal steps—one at $\frac{2}{3} V_{cc}$ and one at $\frac{1}{3} V_{cc}$. These serve as reference voltages.

Connected to the reference voltages are blocks labeled *trigger comparator* and *threshold comparator*. A *comparator* is nothing more than a circuit whose output indicates which of its two inputs is greater. If the + input is greater, the output is *high*. If the − input is greater, the output is at ground or *low*.

The trigger comparator in the 555 is wired so that its output is *high* whenever the trigger input is *less* than $\frac{1}{3} V_{cc}$ and vice versa. Similarly, the threshold comparator output is *high* whenever the threshold input is *greater* than $\frac{2}{3} V_{cc}$. These two outputs control a circuit called a *flip-flop*.

The flip-flop output, *Q,* changes to *high* or *low* when the state of its *set* and *reset* input changes. The Q output stays *high* or *low* (it *latches* or *toggles*) until the opposite input

changes. When the set input changes from *low* to *high*, Q goes *low*. When reset changes from *low* to *high*, Q goes *high*. The flip-flop ignores any other changes. An inverter makes the 555 output *high* when Q is *low* and vice versa—this makes the timer circuit easier to interface with external circuits.

The transistor connected to Q acts as a *switch*. When Q is *high*, the transistor is *on* and acts as a closed switch connected to ground. When Q is *low*, the transistor is *off* and the switch is open. These simple building blocks—*voltage divider*, *comparator*, *flip-flop* and *switch*—allow us to build a surprising number of useful circuits.

## The Monostable or "One-Shot" Multivibrator

The simplest 555 circuit is the *monostable* circuit. This configuration will output one fixed-length pulse when triggered by an input pulse. **Figure 12.23** shows the connections for this circuit. How does it work?

Starting with capacitor C discharged, the flip-flop output, Q, is *high*, which keeps the discharge transistor turned on and the voltage across C below $\frac{2}{3} V_{cc}$. The circuit is in its stable state, waiting for a trigger pulse.

When the voltage at the trigger input drops below $\frac{1}{3} V_{cc}$, the trigger comparator output changes from *low* to *high*, which causes Q to toggle to the *low* state. This turns *off* the transistor (opens the switch) and allows C to begin charging toward $V_{cc}$.

When C reaches $\frac{2}{3} V_{cc}$, the threshold comparator switches its output from *low* to *high* and that resets the flip-flop. Q returns *high*, turning *on* the transistor and discharging C. The circuit has returned to its stable state. The output pulse length is:

$$T = 1.1 \, RC \qquad [1]$$

Notice that $V_{cc}$ doesn't really matter in the timing—the output pulse width is the same with a 5 V supply as it is with a 15 V supply. This is because the 555 design is based on ratios and not absolute voltage levels.

## Testing the Monostable Multivibrator

• Use the wiring diagram of Figure 12.23. Let's aim for a 1 second output pulse, which requires RC = 1/1.1 = 0.91. If

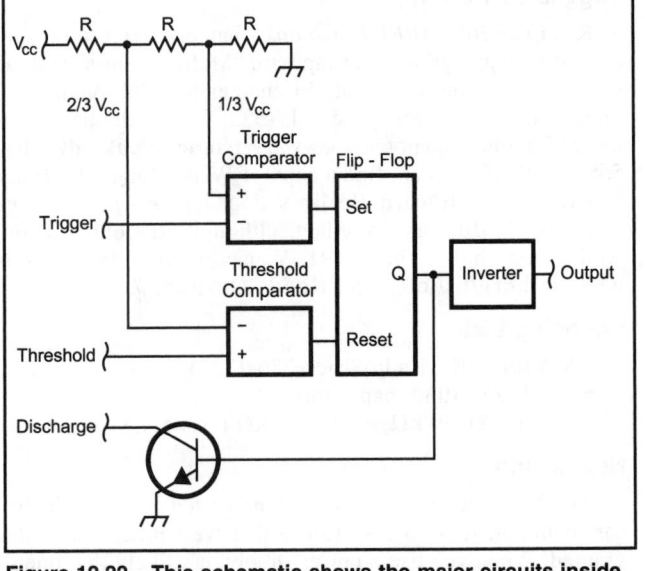

Figure 12.22—This schematic shows the major circuits inside the 555 timer.

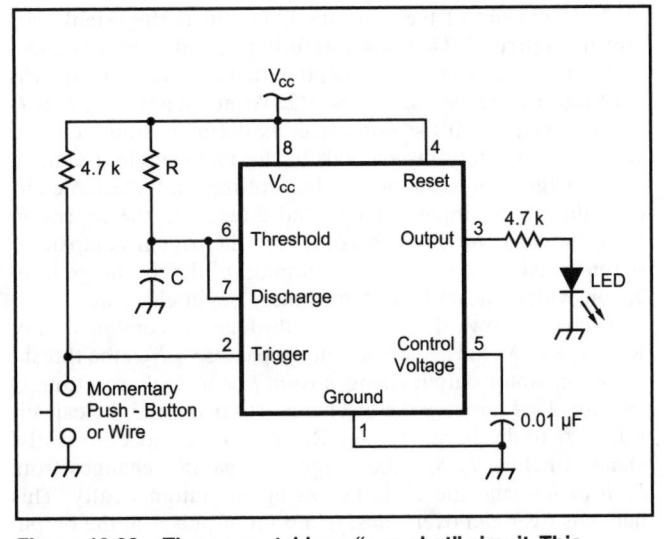

Figure 12.23—The monostable or "one-shot" circuit. This circuit generates a single pulse when the trigger input is shorted to ground. An LED is used to indicate whether the output is high or low.

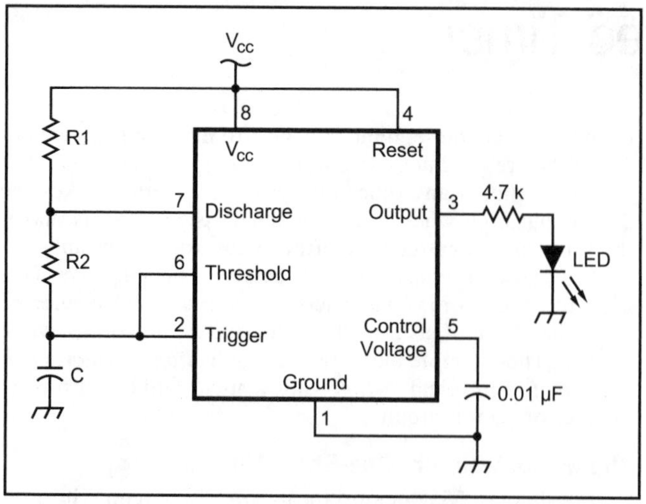

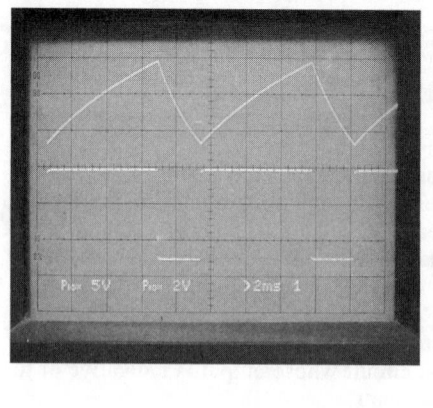

Figure 12.24—The astable or "free-running" circuit. This circuit generates a continuous train of output pulses.

Figure 12.25—A photo of the oscilloscope showing the capacitor and output voltages for the astable circuit with a 0.1 μF timing capacitor for a 100 Hz oscillation frequency. The top trace shows capacitor voltage and the bottom trace the 555 output. Capacitor charging and discharging can be seen clearly.

we choose C = 10 μF, then R = 91 kΩ.

• Connect a 4.7 kΩ resistor between $V_{cc}$ and pin 2. The symbol at pin 2 indicates a jumper to ground—you can use a switch or a piece of wire to temporarily ground pin 2, supplying the trigger pulse.

• The 4.7 kΩ resistor and LED at the output will give a visual indication when the output is *high*.

• The 0.01 μF capacitor at pin 5 filters out any noise that might cause changes in the threshold comparator reference voltage. Pin 4 resets the flip-flop that drives the output and it can be used to prematurely force the output low, regardless of the output state. It should be connected to $V_{cc}$ when not used, to prevent resets from noise. The power supply voltage can be any positive voltage between 4.5 and 18 V.

• With your circuit ready to go, press the switch (or insert the jumper for a brief instant) and watch the output LED light up. It should be on for about 1 second and then turn off until you retrigger the circuit.

• Change either R or C, recalculate the expected output pulse length, and give it a try. R can be a potentiometer, as well, for adjustable pulse length.

## The Astable Multivibrator

The opposite of the monostable circuit is the astable circuit in **Figure 12.24**. Look carefully at the different connections of pins 2, 6 and 7. Notice, too, that the timing resistor is split into two resistors, R1 and R2. What's happening here?

Let's start from the same state as the monostable circuit, with C completely discharged. In the monostable circuit, it took a trigger signal to get the ball rolling. In the astable circuit, the trigger input is connected directly to the capacitor, so if the capacitor is discharged, then the trigger comparator output must be *high*. Q is *low*, turning *off* the discharge transistor, which allows C to immediately begin charging.

C charges toward $V_{cc}$, but now through the combination of R1 and R2. As the capacitor voltage passes $^2/_3$ $V_{cc}$, the threshold comparator output changes from *low* to *high*, resetting Q to *high*. This turns *on* the discharge transistor and the capacitor starts to discharge through R2. When the capacitor is discharged below $^1/_3$ $V_{cc}$, the trigger comparator changes from *high* to *low* and the cycle begins again, automatically. This happens over and over, causing a train of pulses at the output while C charges and discharges between $^1/_3$ and $^2/_3$ $V_{cc}$ as shown in Figure 12.24.

The design equations are a little more complex for this cir-

cuit. The total time it takes for one complete cycle is the charge time, $T_c$, plus the discharge time, $T_d$:

$$T = T_c + T_d = 0.693 (R_1 + R_2) C + 0.693 R_2C$$
$$= 0.693 (R_1 + 2R_2) C \qquad [2]$$

and the output frequency is:

$$f = 1/T = 1.443 / [(R_1 + 2R_2) C] \qquad [3]$$

Let's try it out!

## Testing the Astable Multivibrator

• Split the original 91 kΩ resistor into a 62 kΩ for R1 and 39 kΩ for R2. Use the same 10 μF capacitor for C. The total cycle time should be close to 1 second. If you have a stopwatch, count 10 or more cycles and average for a good cycle time measurement.

• You may have noted that the LED is not on and off for equal periods—it's on longer than it is off. This is because the capacitor has to both charge and discharge through $R_2$. The ratio of on-time to off-time is called the *duty cycle* and is calculated as:

$$\text{duty cycle} = (R_1 + R_2) / (R_1 + 2R_2) \qquad [4]$$

• Experiment with different combinations of R1 and R2 to observe the effect of their ratio on duty cycle. (Keep R1 greater than 1 kΩ to avoid overloading the discharge transistor.) If you have an oscilloscope, watch the capacitor voltage on one channel and the output voltage on the other. **Figure 12.25** shows an example.

## Suggested Reading

Read *The 2003 ARRL Handbook*, chapter 7, page 7.14, specifically the paragraphs starting with "Multivibrators" and the section "RC Time Constant" in chapter 6. Additionally, see *The Art of Electronics*, pages 517-522. One of the better on-line 555 application notes is **www.doctronics.co.uk/pdf_files/555an.pdf**. If you can, find a copy of Walter Jung's *IC Timer Cookbook* or Howard Berlin's *555 Timer Applications Sourcebook*. Both are excellent, although now out of print. And, remember... the ARRL Web site for this series is **www.arrl.org/tis/info/html/Hands-On-Radio/**.

## Shopping List

• 555 timer IC (RadioShack 276-1723).
• 10 μF and 10 nF capacitors.
• 4.7 kΩ (2), 39 kΩ, 62 kΩ, 91 kΩ resistors, ¼ W.

## Next Month

Another popular well-designed integrated device is the linear regulator. It is so easy to use that we tend to take it for granted. When you use a power supply, it's likely that one of these is integral to its design. See you next month!

# Experiment #6—Rectifiers and Zener References

## Background

This month begins a three-part series of experiments on power supply circuits. We'll start with a basic rectifier and a Zener diode voltage reference. In the second step we'll experiment with some voltage multipliers. Finally, we'll design a linear voltage regulator.

## Terms to Learn

- *Anode*—diode electrode into which current flows.[1]
- *Cathode*—diode electrode out of which current flows.
- *Half-wave or Full-wave*—rectification during one-half of or an entire ac cycle, respectively.
- *Peak Inverse or Reverse Voltage (PIV or PRV)*—the maximum voltage from cathode to anode a diode can safely withstand.
- *Avalanche Breakdown / Conduction*—current flow from cathode to anode when a diode's PIV or Zener voltage is exceeded.

## The Basic Rectifier

The term *rectifier* can refer to either a semiconductor device (a diode) or to a circuit. Both convert alternating current (ac) into direct current (dc). The diode performs no other function besides controlling current flow, while the rectifier circuit may include several other functions. For this experiment, the term *rectifier* will refer to the circuit.

For a diode to be used in a power rectifier, we need to know two basic things about it: its PIV and its average forward current ratings. Diodes convert ac to dc by preventing current flow from cathode to anode. If ac is applied to a diode, current will flow only during the half-cycle in which the voltage from anode to cathode is positive.

During the non-conducting half-cycle, the diode blocks current flow as long as the voltage from cathode to anode does

not exceed the PIV rating. At higher voltages, the diode will begin to conduct in its reverse mode and may suffer damage.

The diode's average current rating specifies how much power the diode can dissipate while conducting current without overheating. When conducting, a regular P-N silicon diode will have about 0.7 V *forward voltage drop* from anode to cathode[2] and will dissipate a power of $(0.7 \text{ V} \times I_{avg})$ W.

Now let's go on to the rectifier. **Figure 12.26** shows three types of diode-based rectifier circuits—a half-wave, a full-wave center-tapped and a full-wave bridge. In our experiments, we'll use a function generator as an ac signal source, but the principles are the same for a transformer in a real power supply. We'll use 1 kHz (1000 Hz) as our ac frequency (because it's convenient and the filter components are smaller)—a transformer in a real power supply will usually be operating at the ac power line frequency of 60 Hz (as commonly used in the Western Hemisphere). Resistor $R_L$ is the load.

The half-wave rectifier with its single diode can only supply current to the load during one-half of each applied ac cycle—thus the term *half-wave*. The full-wave center-tapped requires two out-of-phase voltage sources with a common center connection, such as a transformer's center-tapped secondary winding. Each source supplies current to the load on opposite half-cycles—thus the term *full-wave*—and doubling the output voltage.

The full-wave bridge achieves full-wave rectification by using an extra pair of diodes. On the first half-cycle, the full-wave bridge conducts through D1 and D3. On the next half-cycle, D1 and D3 are *reverse-biased* and don't conduct current, while D2 and D4 are *forward-biased* and supply current to the load.

## Testing the Half-Wave Rectifier

- Because function generator outputs usually have a ground-referenced output, we will only test the half-wave rec-

---

**Table 12.1**

**Important Characteristics of Rectifier Circuits ($V_{in}$ is the input RMS voltage and $I_{avg}$ is the average load current)**

| Rectifier Type | Number of Diodes | Average Output Voltage | Power Loss | Diode PIV Required |
|---|---|---|---|---|
| Half-Wave | 1 | $0.45 \ V_{in}$ | $0.7 \times I_{avg}$ | $2.8 \ V_{in}$ |
| Full-Wave, Center-Tap | 2 | $0.9 \ V_{in}$ | $0.7 \times I_{avg}$ | $2.8 \ V_{in}$ |
| Full-Wave Bridge | 4 | $0.9 \ V_{in}$ | $2 \times 0.7 \times I_{avg}$ | $1.4 \ V_{in}$ |

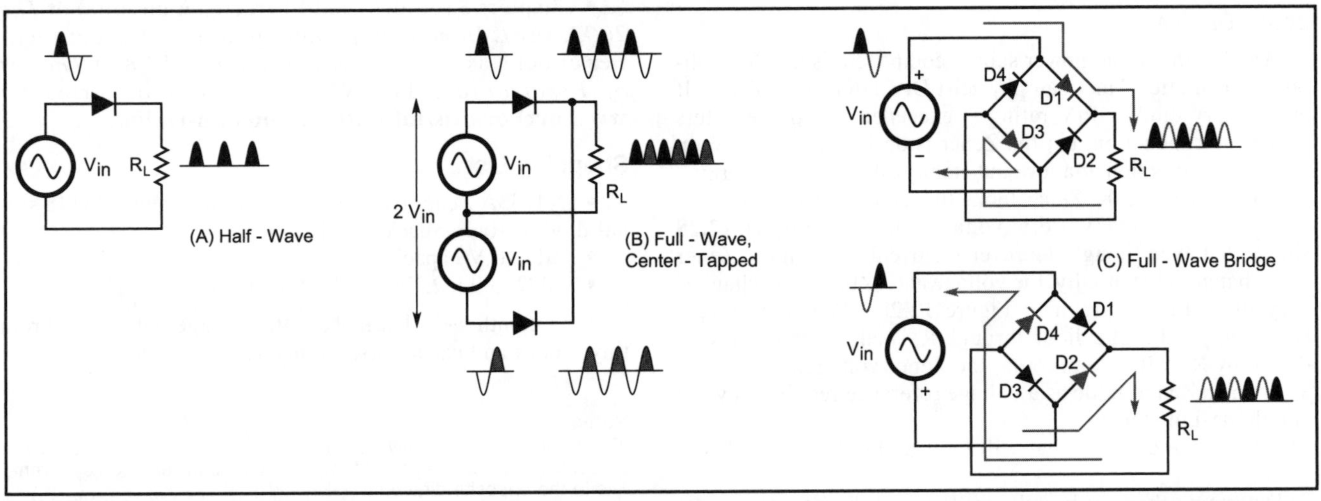

---

Figure 12.26—The three diode-based rectifier circuits: (a) the half-wave, (b) the full-wave, center-tap, and (c) the full-wave bridge. Table 12.1 shows some important characteristics of each circuit.

Figure 12.27—The bottom trace in this photo-graph shows the sine wave input from the signal generator. The upper trace shows the voltage across the load with a 1 µF capacitor. Note that the charging peaks in the upper trace correspond to the positive peaks of the input voltage.

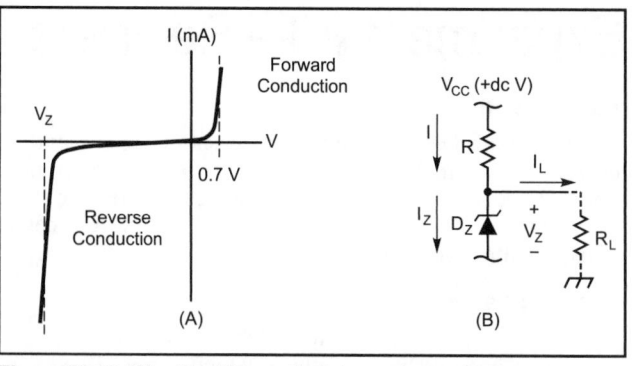

Figure 12.28 (A)—The Zener diode's current-voltage characteristics. Current from anode to cathode is considered to be positive or forward current and voltage from anode to cathode is positive. (B)—A common circuit for making a voltage reference with a Zener diode.

tifier. Build the half-wave circuit of Figure 1a using a 1N4148 diode and a 3.9 kΩ load resistor.

• Set the function generator to output a sine wave of 5 V$_{peak}$ (3.5 V$_{rms}$ on the DMM's ac scale) at 1 kHz. The DMM will show about 1.3 V dc across the load resistor. An oscilloscope will show the load voltage pulsing on every positive half-cycle of the input sine wave. Note that the diode doesn't conduct for exactly one-half cycle because of the 0.7 V forward drop.

• Connect a 1 µF capacitor with at least a 10 V rating in parallel with the resistor. The DMM will show a load voltage of about 3.6 V dc because the capacitor stores energy during the non-conducting half-cycles. The 'scope will show the load voltage as a series of short ramps (as the capacitor charges through the diode) followed by long ramps (as the capacitor discharges through the resistor). This can be seen in **Figure 12.27**.

• Experiment by trying different input voltages, load resistors, and capacitors. Try different input waveforms—square and triangle waves, for example. Observe the shape of the charging ramp as you try different waveforms. If you have a function generator with a ground-independent (or *floating*) output, try building the full-wave bridge rectifier.

### Rectifier Characteristics

Why would one select a particular rectifier circuit over another? There are certain differences, or *trade-offs*, in the characteristics of each that make them suitable in various circumstances, as shown in **Table 12.1**.

The full-wave bridge, because it has two diodes in the current path, is dissipating twice the power of the half-wave and full-wave center-tapped rectifiers. The benefit of the full-wave bridge is that each diode needs only one-half the PIV rating of a full-wave, center-tapped circuit. The other two circuits have fewer diodes and less power dissipation, but they require higher diode PIV ratings.

### Zener Diodes

Another important power supply component is the Zener diode, named after American physicist Dr Clarence M. Zener. If an ordinary diode's PIV rating is exceeded, the diode enters avalanche conduction, but the Zener is designed to conduct in the reverse direction at a low, but stable voltage. In the normal, forward direction, the Zener looks like an ordinary diode.

The Zener is a very useful voltage reference. **Figure 12.28** shows that even though the reverse current through the Zener may change substantially, the voltage across the diode changes very little. In the circuit of Figure 12.28, if enough current (I$_z$) is supplied to the diode through R, small amounts may be drawn by R$_L$ without affecting the Zener voltage.

Using a Zener diode as a voltage reference requires several simple design steps:

1) Add up the currents that will be used by the load—this is I$_L$.
2) Determine the supply voltage, V$_{cc}$, and the Zener's power rating, P$_z$.

3) Select a current I$_z$ so that P$_z$ = V$_z$ × I$_z$ is, at most, less than one-half of the Zener's rated power—this is for safety and to keep the Zener voltage from changing with temperature.
4) Find I by adding I$_L$ and I$_z$. Use Ohm's Law to find R.
R = (minimum V$_{cc}$ – V$_z$) / I

By using this procedure, R is set so that even at the minimum value of supply voltage, there is enough current to supply the Zener and the loading circuitry. Give it a try!

### Testing a Voltage Reference

• Use a 12 V supply voltage (V$_{cc}$ minimum is 12 V) and a 5.1 V 1N4733A 1 W Zener diode. (The letter following the Zener type number usually refers to the Zener's voltage tolerance, "A" being ±10%, "B" being ±5% and no following letter being ±20%.) Assume that the circuitry loading the voltage will draw 1 mA.

• Follow the design procedure, limiting the Zener's power dissipation to 100 mW.

5.1 V × I$_z$ = 100 mW, so I$_z$ = 19.6 mA. Now, I = 19.6 + 1 mA = 20.6 mA and R = (12 – 5.1 V) / 20.6 mA = 335 Ω; use a 330 Ω resistor.

For the load, use a 5.1 kΩ resistor connected from the Zener's cathode to ground.

• Connect the components as in Figure 12.28B and verify the Zener voltage is close to 5.1 V. Vary the supply voltage up and down while watching the Zener voltage on a DMM—it should remain stable until V$_{cc}$ falls below V$_z$ + (I × R).

### Suggested Reading

• Chapters 8 (diodes) and 11 (rectifier circuits) of *The 2003 ARRL Handbook* go into great detail about rectifier circuits as do sections 1.25 through 1.28 of *The Art of Electronics*. The Web site for our series is: **www.arrl.org/tis/info/html/hands-on-radio/**.

### Shopping List

• 1N4733A Zener (RadioShack 276-565) and 1N4148 signal diodes (RadioShack 276-1122)
• 1 µF, 16 V capacitor
• 330 Ω, 3.9 kΩ, 5.1 kΩ ¼ W resistors

Next month we'll learn about the voltage multiplier. From tiny diodes and capacitors, mighty voltages come!

**Notes**
[1]Electronics texts typically use "conventional current" or the flow of positive charge. The actual flow of electrons or "electronic current," is in the opposite direction.
[2]Other types of diodes, such as PIN, Schottky, or those made from germanium have different forward voltage drops when conducting.

# Experiment #7—Voltage Multipliers

## Background

This is the second of a three-part series of experiments on power supply circuits. Last month we studied the rectifier. This month we take the rectifier one step further to create output voltages higher than that of the power source...even of the opposite polarity!

## Terms to Learn

• *Commutation*—periodic switching that is synchronized to a clock signal or a time reference

• *Floating*—a voltage source is floating if neither of its output connections are connected to ground

• *Ripple*—the regular (ac) variation of rectifier output voltage at the frequency at which the output capacitor (filter) is charged

• *Surge Current*—the large inrush of current into discharged capacitors when voltage is first applied

• *Voltage Regulation*—the change in output voltage with load current (usually expressed as a percentage change in voltage for a given change in output current)

## The Voltage Multiplier

There are many instances where an ac power source is available but a dc voltage is needed by a circuit that can't be obtained by using a simple rectifier. Sometimes, a circuit just needs a "dab" of higher voltage...and it's not worth the expense of using a higher-voltage transformer or adding another secondary winding to get it. For other applications, such as high-voltage supplies for amplifiers or other tube circuits, a full-voltage transformer may be too expensive (or too difficult to insulate for the high voltage needed). Voltage multiplier circuits are used to address both situations.

In the full-wave rectifiers of the previous experiment, we saw how diodes are used to route charging current into a storage capacitor. The diodes effectively double the frequency at which the capacitor can be charged. The doubling of the charge frequency also doubles the amount of current a rectifier can supply for a given voltage variation or ripple.

What if, instead of doubling the output current, there was a way to use the same diodes to double the output voltage? By arranging the diodes and capacitors properly, we can create a "bucket brigade" effect where the voltages of the capacitors can be added together.

**Figure 12.29A** shows the simplest voltage multiplier—a half-wave doubler—supplied from a source with an RMS voltage of $V_{RMS}$ and whose peak voltage is 1.4 $V_{RMS}$. Starting with both capacitors discharged, a negative half-cycle from the voltage source charges C1 to 1.4 $V_{RMS}$ through D1, as shown in Figure 12.29B. On the following half-cycle, in Figure 12.29C, the output capacitor C2 is charged through D2 but, like an acrobat springing onto another's shoulders, the voltage of C1 adds to the source voltage and C2 is charged to 2.8 $V_{RMS}$. Because one diode is always in the current path, the actual output voltage is less by one diode's forward voltage drop, $V_f$, of 0.7 V.

The half-wave doubler only charges the output capacitor once every other half-cycle, limiting the amount of current that can be drawn from the supply. Each diode and capacitor in the half-wave doubler must be rated to handle the full output voltage. These limitations can be a problem at high output voltages.

To increase the amount of output current and reduce the necessary ratings of individual components, the diodes and capacitors can be rearranged as shown in the full-wave doubler circuit of **Figure 12.30**. For the half-wave doubler, one side of the voltage source may be grounded, but for the full-wave doubler, the source must be floating.

Figure 12.30A shows the customary way of drawing the full-wave doubler circuit on a schematic, where the voltage

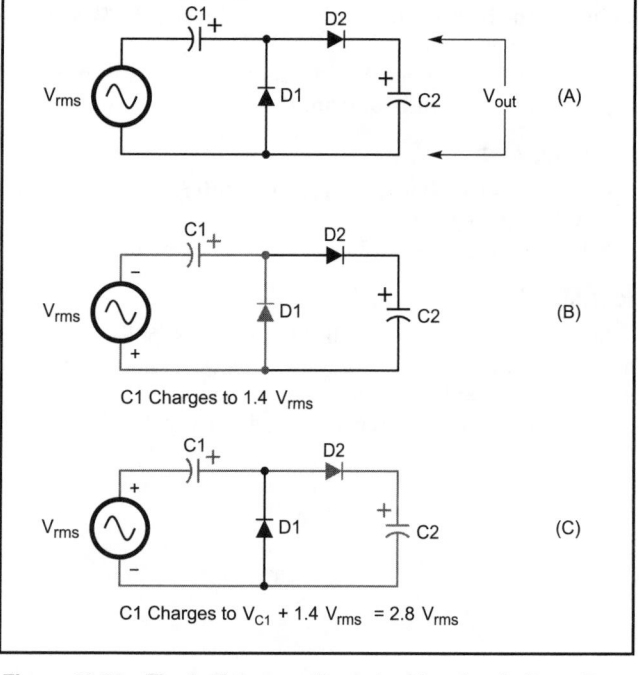

Figure 12.29—The half-wave voltage doubler circuit. Parts B and C show how the capacitors charge on alternating half-cycles. The voltages of C1 and C2 are added together as C2 is charged.

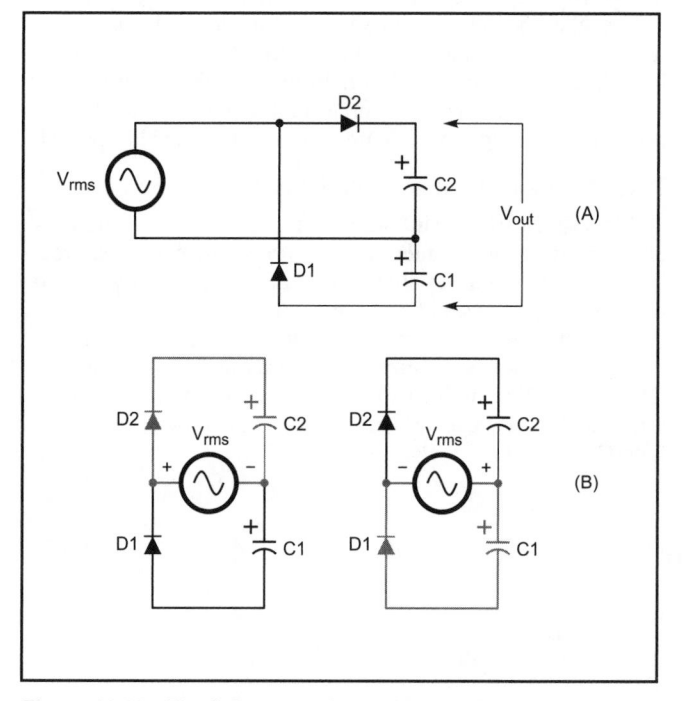

Figure 12.30—The full-wave voltage doubler. Part A shows the usual schematic for the circuit. Part B redraws the circuit for clarity and illustrates how the capacitors charge on alternate half-cycles.

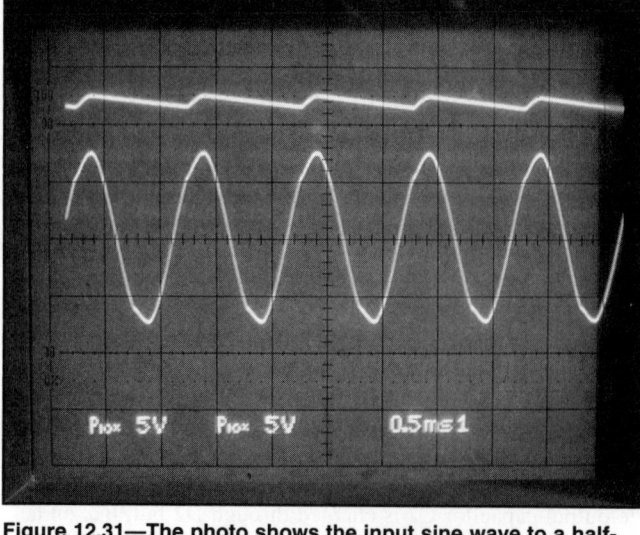

Figure 12.31—The photo shows the input sine wave to a half-wave voltage doubler and the output waveform across C2. Note that capacitor C2 is charged once every other half-cycle. Ground potential for both channels is at the center of the sine wave.

source is usually a transformer secondary winding. However, it's a little easier to understand when redrawn as in Figure 2B. On alternate half-cycles, the source charges each capacitor to its peak voltage, 1.4 $V_{RMS}$. The output voltage is developed across C1 and C2 in series. This also means that the value of output capacitance that supplies current to the load is less than C1 or C2 by the equation:

$$C_{output} = (C1 \times C2) / (C1+C2)$$

In addition, one diode drop is subtracted from the charging voltage of each capacitor, so the actual output voltage will be 2.8 $V_{RMS}$ − [2×0.7 V].

Note that when using these voltage multiplier circuits for powering actual equipment at higher power, it is necessary to limit the surge current into the capacitors when the supply is first powered up. The discharged capacitors look like short circuits to the transformer secondary and diodes and can blow a fuse or damage components on those first few cycles of charging. That is why, in *The ARRL Handbook*, the discussion of voltage multipliers includes surge-limiting resistors. In our experiments, the surge currents are quite small and can be ignored.

### Testing a Pair of Voltage Multipliers

Let's start with the half-wave doubler. As with last month's experiment, use your function generator as the voltage source. Construct the circuit as shown in Figure 12.29 taking care to observe the polarities of the capacitors.

• Set the function generator to output a 1 kHz sine wave at 5 $V_{RMS}$. Use your voltmeter to measure the dc voltage across C1 and C2. With no load to drain charge from either capacitor, you should measure nearly 2.8 × 5 V = 14 V dc across both C1 and C2.

• Connect a 10 kΩ load resistor across C2 and re-measure the capacitor voltages. You will see the voltage across C1 drop to just below 1.4 × 5 V = 7 V dc while the voltage across C2 stays about one diode forward voltage drop (0.7 V) below 14 V dc. If you are using an oscilloscope you should see waveforms like those of **Figure 12.31**.

• You can experiment with the doubler by varying the load resistance or capacitance values. Less load resistance (a heavier load) or less capacitance will drop the output voltage dramatically as C2 is discharged more during each half-cycle. Vary the frequency of the source. Raising the source frequency also charges the capacitors more frequently, so for a given load resistance, this will increase output voltage.

• Make a voltage inverter by switching the polarity of the diodes and capacitors.

• Construct a full-wave doubler, as in Figure 12.30, using the same diodes and capacitors as for the half-wave doubler. You won't be able to use the oscilloscope unless the function generator output is floating, so rely on your voltmeter.

• With no load resistor connected, the output voltage will be close to 14 V dc, but with the 10 kΩ load, the output voltage will be lower than for the half-wave doubler because the effective output capacitance is less—C1 in series with C2—and there is an extra diode forward voltage drop. However, the *voltage regulation* of the full-wave doubler is better than the half-wave circuit because the output capacitors are charged more frequently, doubling the ripple frequency.

• If you add a 1 µF capacitor in parallel with both C1 and C2, the output voltage should increase.

It should be obvious from your experiments that the voltage regulation of these voltage multiplier circuits is not outstanding. They should not be used where large variations in load current are to be expected. They are useful circuits, however, and can be used effectively where load currents are low and where "stiff" voltage regulation is not important.

### Suggested Reading

• Chapter 11 (rectifier circuits) of *The 2003 ARRL Handbook* has an excellent section on voltage multipliers, including triplers and quadruplers. A set of graphs is provided to aid in figuring how much capacitance is needed for given loads with a 60 Hz ac supply.

• And don't forget our Web site for this series is **www.arrl.org/tis/info/html/hands-on-radio/**.

### Shopping List

• 2—1N4148 diodes (any silicon rectifier will do)
• 10 kΩ, ¼ W resistor
• 4—1 µF and 2—10 µF capacitors, 25 V dc or higher

### Next Month

So what do you do with all these power supplies? To get the best results from most circuits, it's necessary to power them with a smooth, constant voltage. Next month, we'll design and build a voltage regulator to do just that.

# Experiment #8—The Linear Regulator

Voltage regulators provide stable power for sensitive electronic circuits. In our final power supply experiment, we combine our experience with transistor amplifiers, op-amps and Zener diodes into a linear voltage regulator.

## Terms to Learn

- *Linear*—a circuit in which the current and voltage can take on any value within a continuous range
- *Regulate*—to control a voltage or current such that it matches an established level
- *Setpoint*—the desired level at which the regulator output is to be maintained
- *Pass transistor*—the transistor in a regulator circuit through which current flows to the output circuit

## The Linear Regulator

**Figure 12.32A** shows the block diagram of a *pass-type* voltage regulator. The *control element* is the decision-maker. It compares the output with its *setpoint* and varies the *control signal* to the *pass element* so that the output matches the setpoint. A simple example is squirting water from a hose with your thumb. The setpoint is where your eyes tell you the water is supposed to go. Your thumb is the pass element and your brain is the control element, constantly monitoring where your eyes say the water is actually going.

The control element in a linear regulator is a high-gain amplifier with one input connected to the setpoint and the other to the output. Any imbalance results in a strong response at the amplifier's output that causes the pass element to restore the output to the expected value. In our experiment, the control element will be an op-amp with the setpoint provided by a Zener diode. Figure 12.32B shows the complete circuit.

We can break this circuit down into three familiar parts—a Zener diode reference, an amplifier and an op-amp. The Zener diode that supplies the setpoint is the same one that we used in experiment #6 with an extra 0.1 µF capacitor to filter high-frequency noise. The pass transistor circuit is just an emitter-follower (EF) amplifier (Experiment #2) turned on its side! The EF's input is the control signal and its output is the load current. It is the job of the op-amp to supply enough base current ($I_b$) to the pass transistor so that its emitter current ($I_e$) can drive the load to the desired voltage, balancing the output and setpoint voltages at its inputs.

## Testing the Linear Regulator

- The object is to design a fixed-voltage regulator that supplies 10 mA to a 470 Ω load at 5.1 V dc.
- Using Experiment #6's Zener (1N4733A) circuit and assuming that the load current going into the op-amp is very small, we can use the same 330 Ω resistor for $R_z$ to supply current to $D_z$, which then supplies a 5.1 V dc setpoint.
- How much base current is needed for the transistor to drive the load?

$$I_e = I_b (\beta+1), \text{ so } I_b = I_e / (\beta+1) \qquad [Eq\ 1]$$

The 2N4401 transistor's data sheet shows that its minimum dc current gain ($\beta$ or $h_{FE}$) is 80 for an emitter current of 10 mA. That means $I_b$ must be 125 µA or more to drive the transistor hard enough to allow $I_e$ to reach 10 mA. This is well within the op-amp's capability.

- Take particular care to connect the op-amp's inverting (–) and noninverting (+) terminals correctly.
- Supply 12 V dc to the regulator's input—the Zener diode and output voltages should be almost identical and close to 5.1 V dc. The output of the op-amp should be about 0.7 V greater than the load voltage. How much power is the transistor dissipating?

$$P = I_e \times (V_{in} - V_{load}) \text{ and } I_e = V_{load} / 470\ \Omega$$

- Vary the input voltage up and down by 3 V. What is the effect on load voltage? How low can the input go before the output voltage drops?

## Variable Regulators

In many cases a variable output voltage is needed. **Figure 12.33** shows two types of variable regulators that use a single reference Zener diode. The 0.1 µF capacitors remove high-frequency noise from the control voltages.

To regulate at load voltages greater than that of the Zener diode, a resistive voltage divider reduces the load voltage so that a fraction of the actual load voltage is supplied to the op-amp's inverting (–) terminal in Figure 12.33A.

$$V- = V_{load} (R_B / [R_A + R_B])$$

In order to balance its input voltages, the op-amp must drive the transistor until the load voltage is greater than the setpoint by the inverse of this fraction.

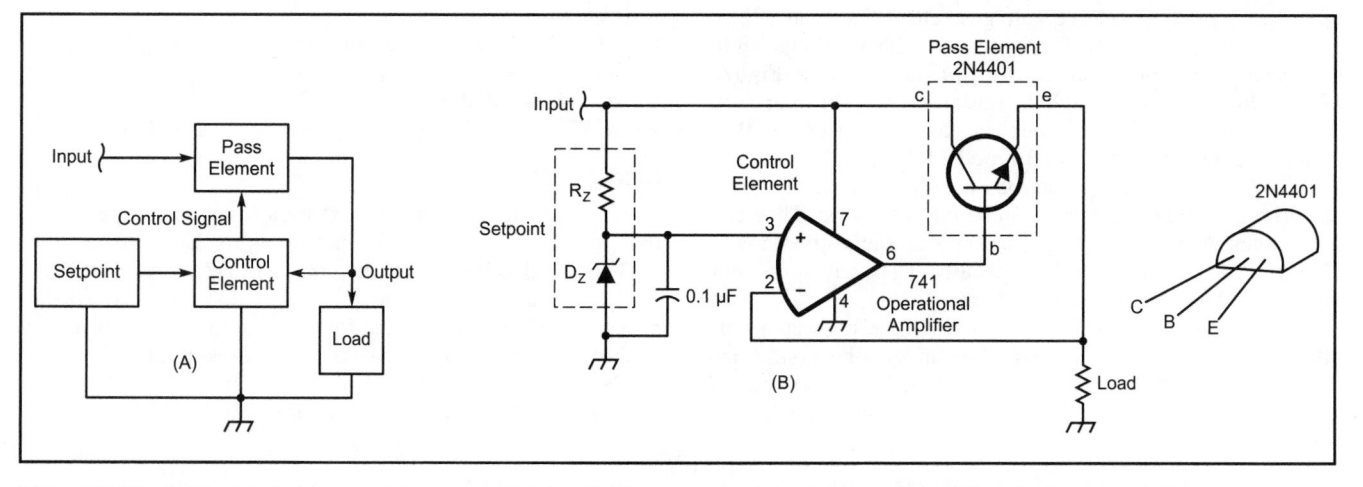

**Figure 12.32—A: The block diagram for a pass regulator. B: The pass regulator implemented with actual components.**

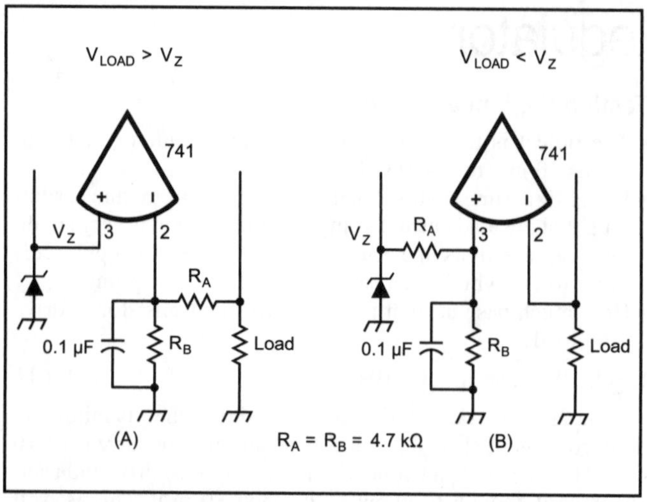

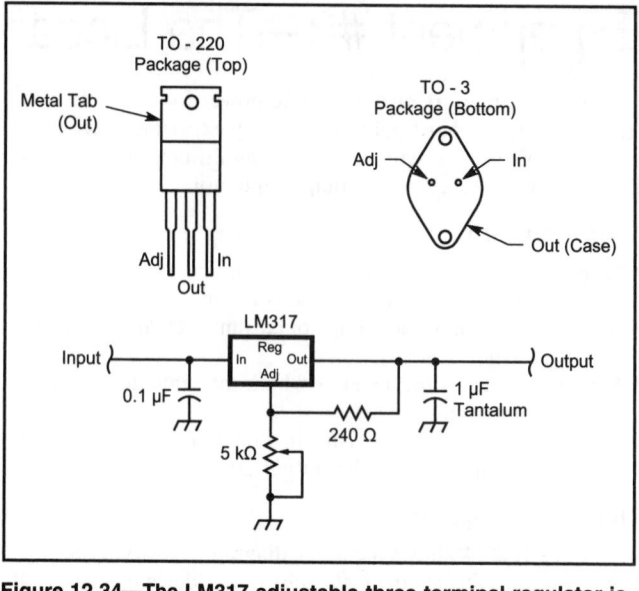

Figure 12.33—A: The voltage divider of $R_A$ and $R_B$ causes the op-amp to drive the pass transistor so that the load voltage is higher than the Zener voltage, $V_Z$. B: Performing the same trick for load voltages lower than $V_Z$.

$$V_{load} = V_Z ([R_A + R_B] / R_B) \qquad \text{[Eq 2]}$$

To obtain load voltages less than the Zener's voltage, use the circuit of Figure 12.33B. The voltage divider to reduces the Zener voltage, causing the setpoint to be reduced.

$$V_{load} = V_Z (R_B / [R_A + R_B]) \qquad \text{[Eq 3]}$$

## Testing a Variable Regulator

- Add two 4.7 kΩ resistors for $R_A$ and $R_B$ as shown in Figure 12.33A. The output voltage should change to nearly 10.2 V dc and the op-amp's output to around 10.9 V dc.
- Move the 4.7 kΩ resistors to divide the Zener voltage as in Figure 12.33B. Now the output voltage should be about 2.5 V dc and the op-amp's output about 3.2 V dc.
- Create an adjustable output regulator by replacing the two 4.7 kΩ resistors with a 10 kΩ potentiometer. Keep the 0.1 µF capacitor at the midpoint of the divider.

## The Three-Terminal Regulator

There are many integrated regulators available for fixed and variable positive and negative voltages. These generally have three terminals—input, output and ground—thus creating the generic term "three-terminal regulator."

The most popular IC regulator family is the 78xx, where "xx" denotes the output voltage. A type 7805 delivers 5 V dc output, a 7812 supplies 12 V dc, and so on. The 79xx regulator series regulates negative voltages. The 78Lxx and 79Lxx are low-power regulators. There are also numerous adjustable integrated regulators, such as the LM317 shown in **Figure 12.34**. One of the earliest IC regulators was the Fairchild µA723; it's still in use. It's possible to regulate up to 10 A with an IC regulator (the TO-3 type LM396).

These packages have numerous useful features. The voltage drop from input to output can be up to 40 V dc. They can sense when they're getting too hot and shut themselves down. They're protected against short circuits. They have excellent regulation. You can see why they're so popular!

Two caveats, however. The regulators use high-gain amplifiers. These amplifiers can oscillate under some conditions and input and output capacitors are sometimes required, as shown in Figure 12.34. If overloaded, the regulators will tem-

Figure 12.34—The LM317 adjustable three-terminal regulator is very versatile and rugged. The capacitors are required to ensure that the regulator's internal amplifiers remain stable under all conditions. The 240 Ω resistor limits the current through the 5 kΩ potentiometer. This regulator has an adjustable output from 1.2 V to a maximum that is about 3 V lower than the input voltage.

porarily shut themselves off until they cool, then turn back on. If the overload is persistent, this cycle can repeat as fast as tens of times per second. On a 'scope this appears as high-frequency "noise" from oscillation or a repeating "hiccup" as the chip switches between overheating and shutdown.

Try a 7805 or LM317 and learn how to use these valuable parts. Keep the current to 500 mA or less to avoid overheating the prototype board terminals.

## Suggested Reading

Chapter 11 of *The 2003 ARRL Handbook* has a substantial discussion of power supply regulation. *The Art of Electronics*, by Horowitz and Hill, really shines, with page after page of Chapter 6 devoted to regulators and an excellent discussion of the 723 regulator IC.

## Shopping List

- 2N4401 NPN transistor (RadioShack 276-2058)
- 470 Ω, 2 - 4.7 kΩ, 1 kΩ, 2.2 kΩ, ¼ W resistors
- 10 kΩ potentiometer
- 2 – 0.1 µF, 50 V ceramic capacitors and a 1 µF, 35 V tantalum capacitor
- 741 op-amp (RadioShack 276-007)
- LM317 adjustable regulator (RadioShack 276-1778)

## Next Month

Let's get back to basics next month with an experiment that shows how to design driver circuits for heavy loads.

This month brings a generous contribution from Steve Alpert, W1GGN. He constructed a spreadsheet that performs all the necessary calculations for the common emitter amplifier in our first experiment. It also includes a nifty lookup table for standard resistor values. It's available on the Hands-On Radio Web site: **www.arrl.org/tis/info/html/hands-on-radio/**.

# Experiment #9—Designing Drivers

Transistors make great switches as well as amplifiers. In fact, computers are built of millions of transistors acting as switches. Any circuit that controls or supplies power to a heavy load is called a *driver*. In this experiment we will learn how to make a transistor switch that can turn a heavy load on and off reliably. (Thanks to George, KF6VSG, for suggesting the topic.)

## Terms to Learn

- *Cutoff*—the point at which collector current reaches zero
- *Linear Region*—when a transistor is operating between cutoff and saturation, it is in its linear region.
- *Saturation*—the point at which increases in base current do not cause a further increase in collector current
- *Transconductance*—the change in output current in response to a change in input voltage

## The Transistor as a Switch

The goal when designing amplifiers is to make the transistor's collector current linearly and faithfully follow (proportionally) its base current. This requires that the transistor stay within its *linear region*—conducting some current at all times. A switch has completely different properties—its output current is either zero or some maximum value. **Figure 12.35** shows both a bipolar and metal-oxide semiconductor field-effect transistor (or MOSFET) switch circuit. You'll notice that there are no bias resistors in either circuit.

Before we proceed, a primer on the MOSFET—just "FET" from here on—is in order. The FET drain corresponds to the bipolar collector, the gate to the base and the source to the emitter. The FET's drain-to-source current, $I_{DS}$, is controlled by the gate-to-source voltage, $V_{GS}$.

Similar to the NPN or PNP bipolar transistor, the FET comes in N-channel and P-channel flavors. (The arrowhead points into the symbol for N-channel devices.) Unlike the bipolar transistor, the FET has both depletion and enhancement modes. An enhancement mode device is similar to a bipolar transistor—it does not conduct without an input signal. In an enhancement-mode FET, as $V_{GS}$ increases, so does $I_{DS}$. The depletion mode acts just the opposite. The FET symbol in Figure 12.35 is of an N-channel, enhancement mode device.

When a bipolar transistor's collector current reaches zero, the transistor is said to be in cutoff. As base current increases, so will collector current until the transistor reaches saturation. In saturation, collector current can't increase any further, even if base current is increased, and $V_{CE}$ is at its minimum value. The analogous states in a FET are called *fully on* and *fully off*. The voltage and current waveforms below the circuit show how the load current reacts to $V_{IN}$.

Since the FET uses voltage to control its drain current, forward transconductance, $g_{fs}$ measures the effect of the control signal.

$$g_{fs} = \Delta I_D / \Delta V_{GS} \qquad [1]$$

This parameter has the same units (Siemens, S) as conductance, which is the reciprocal of resistance (1/R). One can think of the FET acting as a voltage-controlled resistor, with $g_{fs}$ showing how much the resistance value changes in response to changes in the gate voltage.

## Designing Driver Circuits

First, select a transistor that can handle the load current and dissipate whatever power is lost as heat. Second, be sure that the input signal source can supply an adequate input sig-

nal (drive). You must meet both of these conditions to ensure reliable driver operation.

To choose the proper transistor, the load current and supply voltage must both be known. The supply voltage often varies widely. For example, a car's 12 V dc power bus may vary from 9 to 18 V dc, depending on battery condition and the state of the vehicle's charging system. The transistor must withstand the maximum supply voltage, $V_{MAX}$, when it is off.

The load resistance, $R_L$, must also be known. The maximum current the switch must handle is:

$$I_{MAX} = V_{MAX} / R_L \qquad [2]$$

Beware of surge currents at turn-on. Loads with capacitors may temporarily act like short circuits at turn-on. Also beware of voltage transients or "spikes" during switching. Inductive loads will present high voltages during the switch period (Remember that, for an inductor, V = L di/dt—the faster we try to change current through it, the higher the voltage). Your driver will therefore have to handle any current surges or voltage spikes induced by the load. ("Snubber" circuits, consisting of a clamp diode and a resistor-capacitor network, are frequently used to protect the driver from the spikes of inductive loads.) If you are using a bipolar transistor, you now can calculate how much base current you must supply to the switch:

$$I_B = I_{MAX} / \beta$$

$\beta$ changes with collector current (it usually decreases as $I_C$ increases), so use a value for $\beta$ with $I_C$ near $I_{MAX}$. This is specified on the transistor's data sheet. Using the *minimum* value for the input voltage, calculate the value of $R_B$:

$$R_B = (V_{INmin} - V_{BE}) / I_B \qquad [3]$$

The minimum value of input voltage must be used to accommodate the *worst-case* combination of circuit voltages and currents.

Designing with an FET is a little easier because the manufacturer usually specifies what the value of $V_{GS}$ must be for the transistor to be fully on. The FET's gate, being insulated from the conducting channel, acts like a small capacitor of a few hundred pF and draws very little dc current. $R_G$ in Figure 1 is required if the input voltage source does not actually output 0 V when off, such as a switch connected to a positive voltage. The FET won't turn off reliably if its gate is allowed to "float." $R_G$ pulls the gate voltage to zero if the input is open-circuited. The input source must be able to supply current of $V_{GS}/R_G$.

Power dissipation is the next design hurdle. Even if the transistors are turned completely on, they will still dissipate some heat. Just as for a resistor, the switch power dissipation is:

$$P_D = V_{CE} I_C = V_{CEsat} I_{MAX} \text{ (for a bipolar transistor)} \qquad [4]$$

and

$$P_D = V_{DS} I_D = R_{DSon} I_{MAX}^2 \text{ (for a FET)} \qquad [5]$$

$R_{DSon}$ is the resistance of the channel from drain to source when the FET is on. Modern FETs have a very low on-resistance, but still dissipate power when driving a heavy load. Some FETs have gotten so good, however, that their on-resistance is now below 2 milliohms (that's 0.002 $\Omega$!). To put this in perspective, some modern power MOSFETs can handle 20 A of current, dissipate less than 1 W and not require a heat sink under moderate ambient conditions! Look at the transistor's data sheet for the manufacturer's $R_{DSon}$ specification.

Power dissipation is why a switching transistor needs to be kept out of its linear region. When it's turned off or fully on, either the current through the transistor or the voltage

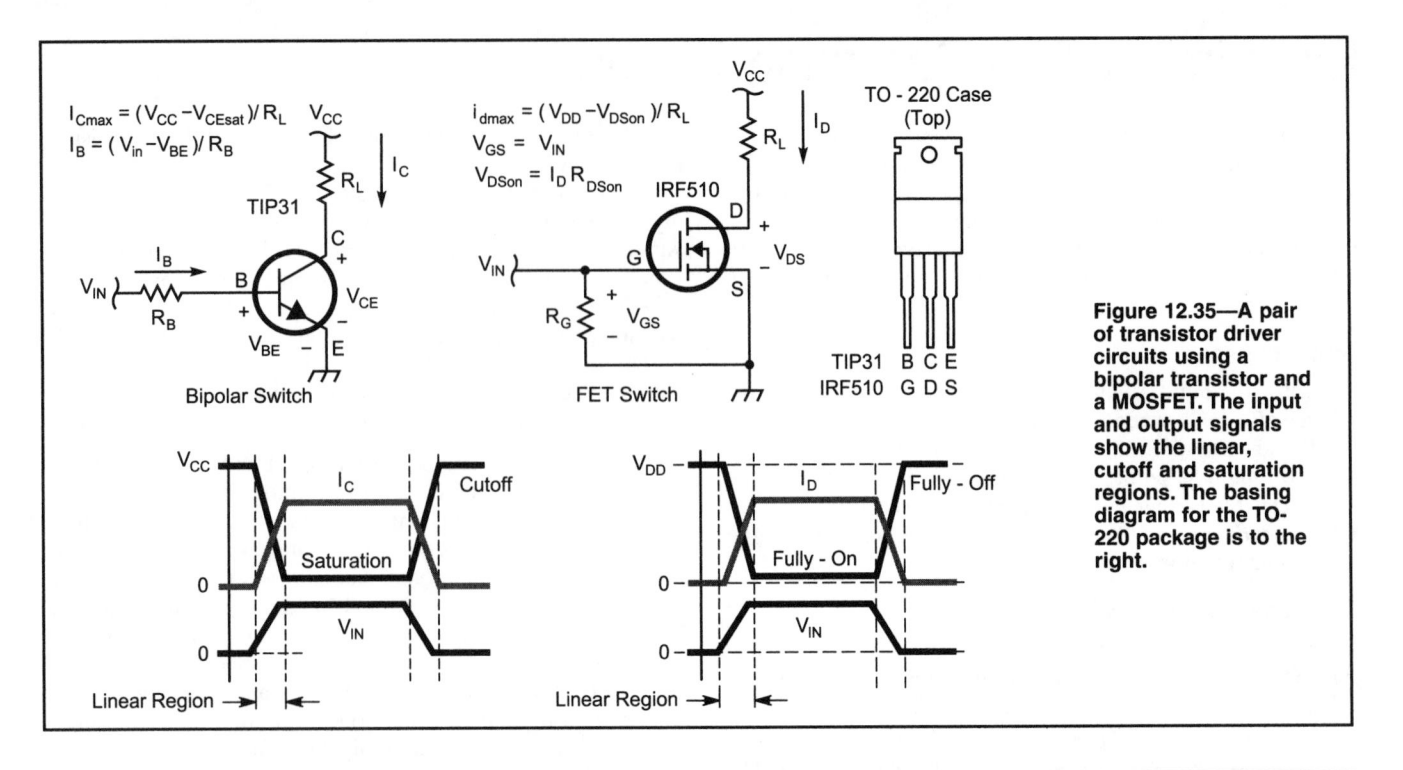

Figure 12.35—A pair of transistor driver circuits using a bipolar transistor and a MOSFET. The input and output signals show the linear, cutoff and saturation regions. The basing diagram for the TO-220 package is to the right.

across it is low, thus keeping the product of voltage and current (dissipated power) low. As the waveforms in Figure 12.35 show, while in the linear region, both voltage and current have significant values and the transistor is generating heat. It's important to make the transition through the linear region quick enough to keep the transistor cool.

Once you have calculated the power dissipation the switch must handle, you must check to see whether the transistor can withstand it. The manufacturer of the transistor will specify a *free-air dissipation* that assumes no heat-sink and room-temperature (ambient) air circulating freely around the transistor. This should be at least 50 percent higher than your calculated power dissipation. If not, you must either use a larger transistor or provide a heat sink. Let's make a driver!

### Testing a Driver Circuit

- We're going to use a 25 Ω power resistor as a 0.5 A load, much like a heavy-duty solenoid or a small motor. Bipolar and MOSFET drivers will use a 12 V input signal. **Table 12.2** shows the typical rating for two popular transistors.
- Solder the two 50 Ω resistors in parallel to create the load. Don't use your prototype board for this experiment due to the large currents—temporarily solder components together by their leads or use a terminal strip. The power supply should be able to deliver 12 V at 1 A.
- For the TIP31, if the collector current is to be 0.5 A and β is 25, base current must be at least 0.5/25 = 20 mA. From equation 3, the value of $R_B = (12 - 1.8)/0.02 = 510$ Ω.
- For the IRF510, since 10 V of gate drive is needed, the 12 V input signal can be used directly. Use a 4.7 kΩ resistor for $R_G$.
- Use equations 4 and 5 to calculate power dissipation for each transistor:
  TIP31: $P_D = 1.2 \times 0.5 = 0.6$ W
  IRF510: $P_D = 0.6 \times (0.5)^2 = 0.15$ W
  Load: $P_D = 25 \times (0.5)^2 = 6$ W — it will get warm, so keep it in the clear!
- Power up the circuit and use your voltmeter to check all of the transistor voltages. Load current can be calculated by measuring the voltage across the load and using Ohm's Law.
- Vary the amount of input current (TIP31) or voltage (IRF510)

### Table 12.2
**Comparison of Bipolar and MOSFET Power Transistors**

| Transistor Parameter (Typical Values) | TIP 31 | IRF510 |
|---|---|---|
| $V_{CEsat}$ | 1.2 V | N/A |
| $R_{DSon}$ | N/A | 0.4 Ω |
| $V_{BE}$ or $V_{GSon}$ | 1.8 V | 10 V |
| $I_C$ or $I_D$ | 3.0 A | 3.0 A |
| β or $g_{fs}$ | 25@$I_C$ = 1 A | 2 S (A/V) |
| $P_{Dmax}$ | 40 W | 20 W |

and observe the effect on the transistor's ability to drive the load. The base current can be varied by changing the value of $R_B$. The gate voltage can be varied by using a 20 kΩ potentiometer in series with $R_G$ as a voltage divider.
- Place the transistor in its linear region for a short period by reducing the input signal and see how hot it gets—careful! You'll see why it's important to supply adequate drive.

### Suggested Reading

Chapter 8 of *The 2004 ARRL Handbook* discusses both bipolar and MOSFET transistor construction. Chapter 3 of *The Art of Electronics*, by Horowitz and Hill, has a good section on power MOSFET switches and Chapter 6 reviews heat sinking. A list of Web links with technical tutorial information can be found on the Hands-On Radio Web site: **www.arrl.org/tis/info/html/hands-on-radio/**.

### Shopping List

- TIP31 bipolar power transistor (RadioShack 276-2017), IRF510 MOSFET (RadioShack 276-2072)
- 1 package (2) of 50 Ω, 10 W resistors (RadioShack 271-133)
- 510 Ω, 4.7 kΩ $^1/_4$ W resistors
- 20 kΩ potentiometer

### Next Month

As long as we're experimenting with power control, this would be a good opportunity to explore the SCR—a thyristor that acts like a switch and is widely used for ac power control and switching.

# Experiment #10—Using SCRs

*Thyristors*—what a strange word! What do they do? Thyristors are common components found around the ham shack in power supplies and ac control circuits. They are solid-state replacements for *thyratrons*—tubes that act as current switches. Like transistors, a small current can switch a much larger current. In this experiment, we'll use the most common thyristor—a silicon-controlled rectifier or *SCR*—to control both ac and dc.

## Terms to Learn

- *Breakover* and *breakdown voltage*—the voltages at which an SCR begins to conduct current without gate drive from anode-to-cathode (forward) and cathode-to-anode (reverse), respectively.
- *Conduction angle*—the number of degrees of an ac cycle during which the SCR is conducting forward current.
- *Holding current* ($I_H$)—the amount of forward current required to keep an SCR conducting.
- *Latch*—to change state and remain in that state.

## How the SCR Works

The SCR has an NPN transistor's layered structure of N and P-type material but adds one additional P-type layer as shown in **Figure 12.36**. Starting at the cathode and moving left, you see what looks like the three layers of a regular NPN transistor. The extra P-type layer then creates a PN-diode at the anode. The SCR "looks like" a rectifier attached to an NPN transistor.

The SCR operates in just two states: ON and OFF. When OFF, the SCR acts like an open-circuit to voltages between the anode and cathode as long as the value is less than either the breakover or breakdown voltages. The SCR will remain OFF until gate-to-cathode current reaches the *gate trigger current*, $I_{GT}$, or *gate turn-on voltage*, $V_{GTO}$, at which point forward current flows from the anode to cathode and the SCR is ON.

It's important to understand that while the SCR is turned ON by gate current, it can't be turned OFF the same way. Once ON, the SCR is *latched* ON until forward current falls below the *holding current*, $I_{HO}$, when it resets to the OFF state. Forward current will fall below $I_{HO}$ when the power source stops supplying or the load stops drawing current. In an ac circuit, the reversal of voltage across the SCR stops current flow.

## Demonstrating SCR Functions

This is unfamiliar territory for many electronic designers,

so let's start with a simple experiment that demonstrates the basic SCR functions to discharge a capacitor into a load.

- Construct the circuit of **Figure 12.37**. Don't use your prototype board; either solder the components together or use a terminal or barrier strip. A clip lead or jumper wire can be used for the switches.
- Open S2 then close S1. Connect the 12 V power supply. Monitor voltage across the capacitor to be sure it charges to 12 V. No voltage should appear across the 100 Ω load resistor.
- Open S1, leaving the charged capacitor connected to the SCR. Monitor voltage across the load resistor while *momentarily* closing S2. (If you leave S2 closed, gate current will continue to flow, overheating the 47 Ω resistor.) You will see a pulse of voltage across the load resistor as the capacitor discharges through it. The duration of the pulse will be approximately R × C = 100 × 9400 µF = 0.94 seconds.
- Observe the trailing edge of the pulse as the capacitor discharges. You will see load voltage abruptly drop to zero as current through the SCR falls below $I_{HO}$. This will happen with capacitor voltage around 2.2 V due to the 1.8 V forward voltage drop of the SCR, which leaves only 30-40 mA flowing in the load resistor. (This is clearest if you are able to monitor both capacitor and load voltage.)
- As soon as load voltage drops to zero, indicating that the SCR is reset, you can close S1 again to repeat the cycle.
- Experiment with the circuit by increasing the value of the gate resistor until the SCR no longer triggers. Similarly, if the load resistance is increased, maximum current will fall below $I_{HO}$ and the capacitor will no longer discharge through the SCR.

## Designing with SCRs

The circuit you just tested is similar to over-voltage protection circuits found in dc power supplies, called *crowbars*. A heavy-duty SCR is connected directly across the power supply output and triggered to act as a short circuit if the output voltage gets too high. SCRs can handle a large surge current, so this either trips the supply's current limit circuit or blows a fuse. Either way, equipment connected to the supply is not subjected to excessive voltage.

Another popular use of SCRs is in ac circuits that control power to a load such as a light bulb dimmer or motor speed control. The circuit of **Figure 12.38A** shows a simple dimmer circuit. Starting with the gate control potentiometer set to a

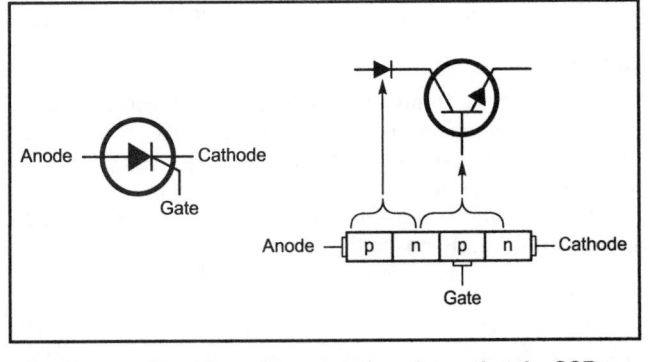

Figure 12.36—The internal construction shows that the SCR may be thought of as a rectifier in series with an NPN transistor.

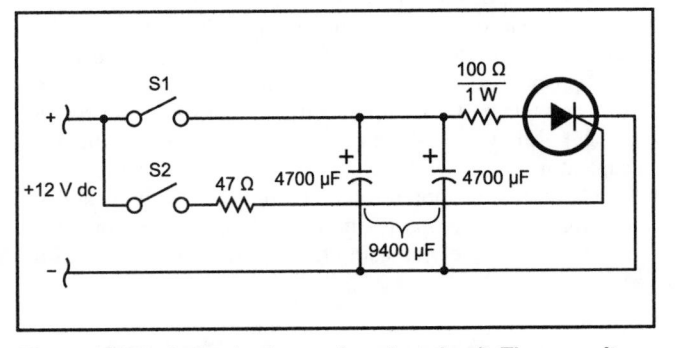

Figure 12.37—A simple charge-dumping circuit. The capacitor discharges through the load resistor and the SCR when a current pulse through the gate turns the SCR ON.

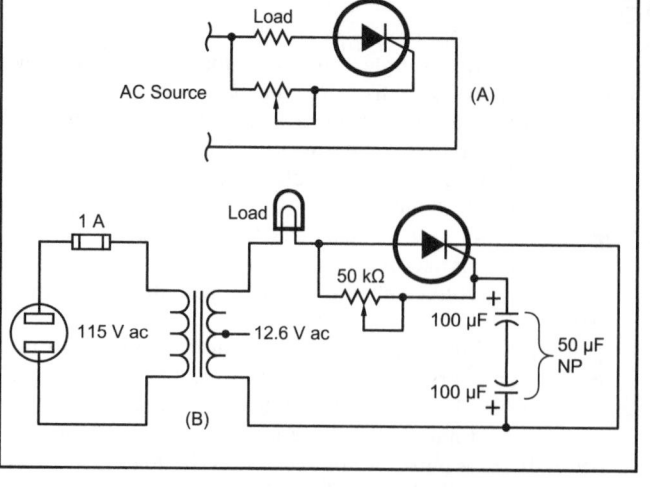

Figure 12.38—An RC-controlled dimmer circuit. To run this circuit at 115 V ac, the capacitor value can be reduced by a factor of 10 or more.

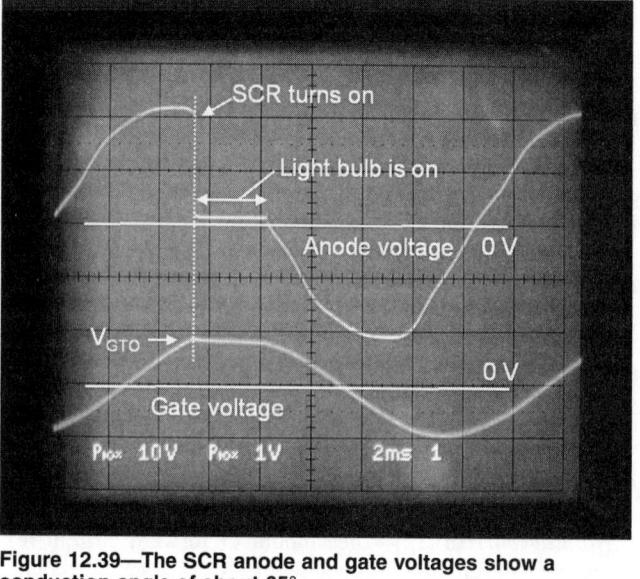

Figure 12.39—The SCR anode and gate voltages show a conduction angle of about 65°.

high value, the SCR remains OFF over the entire ac cycle. As the control resistance is reduced, eventually enough current enters the SCR gate at the very peak of the ac cycle, turning it ON for the duration of the positive half-cycle. As the control's resistance is reduced further, the SCR turns ON at lower and lower voltages, conducting over more of the positive half-cycle and delivering more power to the load.

In Figure 12.38B, the load—a light bulb—has been moved to the supply side of the potentiometer and a gate capacitor has been added. This allows smoother control of the *conduction angle*. Starting once again with the SCR in the OFF state, all of the applied voltage appears across the SCR and the gate capacitor charges through the potentiometer. When the capacitor has charged to the SCR's gate turn-on voltage, $V_{GTO}$, the SCR turns ON. The SCR stays ON until the voltage reverses.

By choosing the right values for the potentiometer and capacitor, the SCR's conduction angle can be varied from about 30°, turning on near the end of the positive half-cycle, to almost 180°, conducting over the entire positive half-cycle. Ready to try it for real?

### Testing a Dimmer Circuit

- Construct the circuit of Figure 12.38B taking special care with the ac supply. All 115 $V_{rms}$ line circuits must be insulated and fused. Use a ground-fault interrupter (GFI) circuit, if possible. The gate capacitor must be nonpolarized and is constructed from two electrolytic caps connected back to back with opposing polarities.
- Set the potentiometer to its maximum value. Monitor SCR anode voltage and gate capacitor voltage with an oscilloscope. Connect a voltmeter across the light bulb set to measure ac voltage. Power up the circuit. The light bulb should be OFF. You will observe a small ac voltage across the gate capacitor.
- Slowly reduce the potentiometer value until voltage across the light bulb begins to increase. You will see the gate capacitor voltage increasing to $V_{GTO}$ (about 1 V) at which

point the SCR turns ON. Continue decreasing the potentiometer resistance. The gate capacitor will charge to $V_{GTO}$ faster and the SCR will conduct over more of the ac cycle, increasing bulb brightness and the voltage across it. **Figure 12.39** shows one ac cycle of the SCR gate and anode voltage.

- Try to maximize the range of the SCR's conduction angle by changing the gate capacitor or control pot values. A 25 kΩ pot and 100 µF capacitors worked best for the SCR I used.

### Suggested Reading

The amateur literature is sparse in the area of thyristors, but manufacturers offer detailed design and application information. The Teccor Electronics Web site has an excellent series of downloadable application notes on thyristors at **www.teccor.com/web/menuitems/downloads/appnotes. htm**. The classic, but old data book by RCA—the *Transistor, Thyristor and Diode Manual*—also has an excellent tutorial section on thyristor basics.

### Shopping List

- SCR—RadioShack 276-1067, 267-1020 or similar.
- 115 $V_{rms}$ to 12.6 $V_{rms}$ power transformer—RadioShack 273-1365 or similar.
- Two 4700 µF @ 16 V or greater, two 100 µF @ 16 V or greater capacitors.
- 100 Ω-1 W, 47 Ω-1/4 W resistors.
- 50 kΩ potentiometer—RadioShack 271-1716.
- 12 V incandescent lamp—RadioShack 900-2665 or similar.

### Next Month

Next month we'll jump back to one of my favorite op-amp circuits—the comparator. These handy circuits are used for all sorts of detection and sensing duties, so get the prototype board and 741s dusted off!

Remember the Hands-On Radio Web site: **www.arrl.org/ tis/info/html/hands-on-radio/**.

# Experiment #11—Comparators

The *comparator* made an appearance in Hands-On Radio experiment #5 on timers. As a crucial part of the type 555 integrated circuit (IC), it made the decision about when it was time to change the timer's operation from one state to another. We'll now delve deeply into comparator functions including the mysterious property called *hysteresis*.

## Terms to Learn

- *Hysteresis*—a shift in the switching threshold of a comparator purposely caused by positive feedback.
- *Chatter*—oscillations of a comparator output when the input signal is near the threshold.
- *Open-collector output*—an IC output consisting of the isolated collector of a bipolar transistor or FET drain.
- *Threshold*—the voltage at which a comparator circuit switches states.

## Background

The basic function of a comparator is, surprisingly (!), to compare the magnitudes of two inputs and indicate which is greater. The comparator is found in many places around the shack—battery chargers, power supplies, antenna tuners and switches, just to name a few.

While there are lots of circuits that can compare voltages, the most common is a high-gain amplifier with two high-impedance inputs. If this sounds like an op-amp, it should—the comparator is basically an op-amp with an *open-collector output*. This is an NPN transistor with its collector connected to the OUTPUT pin, but nothing else. It allows the comparator to interface to digital circuits and drive switched loads better than an op-amp. It also supports a neat noise-control design trick, as we'll see later.

**Figure 12.40** shows a comparator in a simple temperature control circuit. No feedback is used, so its full voltage gain (in the thousands at dc and low frequencies) turns the output transistor OFF if the + input voltage is greater than that of the – input (by even a few millivolts) and vice versa. The point at which the comparator changes state is called the *threshold*. The output states can be reversed by switching the input connections.

In this circuit, the negative input (–) voltage is fixed at a value representing the desired temperature (the system setpoint), $V_{SP}$. If the sensor's output voltage is lower than $V_{SP}$, the comparator's output transistor will be turned ON and the heater will be ON, raising the temperature. When the sensor is hotter than the desired temperature, the output transistor is turned OFF, turning the heater OFF. The system cycles between a little too hot and a little too cold.

## Testing a Simple Comparator

Let's start with the simple voltage detector circuit of **Figure 12.41**, such as might be used in a power supply to detect overvoltage. We want the LED to turn ON whenever the variable input voltage is higher than the fixed input voltage (setpoint). Fixed resistors R1 and R2 form a resistive divider that creates the setpoint voltage, $V_{SP}$.

Use an LM311 with its V+ power supply pin connected to +12 V and its V– pin connected to ground. Be sure to connect pins 1 and 4 together so the emitter of the output transistor is grounded.

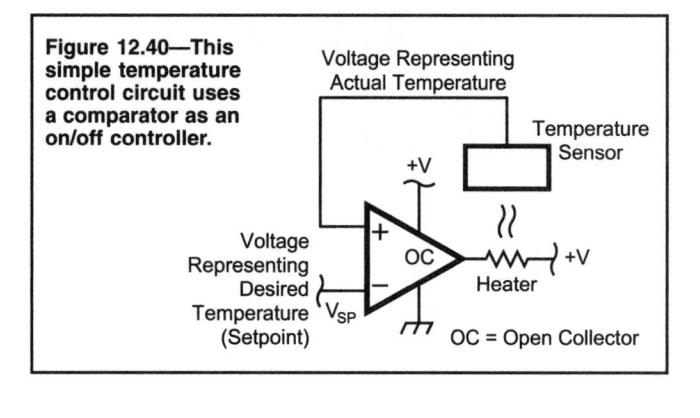

Figure 12.40—This simple temperature control circuit uses a comparator as an on/off controller.

To keep current through the resistive divider small, assume R1 + R2 = 50 kΩ, and R1 = 50 kΩ – R2.

- Create a setpoint of $V_{SP}$ = 5 V. Use the voltage divider equation: $V_{SP}$ = V+ × [R2/(R1+R2)]=12 V × [R2/(50 kΩ)]. So R2 =5 V×50 kΩ/12 V=20.8 kΩ. Use 22 kΩ for R2. R1=50 kΩ – 22 kΩ =28 kΩ, so use a 27 kΩ resistor.
- Build the circuit and vary the potentiometer while watching the LED. Measure the setpoint and variable voltages at threshold to be sure they agree with the calculated values. Redesign the resistive divider for different setpoint values or use a 10 kΩ potentiometer to change the setpoint.
- Adjust the variable input slowly through the setpoint value. Do you see the LED flicker or light dimly before staying ON or OFF? If you are using an oscilloscope, watch the LM311 output voltage as the setpoint is passed for rapid changes between ON to OFF before settling at the final value.
- Measure the comparator's output voltage, $V_{OH}$, with the LED turned OFF for use in the next part of the experiment. The forward voltage drop across the LED, even when OFF, will make $V_{OH}$ about 1.5 V lower than V+.

## Hysteresis

Comparators are often used to drive relays. The audible noise of the relay contacts rapidly opening and closing as the comparator output switches states is called *chatter* and it is damaging to the relay and to the circuit it controls. Chatter is caused by noise on either the setpoint or the input voltage. As shown in **Figure 12.42A**, even small noise peaks can cause a temporary crossing of the threshold. When the input voltage is close to the threshold, the effect of the noise is multiplied by the comparator's high gain. The noise from the load current switching can also feed back into the inputs and cause extended oscillations.

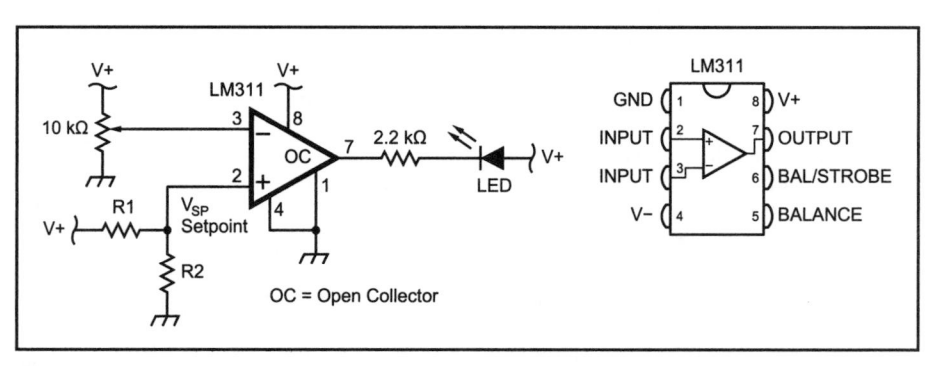

Figure 12.41—This voltage detector uses a resistive divider to create a fixed setpoint. Note that the input connections for the LM311 are reversed from those of the 741 op-amp.

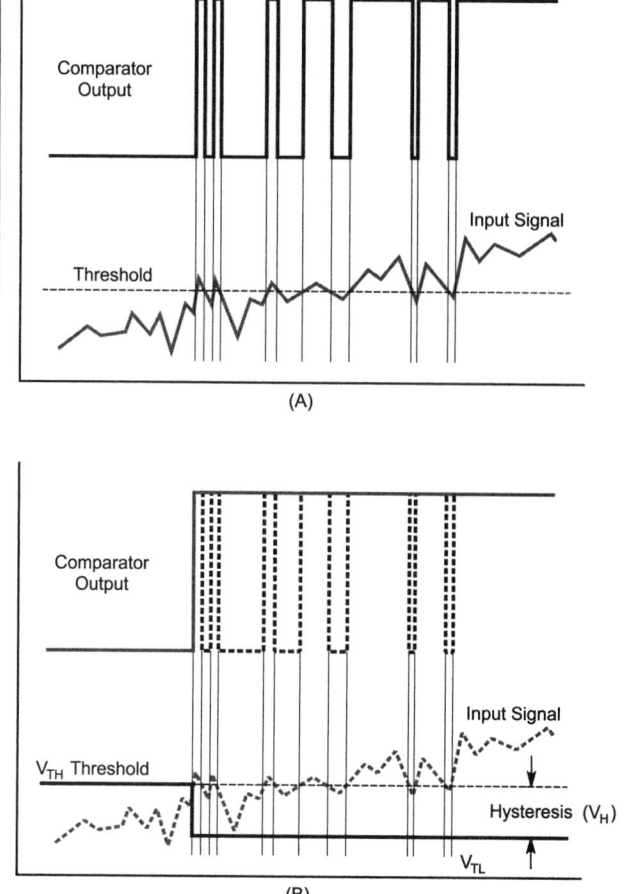

Figure 12.42—A shows chatter as the noisy input signal crosses and recrosses the comparator's switching threshold. B shows how moving the threshold after switching reduces chatter.

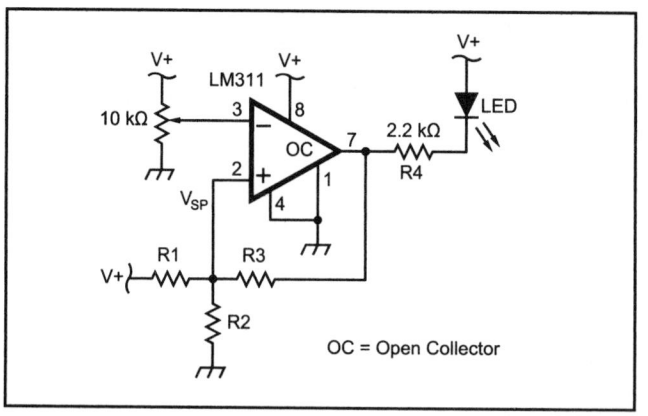

Figure 12.43—The Schmitt Trigger circuit incorporates hysteresis into the switching threshold by providing positive feedback by using R3.

parallel with R2
● R4 is much smaller than R3

You can calculate the amount of hysteresis by assuming that R3 only adds current to R2 or removes a little current from R2, depending on whether the comparator output is ON or OFF.

$$V_H \approx (V_{OH}) (R1 \parallel R2)/[R3 + (R1 \parallel R2)] \qquad [Eq\ 1]$$

Solving for R3 if the other values are known:

$$R3 \approx [(V_{OH})(R1 \parallel R2)/V_H] - (R1 \parallel R2) \qquad [Eq\ 2]$$

### Testing a Schmitt Trigger

Let's add 0.5 V of hysteresis to the voltage detector we just built, keeping the setpoint at 5 V, R1=28 kΩ, and R2=22 kΩ. Leave R4 at 2.2 kΩ, satisfying the assumption R4<<R3. I'll use $V_{OH}$=10.5 V, but you should use the value you measured earlier.

● Using Equation 2, R3 = [(10.5 V)(12 kΩ)/0.5 V]–12 kΩ = 240 kΩ. Use a 220 kΩ resistor. Remember to substitute your own value for $V_{OH}$.
● Monitor the variable input voltage as you slowly increase and decrease it through the 5 V setpoint. Record the point at which the LED turns ON and OFF. Subtract those two voltages to find the circuit's hysteresis voltage. For my circuit, I observed 400 mV (0.4 V) of hysteresis—pretty good for an approximate solution.
● Experiment with the circuit by increasing R3 to reduce hysteresis, and vice versa.

### Suggested Reading

*The Art of Electronics*, by Horowitz and Hill, covers comparators in several sections, primarily 4.23 and 9.07. The National Semiconductor data sheet for the LM311 at **www. national.com/ds/LM/LM311.pdf** (and LP311 data sheet at **www.national.com/ds/LP/LP311.pdf**) includes numerous application hints and circuits.

### Shopping List

● LM311 comparator (The LP311 comparator, RadioShack 900-6272, is available online only. An LM339, part number 276-1712, may be substituted using the pin connections at **www.national.com/ds/LM/LM339.pdf**. Note that V– and GND are connected together internally.)
● 2.2 kΩ, 22 kΩ, 27 kΩ, 220 kΩ ¼ W resistors
● 10 kΩ potentiometer
● Red LED, RadioShack 276-026 or equivalent

*Hands-On Radio Web site:* **www.arrl.org/tis/info/html/ hands-on-radio/**.

Filtering the input signal (as we did in experiment #8) by adding a capacitor to the setpoint divider to reduce noise, can reduce chatter. A more reliable way is to use the comparator output to shift the threshold. It can be shifted a bit in the *opposite* direction of the input signal when the threshold voltage is crossed. This is illustrated in Figure 12.42B. By moving the threshold, chatter is eliminated.

This is accomplished by adding positive feedback from the output to the setpoint as shown in **Figure 12.43**. When the variable input voltage is less than the setpoint, $V_{SP}$, the output transistor is OFF and the voltage at the comparator's output is close to V+. As the variable input voltage increases past the setpoint, the output transistor turns ON, turning the LED ON. This circuit is called a *Schmitt Trigger*.

When the transistor is ON it places R3 in parallel with R2, lowering the setpoint voltage to $V_{TL}$ and moving it away from the variable input voltage shown in Figure 12.42B. The reverse occurs when the threshold is crossed in the opposite direction so that the threshold is raised to $V_{TH}$ as R3 is placed in parallel with R1. This shift in the setpoint depending on whether the input is increasing or decreasing is called *hysteresis*. The amount of hysteresis, $V_H = V_{TH} - V_{TL}$.

In designing a circuit to use hysteresis with specific values for $V_{TH}$ and $V_{TL}$, we can simplify the calculations considerably by making the following assumptions:

● $V_{OL}$ (the comparator output with the output transistor ON) = 0
● R3 is much larger than the combination of R1 in

# Experiment #12—Field Effect Transistors

Welcome to the second year of "Hands-On Radio." After an introduction and 11 experiments, we've covered a lot of ground but it seems like we've only scratched the surface! Radio electronics is a pretty broad field, so there are lots of experiment topics remaining.

The field effect transistor, or FET, is an attractive replacement for bipolar transistors in switches and amplifiers. Why? The FET offers high input impedance, excellent gain, and easy biasing. We'll revisit the first "Hands-On Radio" experiment and find out how these characteristics fit the common-emitter design.

## Terms to Learn

- *Transconductance*—The measure of change in output current caused by a change in input voltage.
- *Channel*—The semiconductor material between an FET drain and source through which current flows.
- *Enhancement and depletion mode*—In enhancement-mode FETs, increasing gate voltage causes channel conductivity to increase. For depletion-mode FETs, the opposite is true.
- *On-resistance*—The drain-to-source resistance of an FET's channel at maximum conductivity.

## Background

While you may know that John Bardeen, Walter Brattain and William Shockley constructed the first bipolar transistor in 1948, you may not know that the idea behind the FET was patented in 1926 by Julius Lilienfield. A working (but very slow) amplifier was made using salt by Robert Pohl in 1938. The FET is actually the oldest transistor and its operation is much closer to the vacuum tube than the bipolar transistor.

**Figure 12.44** shows the rudimentary construction and symbols for the two primary types of FETs, the junction FET (JFET) and the metal-oxide-semiconductor FET (MOSFET), that we met in experiment #9. Metal electrodes attach leads to the semiconductor material. The junction in a JFET is formed by the different material types (P and N) of the gate and the channel. MOS describes the construction of the gate; a metal electrode coating an insulating layer of oxide (usually quartz, silicon dioxide or $SiO_2$) which, in turn, contacts the channel material directly. FET and bipolar transistors have terminals with similar functions—gate and base, collector and drain, and emitter and source.

Where the bipolar transistor uses input current to control output current, the FET uses input voltage. In place of the bipolar transistor's pair of P-N junctions placed back-to-back between collector and emitter, the FET has a *channel* of either P-type or N-type material. In the bipolar transistor, current flows from the base to emitter, controlling current flow through the two P-N junctions. In the FET, gate voltage changes the conductivity of the channel and so the current flowing between drain and source also changes. Very little current flows in the gate of an FET.

Like the bipolar transistor's NPN and PNP devices, the FET comes in different flavors, but it has *four* instead of two. Figure 12.44 shows N-channel devices, but the channels can be made of either N or P-type material and the device can be designed so that increasing gate voltage causes more or less current to flow in the channel. If more channel current flows with increasing gate voltage, it is an *enhancement-mode* device. Conversely, *depletion-mode* devices have less current with increasing gate voltage. The most widely used device is the N-channel enhancement-mode FET.

The change in output current caused by a change in input voltage is called *transconductance*. Analogous to a bipolar transistor's current gain or beta, its symbol is $g_m$ and its units are siemens (S) because it measures the ratio of current to voltage.[1] The input voltage, $V_{GS}$, is measured between the FET gate and source. The output current, $I_{DS}$, flows from drain to source.

$$g_m = \Delta I_{DS} / \Delta V_{GS} \text{ and } \Delta I_{DS} = g_m \Delta V_{GS} \qquad \text{[Eq 1]}$$

The voltage gain of the FET amplifier in **Figure 12.45** depends on the FET transconductance because varying the current in the FET drain causes a varying voltage across the drain resistance. The model for the FET is the variable resistive divider shown in Figure 12.45A, with $V_{GS}$ controlling the value of $R_{DS}$. If $V_O$ is measured at the drain terminal (just as the common-emitter output voltage is measured at the collector), then

$$\Delta V_O = -\Delta I_{DS} R1 = -g_m \Delta V_{GS} R1 \qquad \text{[Eq 2]}$$

Substituting this relationship gives voltage gain in terms of transconductance and the drain load:

$$A_V = \Delta V_O / \Delta V_{GS} = -g_m R1 \qquad \text{[Eq 3]}$$

The minus sign results from the output voltage decreasing as drain current increases, just as with the common-emitter amplifier.

A key difference between the FET and bipolar transistor is that the channel of an FET acts like a variable resistance. That means that drain-to-source voltage can become quite low—lower than a completely saturated bipolar transistor's $V_{CE}$. Note that the *on-resistance* for power FETs can be very low—in the milliohm range. This allows them to switch heavy loads while dissipating little power. In amplifiers, this also allows more output voltage swing.

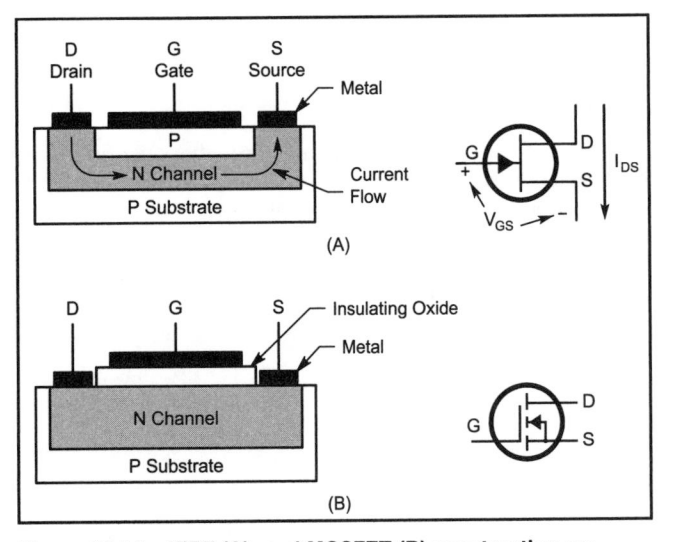

**Figure 12.44—JFET (A) and MOSFET (B) construction are shown along with their symbols. N-channel, enhancement-mode devices are shown.**

---

[1]Siemens (pronounced "see-mins" ) is the international unit for conductance, formerly mhos. Its symbol is a capital "S" and 1 siemens = 1 A/V.

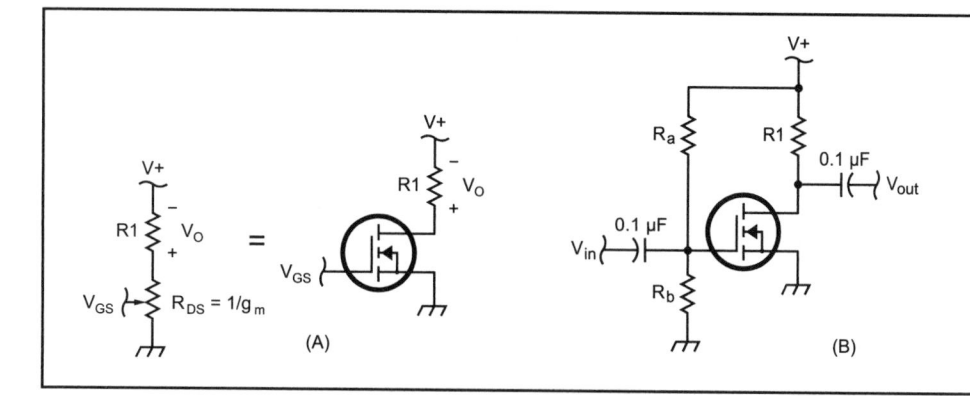

Figure 12.45—(A) A MOSFET common-source amplifier can be modeled as a variable voltage divider between the drain load and the FET. (B) A simple MOSFET amplifier with a voltage divider for supplying gate bias.

Another important parameter of FETs is the gate-to-source voltage at which no more current flows through the channel. This is called the *pinch-off voltage*, $V_p$. Imagine the gate voltage as a pair of fingers tightening or loosening around a hose carrying a stream of water and you'll have a pretty good idea of the mechanics involved. When $V_{GS}$ reaches $V_p$, the area of the channel through which current flows is reduced to zero. Depending on the type of FET, $V_p$ can be positive or negative. Switching MOSFETs are generally designed to have $V_p$ greater than zero to make interfacing with digital logic easier. The voltage at which the MOSFET begins to conduct current is usually shown as $V_{GS(TH)}$, the *gate threshold voltage*.

### Testing a MOSFET Common-Source Amplifier

This experiment will use a common switching MOSFET, the IRF510. This is a large transistor capable of handling several amps of drain current, but it demonstrates the mechanics of MOSFET amplifiers well. You may want to download the data sheet for the transistor.[2]

- When using a single power supply, it's necessary to bias the gate so that output voltage can both increase and decrease. Bias is supplied by $R_a$ and $R_b$ which act as a voltage divider—$V_{GS} = R_b / (R_a + R_b)$. For the divider, use a 10 k$\Omega$ potentiometer with the wiper connected to the FET gate and the remaining leads connected to V+ and ground. Start with the potentiometer set so that the wiper is nearly at ground voltage. Leave the input signal source disconnected.
- The IRF510 can handle a lot of current, but we'll limit drain current to 12 mA by using a 1 k$\Omega$ resistor for R1.
- Monitor the FET drain voltage and slowly adjust the bias pot so that gate voltage increases. When the gate threshold voltage is reached, the FET will start conducting and drain voltage will fall rapidly to zero. Record the gate threshold voltage as well as the voltage when the FET drain is 1 V below V+ and 1 V above ground.

[2]The IRF510 data sheet may be downloaded from **www.rigelcorp. com/__doc/8051/IRF510.pdf**. (Note: There are two consecutive underscores prior to "doc.")

- Set the signal generator to output a 0.1 $V_{p-p}$ 1 kHz sine wave. Set the bias voltage halfway between $V_{GS(TH)}$ and V+. Connect the input signal. Observe the output voltage and experiment by adjusting the bias voltage to get the largest undistorted output.
- Calculate voltage gain, $A_v = -$ (drain voltage change) / (gate voltage change) and transconductance, $g_m = - A_v / R1$. My FET showed a voltage gain of −18 and a transconductance of 0.018 S.
- Experiment by varying R1 and observing the effect on voltage gain. Readjust the bias setting and input voltage to get the maximum undistorted output voltage for each value of R1.

You may be asking yourself why your measured transconductance is so low compared to the specified minimum of 1.3 S in the data sheet. The answer lies in the graph of transconductance versus drain current (Figure 12 in the data sheet). The IRF510 transconductance is optimized for drain currents of several amperes and it falls off drastically at low currents.

### Suggested Reading

Begin by reading *The 2004 ARRL Handbook* sections on FETs, beginning on pages 8.23 and 10.32. *The Art of Electronics* devotes all of Chapter 3 to FETs, with sections 3.07 and 3.08 covering amplifier design.

### Shopping List

- IRF510 transistor (RadioShack 276-2072)
- 10 k$\Omega$ potentiometer (multi-turn preferred, but not required)
- Two 0.1 $\mu$F capacitors
- 1 k$\Omega$, $^1/_4$ W resistor

### Next Month

We have focused on active circuits throughout the first year of "Hands-On Radio." It's time to consider a passive circuit for a change. Next month, we'll explore several types of attenuators and their design equations.

The Hands-On Radio Web site is **www.arrl.org/tis/info/html/hands-on-radio/**.

# Experiment #13—Attenuators

Thus far, we've concentrated on active circuits—those that use applied power to transform an input signal. There are other passive circuits out there that don't need a power supply, yet perform useful functions. Attenuators are an excellent example. This month we'll explore common types and you will have a couple of useful gadgets when we're through.

## Terms to Learn

- *Minimum loss*—an attenuator designed to match two impedances while incurring the minimum amount of power loss.
- *Nepers (Np)*—a logarithmic ratio similar to the decibel, except that the Naperian or natural log (ln or $\log_e$, where e=2.71828...) is used. Np is often used to specify ratios of voltage or current.
- *Symmetrical*—an attenuator whose attenuation and impedance is the same in either direction.

## Background

Attenuators are used in many different audio and radio applications. Your HF rig probably has an attenuator at the front end of its receiver and your signal generator might use one to switch output voltage ranges. Along with voltage reduction, attenuators are used for impedance matching and isolation. Most attenuators are made from fixed and variable resistors, but some RF attenuators are made from PIN diodes. Microwave attenuators may be made from material inserted into waveguide.

There are many types of attenuator circuits and **Figure 12.46** shows the most common, the T, Pi, H, O and L. The T, Pi and L circuits are all *unbalanced*, meaning that all circuit voltages are referenced to the common ground. The H and O circuits are the *balanced* equivalents of the T and Pi, respectively. The balanced circuits do not have a common ground. The adjustable L attenuator is often found in audio systems, called an *L Pad*, with the potentiometers mechanically linked or *ganged*. Attenuators are often referred to as *pads* and attenuation as *padding*.

Attenuators are designed to have specific input and output impedances because the source and load impedances affect how much voltage appears across the attenuator's resistors. The source and load often need to be connected to a specific impedance to operate properly.

## Designing Attenuators

The equations for attenuator resistor values are complex[1] so tables for values of attenuation and impedance are widely available, as in *The ARRL Handbook*, and reproduced as **Table 12.3** for symmetric attenuators. Since most ham equipment uses 50 Ω inputs and outputs, we'll use that as our design impedance. Let's design a 50 Ω, 10 dB attenuator.

Although you may use either the T or Pi circuit, I used the Pi because it requires no center connection. If you choose the Pi, Table 1 gives values of 96.2 and 71.2 Ω for R1 and R2. (R1 = R3 for symmetric attenuators.) I substituted 100 Ω and 75 Ω resistors, which keeps the ratio (and thus the attenuation) close to 10 dB, while raising the impedance to 52 Ω.

- Build this circuit and test it by connecting it to a function generator on one side and a 51 Ω resistor on the other. (It's symmetrical, so it doesn't matter which side you choose as input and output.)
- Input a 1 kHz waveform and measure the output voltage. Calculate the attenuation using the following equation:

$$\text{Attenuation (dB)} = 20 \times \log (V_{out}/V_{in}) \qquad [\text{Eq 1}]$$

- Measure the input resistance with the 51 Ω output resistor connected. It should be within a percent or two of 52 Ω.
- Try some of the other attenuations in the table. A 6 dB Pi-attenuator can be made from 150 Ω and 39 Ω resistors. Use 39 Ω and 10 Ω resistors for a 20 dB T-attenuator.

If you make the attenuator a permanent addition to your tool kit, you don't have to use a fancy enclosure. Find any metal enclosure that will seal tightly. (Some of the hallmarks of a good attenuator are insignificant leakage, constant impedance and accuracy.) Keep the leads short and straight so that the attenuator will work at high frequencies without looking like an inductor.

## Using an Attenuator for Isolation

Attenuators can also provide isolation between two systems. This is useful at RF, where output amplifiers are usually designed to expect a load of 50 Ω. For example, signal generators

[1]Attenuator design equations can be found in *Reference Data for Radio Engineers*, Howard W. Sams & Company / ITT, Indianapolis, 1979 or at **www.microwaves101.com/encyclopedia/attenuators.cfm**.

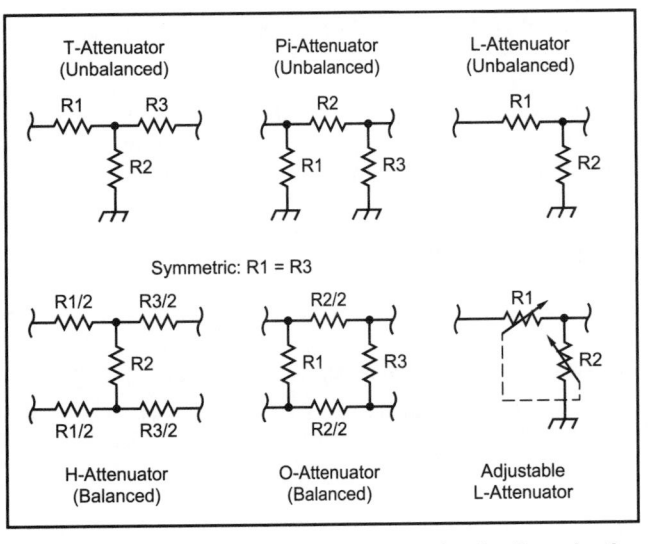

Figure 12.46—Several common attenuator circuits. To make the attenuators symmetric, make the values of R1 and R3 equal.

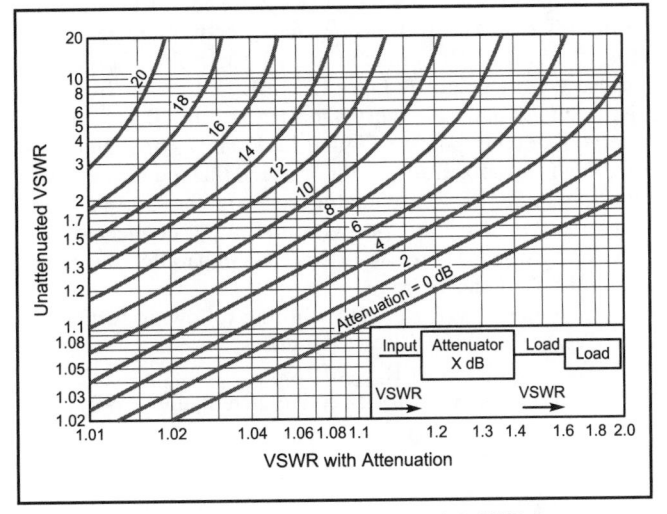

Figure 12.47—Attenuation can prevent a high SWR from upsetting a 50 Ω signal source. It can also mask an SWR problem at your antenna!

## Table 12.3
### Resistance Values for Symmetric T and Pi Resistive Attenuators

| Pi-Network Attenuators (50 Ω) | | | T-Network Attenuators (50 Ω) | | |
|---|---|---|---|---|---|
| Atten (dB) | R1, R3 (Ω) | R2 (Ω) | Atten (dB) | R1, R3 (Ω) | R2 (Ω) |
| 1 | 870.0 | 5.8 | 1 | 2.9 | 433.3 |
| 2 | 436.0 | 11.6 | 2 | 5.7 | 215.2 |
| 3 | 292.0 | 17.6 | 3 | 8.5 | 141.9 |
| 4 | 221.0 | 23.8 | 4 | 11.3 | 104.8 |
| 5 | 178.6 | 30.4 | 5 | 14.0 | 82.2 |
| 6 | 150.5 | 37.3 | 6 | 16.6 | 66.9 |
| 7 | 130.7 | 44.8 | 7 | 19.0 | 55.8 |
| 8 | 116.0 | 52.8 | 8 | 21.5 | 47.3 |
| 9 | 105.0 | 61.6 | 9 | 23.8 | 40.6 |
| 10 | 96.2 | 71.2 | 10 | 26.0 | 35.0 |
| 11 | 89.2 | 81.6 | 11 | 28.0 | 30.6 |
| 12 | 83.5 | 93.2 | 12 | 30.0 | 26.8 |
| 13 | 78.8 | 106.0 | 13 | 31.7 | 23.5 |
| 14 | 74.9 | 120.3 | 14 | 33.3 | 20.8 |
| 15 | 71.6 | 136.1 | 15 | 35.0 | 18.4 |
| 16 | 68.8 | 153.8 | 16 | 36.3 | 16.2 |
| 17 | 66.4 | 173.4 | 17 | 37.6 | 14.4 |
| 18 | 64.4 | 195.4 | 18 | 38.8 | 12.8 |
| 19 | 62.6 | 220.0 | 19 | 40.0 | 11.4 |
| 20 | 61.0 | 247.5 | 20 | 41.0 | 10.0 |
| 21 | 59.7 | 278.2 | 21 | 41.8 | 9.0 |
| 22 | 58.6 | 312.7 | 22 | 42.6 | 8.0 |
| 23 | 57.6 | 351.9 | 23 | 43.4 | 7.1 |
| 24 | 56.7 | 394.6 | 24 | 44.0 | 6.3 |
| 25 | 56.0 | 443.1 | 25 | 44.7 | 5.6 |
| 30 | 53.2 | 789.7 | 30 | 47.0 | 3.2 |
| 35 | 51.8 | 1405.4 | 35 | 48.2 | 1.8 |
| 40 | 51.0 | 2500.0 | 40 | 49.0 | 1.0 |
| 45 | 50.5 | 4446.0 | 45 | 49.4 | 0.56 |
| 50 | 50.3 | 7905.6 | 50 | 49.7 | 0.32 |
| 55 | 50.2 | 14,058.0 | 55 | 49.8 | 0.18 |
| 60 | 50.1 | 25,000.0 | 60 | 49.9 | 0.10 |

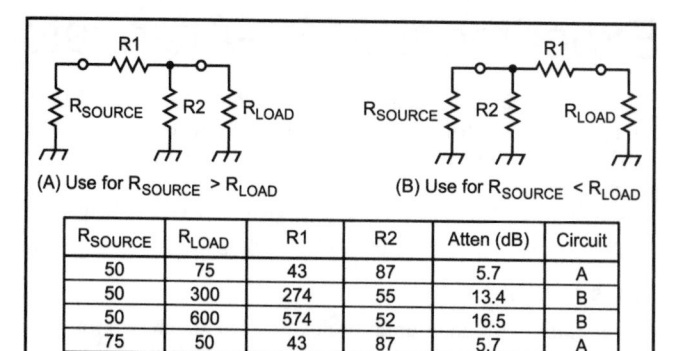

| R$_{SOURCE}$ | R$_{LOAD}$ | R1 | R2 | Atten (dB) | Circuit |
|---|---|---|---|---|---|
| 50 | 75 | 43 | 87 | 5.7 | A |
| 50 | 300 | 274 | 55 | 13.4 | B |
| 50 | 600 | 574 | 52 | 16.5 | B |
| 75 | 50 | 43 | 87 | 5.7 | A |
| 75 | 300 | 260 | 87 | 11.4 | B |
| 75 | 600 | 561 | 80 | 14.8 | B |
| 300 | 50 | 274 | 55 | 13.4 | A |
| 300 | 75 | 260 | 87 | 11.4 | A |
| 300 | 600 | 424 | 424 | 7.7 | B |
| 600 | 50 | 574 | 42 | 16.5 | A |
| 600 | 75 | 561 | 80 | 14.8 | A |
| 600 | 300 | 424 | 424 | 7.7 | A |

Figure 12.48—Minimum-loss attenuators match system impedances while exacting the least amount of signal energy.

expect a low VSWR to maintain their calibrated output level and purity. The input impedance of circuits such as filters, transmission lines and antennas is often not 50 Ω, however. An attenuator in front of the circuit being tested keeps the VSWR low at the generator's output.

Suppose you want to test a series-resonant trap to notch out a strong local broadcast station. The impedance of the filter will be just a few ohms, let's say 5 Ω at the notch frequency, and very high elsewhere. If you have the filter connected across a 50 Ω receiver input, the VSWR at the generator output will rise to 10:1 at the notch frequency. This will likely upset the generator calibration and degrade the accuracy of your filter attenuation measurements.

What happens if you put the 50 Ω, 10 dB attenuator between the generator and the filter? Because energy to and from the filter is reduced by 10 dB in each direction, the generator thinks the 10:1 SWR is much lower, 1.18:1. SWR is reduced because the attenuator reduces the reflected power from the mismatched load to a very small amount—0.7% of the generator's output power.[2] **Figure 12.47** shows how much attenuation from a fixed attenuator or a feed line reduces VSWR.
- Put the 50 Ω, 10 dB attenuator back together and measure the resistance at the input with the output connected to a 51 Ω resistor, a 5 Ω resistor (two 10 Ω in parallel), an open-circuit and a short-circuit.
- Compute the VSWR for each with the following formula:
  VSWR = R$_{meas}$/50 (if R$_{meas}$>50 Ω)
  VSWR = 50/R$_{meas}$ (if R$_{meas}$<50 Ω)
  The 10 dB pad is pretty effective at reducing SWR, isn't it?

## Using an Attenuator for Impedance Matching

You might be more interested in making an attenuator match the impedance of two systems than in creating a fixed amount of loss. This can be done effectively with just a few resistors in an L configuration, similar to that shown in Figure 12.46. It is desired to match the impedances while creating as little extra loss as possible. These are called *minimum loss* attenuators.

**Figure 12.48** shows the L attenuator circuits used for this application and several sets of values that make useful impedance-matching attenuators. If you have other impedances to match, an on-line calculator is available at **home.sandiego. edu/~ekim/e194rfs01/minl_atten/minlosatten.html**.

## Suggested Reading

Enter "audio attenuator" into an Internet search engine to find many different links. If you'd like to try a useful attenuator construction project, see the article at **www.arrl.org/tis/info/ pdf/9506033.pdf**.

## Shopping List
- 10 (2 each)—10, 39, 51, 75 and 100 Ω, ¼ W resistors

## Next Month

To transfer control and data signals between equipment with different grounds, engineers often use electro-optical components. Join in as we attempt to shed light on the workings of the optocoupler.

The Hands-On Radio Web site is **www.arrl.org/tis/info/ html/hands-on-radio/**.

[2]The attenuator reduces the power reaching the load by 10 dB. The reflected power is 1.7 dB below the forward power (return loss), which the attenuator reduces by another 10 dB for a total round trip loss of 21.7 dB. This corresponds to a VSWR of 1.18:1.

# Experiment #14—Optocouplers

Trying to pass a signal between two circuits that don't share a common ground would be quite difficult but for the *optocoupler*. Also called an *optoisolator*, these handy devices use light to transfer a signal between circuits without using a direct connection. You'll find them used to isolate sensitive circuits, provide safety barrier between operators and high-voltage circuits and replace relays in low-power applications. Let's learn how they work.

## Terms to Learn

- *Current-Transfer Ratio (CTR)*—the ratio of output current to the LED input current expressed as a percentage
- *Rise Time and Fall Time*—rise time refers to increasing signals and fall time to decreasing signals. Both refer to the time it takes for a circuit's output to reach 90% of the final output level after a sudden change at its input
- *Isolation Voltage*—the maximum rated voltage difference between an optoisolator's output and input

## Background

The optocoupler was a serendipitous discovery. Early transistors were contained in metal cans with wire leads. Where they passed through the can, tiny glass beads around the wire kept them insulated. Troubleshooting a mysterious current leakage problem, technicians discovered that light entering through the beads caused the transistor to conduct slightly—transistor junctions were light sensitive! After the invention of the LED, the modern optocoupler was created.

One of the most popular IC optocouplers is the 4N35, one of a whole family of similar devices. Inside the IC, an infrared LED is positioned so that it shines on an exposed transistor junction. The photons of light take the place of base current, turning on the transistor. Optocouplers are available with SCRs, FETs, diodes, logic gates and driver amplifiers for outputs.

Central to design with optocouplers is the *current transfer ratio (CTR)*, a factor specified in percent. CTR is very similar to a transistor's current gain, or beta. As in a transistor, for a given input or *forward current*, $I_f$, through the LED, the output current, $I_C$, can only reach CTR $\times I_f$.

$$CTR\ (\%) = [I_C\ /\ I_f\ ] \times 100 \qquad [Eq\ 1]$$

CTR depends on the level of $I_f$ and is usually specified as a maximum and minimum value for a given value of $I_f$ and voltage across the output transistor. For example, the Agilent data sheet for the 4N35 (Figure 4, as shown in **literature.agilent.com/litweb/pdf/5988-4114EN.pdf**) has a graph of CTR versus $I_f$ showing that CTR is optimum for a range in $I_f$ of between 5 and 40 mA, dropping rapidly above and below that range.

Typical CTR values for optocouplers range from 50 to 300, with $I_f$ in a range of 1 to 20 mA. The 4N35 is specified to have a minimum CTR of 100% with an $I_f$ of 10 mA and a $V_{CE}$ of 10 V across the output transistor. On Figure 4 of the data sheet, find $I_f$ of 10 mA and trace upward to the curve on the graph labeled "$R_{BE} = \infty$." All are comfortably over 100%.

What's up with those curves labeled "$R_{BE} = \infty$, 500k and 100k?" Figure 1 shows the internal connections or *pin-outs* of the 4N35. You'll see that the base of the output transistor is connected to pin 6. CTR can be controlled by connecting the base to the emitter with a resistor, $R_{BE}$, so that some of the current created by the LED's light is diverted around the base-emitter junction. Conversely, the base pin can be used to bias the transistor on. For most designs, this connection is left

open—do not ground it or tie it to a power supply voltage.

Optocouplers may be a great solution to isolating circuits from one another, but they are much slower than a transistor to turn on and off. This is because the photons that fall on the phototransistor take some time to diffuse into and out of the base—more time than with direct connections to the base. *rise time*, $t_r$, and *fall time*, $t_f$, are the parameters used to specify the switching speed of the output transistor. You'll find them in the data sheet's "Electrical Specifications" table. Data sheet Figures 9 and 10 show the effect of the load resistance on switching speed and frequency response. As $R_L$ is reduced $I_C$ increases, which means that the transistor reacts quicker to the incoming photons and when turning off, gets rids of them faster. Switching speed is particularly important when the optocoupler is being used to transmit digital data where signal edges need to be clean and fast.

To design an optocoupler circuit, you need to know the output load and power supply voltage. For example, if you are going to drive a reed relay, the coil resistance, say 500 $\Omega$, is $R_L$. If the power supply is 12 V, the optocoupler's output will have to sink 24 mA. For a CTR of 100%, that requires $I_f$ = 24 mA. Assuming an input voltage of 5 V and the typical forward voltage drop of the LED, 1.2 V:

$$R_{in} = (V_{in} - V_f)\ /\ I_f \ \text{ and } \ I_f = (V_{in} - V_f)\ /\ R_{in} \qquad [Eq\ 2]$$
$$= (5 - 1.2)\ /\ 24 = 158\ \Omega\text{—use a 150 }\Omega\text{ resistor}$$

The speed of the optocoupler is often a concern, as well. If you are going to use it to transmit digital data (a common application) the sum of rise and fall times should be less than 10% of the duration of the fastest bit you will send. For example, one bit of 9600 baud data is approximately 10 µs wide, so $t_r + t_f$ must be less than 1 µs. If you look at Figure 9 of the data sheet, you'll see that the 4N35 is not a good choice for 9600 baud data! For a load resistance of 1 kΩ, $t_r + t_f = 40$ µs, so the narrowest data pulse would be 400 µs—about 240 baud.

## Working with Optocouplers

The first set of tests we'll do illustrate the effect of CTR and load resistance, $R_L$, on the ability of the optocoupler to transfer a signal.

Start by connecting the circuit shown in **Figure 12.49**. If your signal generator can add a dc offset to its output signal, you don't need the diode and 2.2 kΩ resistor. Set the signal generator to output a 3 kHz square wave and adjust the voltage

---

### Maximum, Minimum and Typical— The Data Sheet Specifications

Properly interpreting these figures from a data sheet can be crucial to a successful design, particularly if a run of several circuits will be built. Maximum and Minimum are *guaranteed values*. All parts will fall between these two values. Depending on your design, either may be the *worst-case* that your circuit should be able to accommodate. A "typical" value is usually the most common or an average value (they're not always the same). If you're only building one circuit, using a typical value is probably okay, but you may have to test a few parts for getting one with "typical" performance.

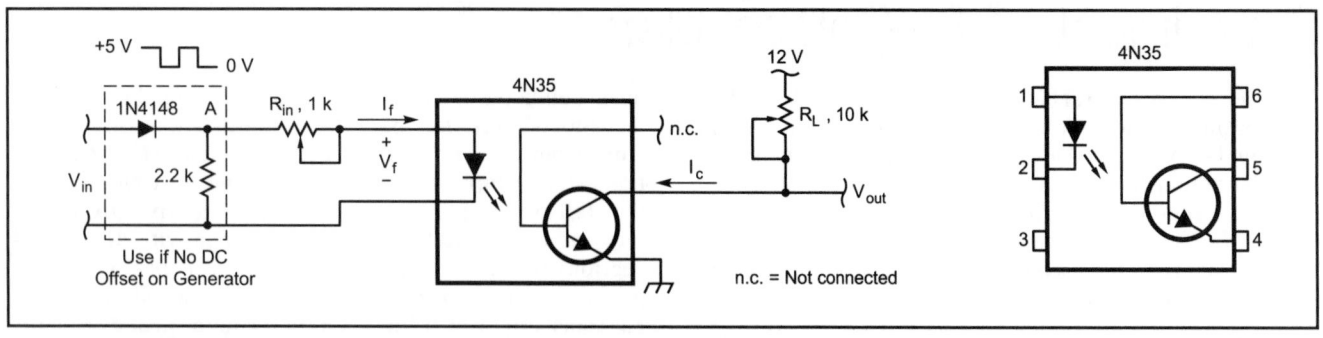

**Figure 12.49—Adjust the input and output resistances to observe the effect of current levels on CTR and on switching speed.**

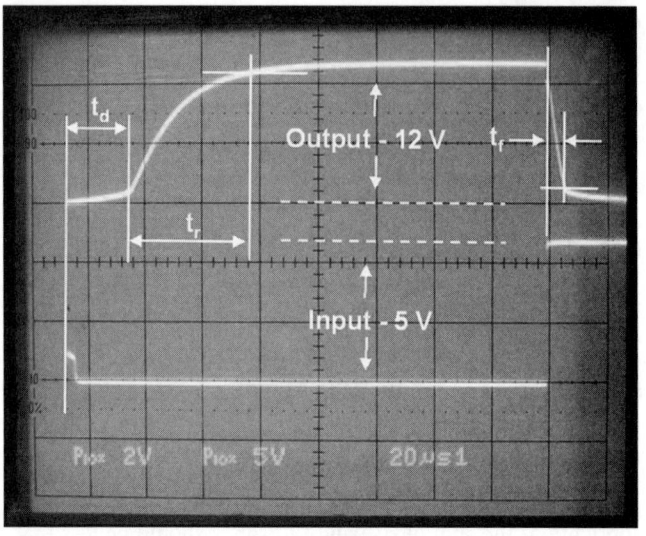

**Figure 12.50—The upper trace shows the output waveform. Notice the significant rise and fall times of the output waveform.**

so that the waveform at point A alternates between 5 V and ground. Set $R_{in}$ to 1 kΩ and $R_L$ to 5 kΩ. Use Eq 2 to calculate $I_f$.

Connect the oscilloscope to point A and to the output. You should see complementary waveforms with the output low with the input high, and vice versa. Once you have the circuit working, zoom in as shown in **Figure 12.50**. Notice that the rising edge of the output is rounded with respect to the falling edge. (Hint—trigger on the falling edge of the input signal and set the sweep speed to 20 μs/division.)

- Measure the delay from the falling edge of the input signal to where the output begins to rise. This is $t_d$. Estimate $t_r$ and $t_f$. Reduce $R_L$ to approximately 2.5 kΩ to see the effect of increasing $I_C$ on $t_r$ and $t_f$. Adjust $R_{in}$ to 600 and 400 Ω and observe the effect of varying $I_f$. Return $R_{in}$ to 500 Ω.
- Continue to reduce $R_L$. The minimum output voltage level will begin to rise above ground. Stop when it reaches 5 V and measure $R_L$. Calculate $I_C = (12\,V–5\,V) / R_L$. Use the previously calculated value of $I_f$ to calculate CTR using Eq 1. My 4N35 had a CTR of 113%, exceeding the specified minimum value.
- Return both potentiometers to their original values. Increase the frequency of the input signal to see what happens as $t_r$ and $t_f$ begin to eat up the signal.
- Experiment by changing input signal level and output voltage while observing the effect on output voltage levels. Try a design—pick a value of $R_L$, an input voltage, and a power supply voltage, then figure out $R_{in}$ and try it!

### Suggested Reading

Chapter 9 in *The Art of Electronics*, by Horowitz and Hill, discusses optocouplers as a means of interfacing with logic circuits. Agilent Technologies publishes a wide variety of excellent application notes and the *Optocoupler Designer's Guide* (Agilent part number 5988-4082EN) is worth the download at **literature.agilent.com/litweb/pdf/5988-4082EN.pdf**.

### Shopping List

- 4N35 optocoupler (available from many suppliers)
- 1N4148 diode
- 2.2 kΩ resistor, 1 kΩ and 10 kΩ potentiometers

### Next Month

We return to power supply design with the first installment of a multipart experiment that will introduce you to switching power supply technology.

The Hands-On Radio Web site is **www.arrl.org/tis/info/html/hands-on-radio/**.

# Experiment #15: Switchmode Regulators—*Part 1*

In case you hadn't noticed, the dc power supply has undergone a radical transformation. A 20 A, 12 V dc supply now weighs just a couple of pounds and is about the same size as a couple of good sized paperback novels. These are *switching* supplies that are much more efficient in delivering power. This month, you'll meet the *switchmode regulator*.

## Terms to Learn
- *Buck* and *boost*—regulators that configure the inductor to subtract from and add to the input voltage, respectively
- *Commutating diode*—a diode that provides a path for inductor current to flow when the switch is turned off

## Background

A power supply with a linear regulator (see Experiment #8)[1] acts like a smart resistor that constantly changes its value to drop the output voltage by just the right amount. This is inefficient, dissipating the unwanted power as heat. Neither can a linear regulator create an output voltage higher than its input.

The pass transistor in a linear regulator is operated in its *linear region* between cutoff (zero collector current, $I_C$) and saturation (minimum collector-to-emitter voltage, $V_{CE}$), and the power it dissipates is equal to $I_C \times V_{CE}$. For example, if I'm drawing 5 A at 12 V from the regulator output and the input voltage is 18 V, the pass transistor must dissipate $(18 - 12) \times 5 = 30$ W. No wonder such big heat sinks are required! 60 W (12 V × 5 A) output for a total of 90 W supplied means only 67% efficiency.

Instead of using the pass transistor as a resistor, the switchmode regulator takes advantage of the fact that when either the current through or the voltage across a device is low, power dissipation (I × V) is also low. This allows the regulator to act more like a power bank, doling out power in small packets, through a switch, at low loss.

Switchmode regulators also make use of the relationship between inductor voltage and current shown in Equation 1:

$$V = L \, DI / Dt = L \times \text{change in I per unit time} \qquad [Eq\ 1]$$

We can also turn Equation 1 around to find inductor current. For a constant applied voltage, current increases linearly with time according to this equation:

$$I = V \times t / L \qquad [Eq\ 2]$$

This is just what a switchmode supply does—apply voltage to an inductor for a fixed amount of time (a quantity measured in *volt-seconds*) in order to build up a certain amount of current. For example, 12 V applied for 10 µs to a 100 µH inductor results in a current that ramps up to 1.2 A. From the equation for energy stored in an inductor:

$$E = \tfrac{1}{2} LI^2 \qquad [Eq\ 3]$$

substitute Equation 2 for current into Equation 3 and come up with:

$$E = \tfrac{1}{2} L(V \times t / L)^2 = \tfrac{1}{2} (V \times t)^2 / L \qquad [Eq\ 4]$$

This means that for a specific value of inductor, the volt-seconds of the pulses determines the rate at which energy is delivered, which is power. With the pulse rate constant, you can vary power by controlling pulse width, and vice versa. Voilà! We have a power supply...almost. We still need a way of smoothing out the current, and we need to take care of one other problem.

The problem is that current through an inductor cannot change value instantaneously. Equation 1 says that if I try to change the current through an inductor, a voltage will be developed across the inductor that resists the change in current. For example, if I try to suddenly interrupt the current, a very large voltage will appear across the inductor. This is why *kickback diodes* are required across relay coils.

To avoid having to deal with these high-voltage transients,

<hr>

[1]See p 12-17.

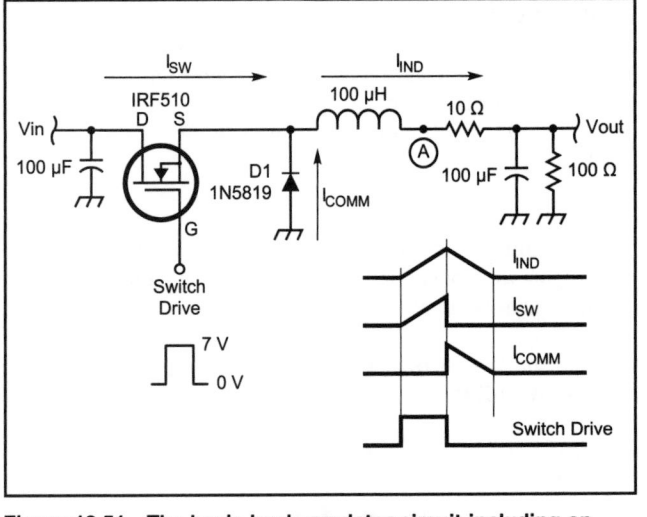

**Figure 12.51—The basic buck regulator circuit including an FET as the switch. Note the commutating diode, D1, which keeps the inductor current flowing between switch drive pulses and avoids the voltage transient at the FET switch.**

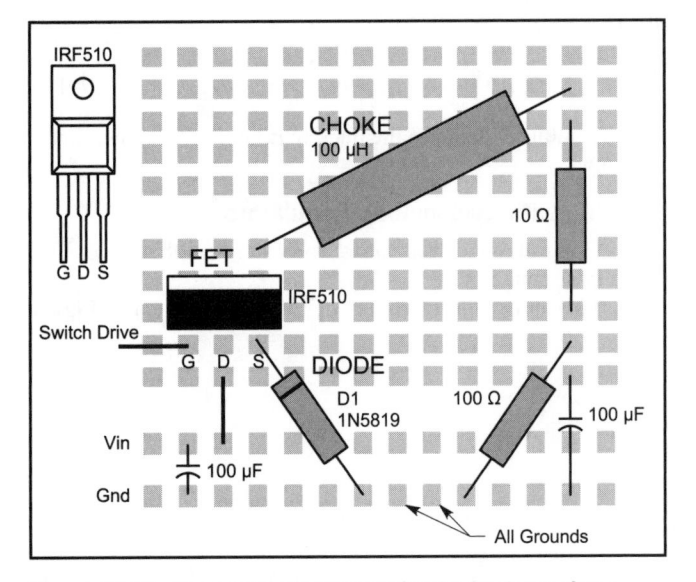

**Figure 12.52—Recommended layout for the buck regulator of Figure 12.51 on a common prototyping board.**

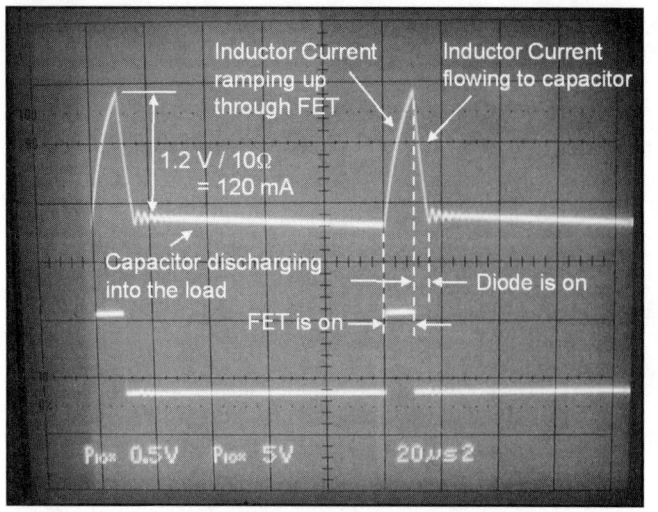

**Figure 12.53—The top trace is the voltage at point A of Figure 1, showing current through the inductor. The bottom trace is the FET gate signal.**

it's better to figure out a way to let the inductor current keep flowing between pulses when the switch is off. The regulator in **Figure 12.51** accomplishes this with a *commutating diode* (D1). The switch transistor applies voltage to the inductor for a fixed length of time. This causes the inductor current to "ramp up" until the transistor is turned off. A high voltage transient would then appear at the FET source because the output capacitor holds voltage on its end of the inductor constant. Instead, a diode is connected from ground to the inductor. When the transistor turns off, the inductor current just switches over to flow through the diode. The current doesn't change and so no big voltage transient is generated. Current continues to flow into the output capacitor, producing an easy-to-filter triangular current waveform as shown in Figure 12.51. The current in the diode is called *commutating current* because it switches with each cycle of operation. When the input switch is turned off, the inductor gradually "discharges" its current into the output capacitor and then waits for the next pulse. The 10 Ω resistor acts as a current sampling resistor so you can look at current with an oscilloscope.

This configuration is called a "buck" regulator because the inductor voltage will *oppose* or *buck* the power supply voltage when it is turned off. The output voltage of a buck regulator is simply:

$$V_{OUT} = V_{IN} \times \text{switch duty cycle} \qquad \text{[Eq 5]}$$

The output voltage of the buck regulator is less than that at the input.

### Working with Switchmode Regulators

Let's build a buck regulator. You can reuse the power FET from Experiment #12.[2]

• Start by building the circuit of Figure 12.51 using **Figure**

[2]See p 12-25.

**12.52** as a layout guideline. Since we are talking about creating rapid current rise and fall times, it's a good idea to keep leads and connection lengths short. Be sure the inductor you use is adequately rated and not a low-power choke that will either saturate or burn out. The commutating diode must be a fast-recovery type so that it can switch current quickly.

• Set your generator to output pulses at 10 kHz with a 10% duty cycle by using the "symmetry" control on the square wave setting to skew the waveform to produce narrow pulses. If you can only generate a 50% duty cycle square wave, increase the frequency to around 50 kHz. See the previous experiment for a way to create a 0 to 7 V signal from a generator with no dc offset capability.

• Apply 3 V (you can also use a pair of D cells in series) to the input of the regulator. We're only using 3 V at the input in order to be able to apply sufficient voltage to the gate of the FET. 4 V between the gate and source is required.

• Put one scope probe on the SWITCH DRIVE signal and one at point A. You should see waveforms like those in **Figure 12.53**. The current (top trace) through the inductor ramps up during the time that the switch is ON and back down when the switch is OFF. The peak current in my circuit is about 120 mA—or 1.2 V across the 10 Ω current sample resistor.

• Remove the output capacitor and measure the output voltage with a voltmeter. You should see a voltage that is close to 10% of the input voltage. Adjust the pulse duty cycle to see if you can verify Equation 5.

• Reconnect the output capacitor and experiment with the pulse duty cycle to see the effect on output voltage. Change the load resistor value to see how much load the regulator can supply without a big change in output voltage.

### Suggested Reading

Not much information on switching supply operation is available in the ham radio press, which is surprising, considering their popularity. Ray Mack, WD5IFS, wrote a detailed two-part article "Understanding Switching Power Supplies" in the Sep/Oct 2002 and Jan/Feb 2003 issues of *QEX*. There is also a good on-line tutorial about switching regulators at **www.web-ee.com/primers/files/webex9.pdf**.

### Shopping List

• 100 µH choke capable of handling 1 A, RadioShack 273-102 or equivalent
• IRF510 transistor (RadioShack 276-2072)
• 1N5819 fast-recovery rectifier (available from Jameco, Digi-Key and other vendors)
• 2—100 µF, 25 V tantalum capacitors
• 10 Ω, 100 Ω, 1/4 W resistors

### Next Month

Continuing with the switchmode theme, next month we'll investigate the boost converter that can create a higher output voltage than its input.

*Hands-On Radio Web site:* **www.arrl.org/tis/info/html/hands-on-radio/**.

# Experiment #16: Switchmode Regulators—*Part 2*

Last month, we looked at the switchmode power converter. We constructed a *buck regulator* that outputs a voltage *lower* than its input. This month, the inductor in that circuit is used to create a *higher* output voltage. Let's examine the *boost regulator*.

## Terms to Learn

- *Continuous and Discontinuous Mode*—In continuous mode, current flows in the inductor at all times. In discontinuous mode, inductor current only flows for part of the time.
- *Converter*—A circuit that transfers energy while converting it from one form to another, such as from a low voltage source to a high voltage load.
- *Saturated*—The state of an inductor core that cannot store any additional magnetic energy.

## Background

Strictly speaking, our circuits are *converters* and not really regulators; they transfer energy from the power supply to a load and in the process change the voltage. Unlike our two circuits, *regulators* control the output so that it matches a desired set point. However, our buck and boost circuits are typical of the fundamental circuitry used in a true switchmode regulator.

The ability of the boost regulator to increase the output voltage over that at the input is very handy. Boost regulators are used in many types of battery-powered equipment, allowing one or two 1.5 V cells to power equipment that requires 5 V or more.

**Figure 12.54** shows the boost regulator schematic. Like the buck regulator, the inductor carries all of the load current, but instead of being "downstream" from the switch transistor, it's now "upstream," with the switch connected between the inductor and ground. The commutating diode is now connected from the output of the inductor to the load capacitor.

At first, this looks funny—how can this possibly work? When the switch is ON, it's shorting the inductor to ground! The diode doesn't really look like it's doing anything at all, just passing current along to the output.

Let's start with the switch and the inductor. If the switch was never turned on at all, dc current would flow from the input source, through the inductor and diode, and on to the output capacitor. Output voltage would be less than the input

voltage by the amount of forward voltage drop across the diode—about 0.7 V.

What does turning the switch ON and routing that current to ground accomplish? As with the buck configuration, the purpose of the switch is to "charge" the inductor with energy stored in a magnetic field by applying voltage to the inductor. When the switch is turned OFF, the inductor current is interrupted, causing the voltage across the inductor to rapidly change from positive to negative in the amount of $L \times (\Delta i / \Delta t)$. Since the input capacitor holds the inductor's input voltage constant during this period, the inductor's output voltage at the FET drain is forced to become greater than that of its input. This higher inductor output voltage forward biases D1 and allows the stored energy to be transferred to the output capacitor as current.

Inductor current gradually decreases until the inductor output voltage is insufficient to keep D1 forward biased. D1 then stops conducting with the output capacitor now charged to a higher voltage than at the power supply input. This is like pulling back a slingshot in order to release it and throw a weight to a higher level.

**Figure 12.56** shows how inductor voltage changes when the switch is turned ON and OFF. Initially, the inductor voltage is at the full input voltage with the switch holding its output at ground potential. (The voltage "droop" observed is due to the relatively small input capacitor being discharged.) When the switch turns OFF, inductor voltage immediately reverses. With its input voltage constant, the output voltage rises to a higher voltage than the input. (Remember that it is the voltage across the inductor that becomes negative, not voltage with respect to ground.) The inductor output voltage gradually decays as the stored energy is transferred through D1 to the output capacitor. This relationship is shown in a simplified way in Figure 12.54.

If all components were lossless and the switch frequency is held constant, the output voltage would be:

$$V_{OUT} = V_{IN} / (1 - \text{Duty Cycle}) \qquad \text{[Eq 1]}$$

This is because the inductor voltage is added to the input voltage only during the period during which it is discharging—a time directly proportional to charging time. The commutating diode, D1, contributes more loss in this circuit because it is in series with the supply current at all times, not just during one-

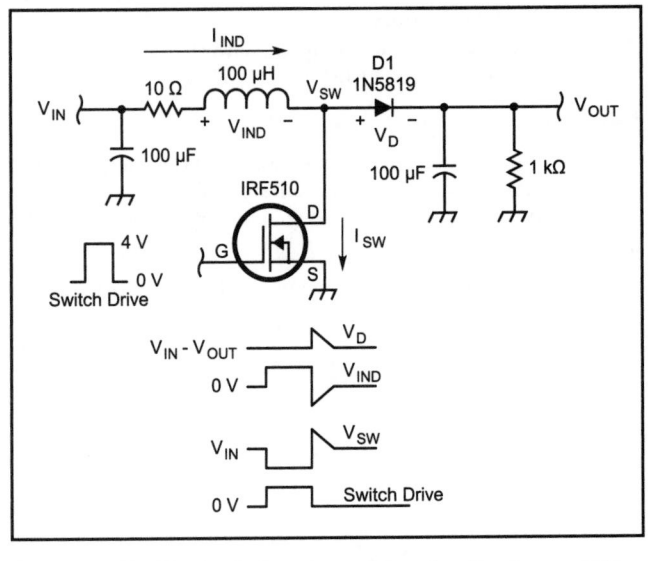

Figure 12.54—The basic boost regulator circuit using an FET as a switch.

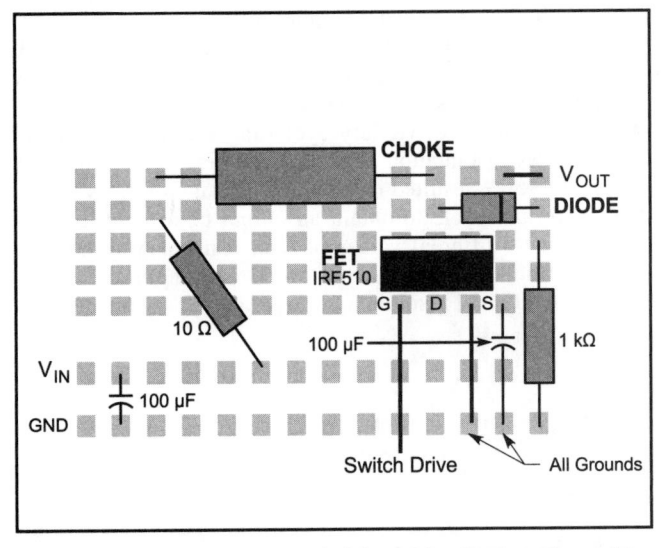

Figure 12.55—The recommended layout for the boost regulator of Figure 12.54. It is constructed on a common prototyping board.

half of the inductor charge/discharge cycle. The diode's forward voltage drop is subtracted from the available output voltage.

Understanding how the inductor energy is stored and released is key to the operation of switchmode regulators. Just as important is the realization that the input and output capacitors temporarily hold voltage constant while the voltage across the inductor can change quickly. This constant voltage enables the changing inductor voltage to be either *added* to the input voltage (as in the *boost* configuration) or *subtracted* from the input voltage (as in the *buck* configuration).

Another important distinction between different types of switchmode designs is whether inductor current flows all the time or just some of the time. The former is called *continuous mode*. If current flows only part of the time, as in our buck and boost regulators, that is a *discontinuous mode* design. Inductors in a continuous mode circuit must be selected so that the energy in the core that is always present does not cause the core to *saturate*, like a bucket being overfilled with water.

## Building a Boost Regulator

Since the switch drain is connected to the inductor and the source to ground, instead of in series with the inductor, the gate drive voltage can be reduced to 4 V. In addition, to more clearly observe the boost function, the output load resistor is increased to 1 kΩ.

- Build the circuit shown in Figure 12.54, and lay it out according to the general guidelines of **Figure 12.55**. As with the buck converter, keep leads short and direct, and use a common ground for the signal and oscilloscope leads.
- Set the function generator to supply 10 kHz pulses, with a duty cycle of approximately 10%, a minimum voltage of 0 V and a maximum of 4 V. Apply 3 V dc to the input (two D cells in series will work). If your function generator can't add a dc offset, see experiment #14 for a method of generating the proper waveform. If limited to a 50% duty cycle, increase the frequency to approximately 50 kHz.
- The output voltage measured on a voltmeter should be somewhat above 4 V dc, depending on the type of inductors and capacitors you use. My circuit's output was 4.7 V dc.
- If your oscilloscope has the ability to add two channels of input together on the screen, this would be an excellent time to learn how to use that facility. Typically, channel 1 is connected to the inductor input, channel 2 to the inductor output, and the two channels are added together, with channel 2 set to invert the input signal. Both channels must be set to the same vertical input sensitivity (volts/division) in order to perform the operation correctly. The result should look something like Figure 12.56 and is a display of channel 1 plus an inverted channel 2.
- Vary the switch drive duty cycle and see how the output compares to Equation 1. In my case, increasing the duty cycle to 50% resulted in an output voltage of 8.3 V dc.
- Set the duty cycle to obtain an output of 6 V dc. Experiment with different values of load resistance to see how that affects output voltage. *Caution*—removing the load completely will result in a fairly large output voltage (pos-

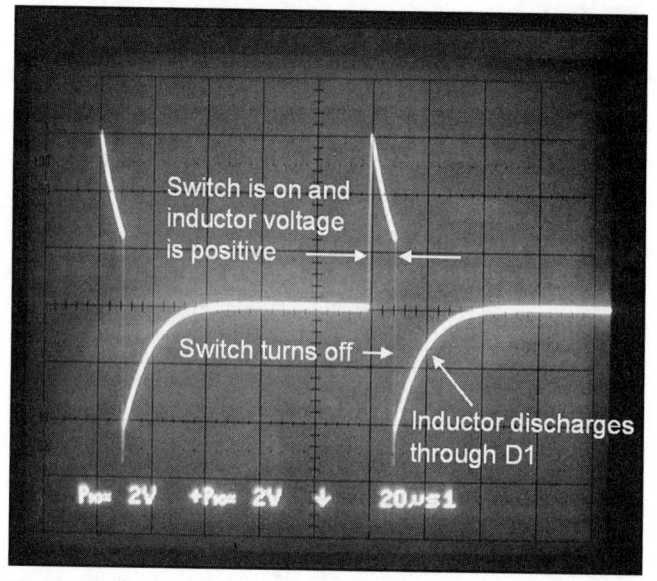

Figure 12.56—An oscilloscope photo of the inductor voltage. The droop on the top portion of the waveform is the input filter capacitor being partially discharged. Note how quickly the voltage reverses when the switch is turned OFF.

sibly as high as 70 to 80 V dc) as the inductor discharges into the open circuit, pumping the capacitor full of charge. This can easily exceed the capacitor's working voltage rating and cause it to fail.
- As you change the load, readjust either duty cycle or frequency to return the output voltage to 6 V dc. This is just what a regulator circuit would do to control the output of a switching supply!

## Suggested Reading

No additional reading material is suggested beyond that recommended last month.

## Shopping List

There are no new parts from last month, but here is the list for those of you just starting:
- 100 μH choke capable of handling 1 A (RadioShack 273-102 or equivalent)
- IRF510 transistor (RadioShack 276-2072)
- 1N5819 fast-recovery rectifier (available from Jameco, Digi-Key and other vendors)
- Two 100 μF, 25 V dc tantalum capacitors
- 10 Ω and 100 Ω, ¼ W resistors

## Next Month

Back into the realm of op-amps we will go for a quick spin cycle through the world of the oscillator. We'll investigate the phase shift oscillator—a simple source for sine waves in the audio region.

*Hands-On Radio Web site:* **www.arrl.org/tis/info/html/hands-on-radio/**.

# Experiment #17: The Phase-Shift Oscillator

Any system having gain and a little output to input feedback can quickly become an oscillator. Anyone who has operated a public-address system can attest to that fact! This month we'll look at a very basic circuit that illustrates the fundamental principles of oscillators—the *phase-shift oscillator*.

## Terms to Learn

- *Network*—circuits with multiple sections of similar components and multiple input and output connections
- *Latch*—to enter and remain in a steady state
- *Loading*—changing the performance of a circuit by placing an impedance at the input or output

## Background

There is an old saying: "Amplifiers are oscillators that *don't* and oscillators are amplifiers that *do*." An amplifier is at the heart of every oscillator, as shown in the block diagram of the basic oscillator in **Figure 12.57**. The feedback network is connected so that some of the output signal is fed back into amplifier's input. If this system is going to work as an oscillator at some frequency, two things must occur. The portion of the signal fed back to the input, $\beta V_{OUT}$, has to arrive with just the right phase to reinforce and not cancel the input signal. The amplifier also has to have enough gain, A, to compensate for losses in the feedback circuit.

In the block diagram, the output signal, $V_{OUT}$, is equal to $AV_1$. $V_1$ is equal to the input signal, $V_{IN}$, minus the fraction of the output signal fed back to the input, $\beta V_{OUT}$. This means that the overall gain of the circuit is:

$$V_{OUT} / V_{IN} = A / 1 + Ab \qquad \text{[Eq 1]}$$

All is nice and stable, unless $A\beta = -1$, in which case gain becomes infinite! When this happens, the amplifier's output heads for infinite voltage, but it reaches the power supply voltage and has to stop. Depending on the circuit's design, the output will either *latch* at that voltage or turn around and head for the other limiting voltage (either ground or the opposite power supply voltage). In the second case, we now have an oscillator because the circuit will continue zoom from one voltage to the other in a continuous cycle.

How do we design a circuit such that $A\beta = 1$? Consider that, to a sine wave, multiplying by –1 is the same as adding 180° of phase shift. The requirement for $A\beta$ can then be rewritten to say that the product must be equal to 1 but with a phase shift of 180°. If you assume that all of the phase shift occurs in the feedback circuit and that the amplifier has enough gain to make up for any losses in the feedback circuit, our equation is satisfied and the oscillator *does*!

Figure 12.58 shows such a circuit, called a *phase-shift oscillator*. To be sure, there are other circuits with better perfor-

mance, but this one is the closest to the basic circuit we've just discussed. Let's start with the feedback network formed by the three pairs of 10 kΩ resistors and 0.1 μF capacitors. Each forms a low-pass RC filter that shifts the phase of the input signal—0 to 90° as frequency is increased. At some frequency, the phase shift will be 60°. When three identical sections are cascaded, each contributes 60° of phase shift to make 180°, the necessary phase shift to form an oscillator. The frequency at which each section contributes 60° of phase shift is:

$$f = (\tan 60°) / 2pRC = 1.73 / 6.28\,RC = 0.28 / RC \qquad \text{[Eq 2]}$$

For our combination of 10 kΩ and 0.1 μF, that frequency is 275 Hz. At the frequency at which 60° of phase shift occurs, the filter also reduces the amplitude of the input signal by half. If three sections are connected back-to-back, then the total reduction in signal level is $1/2 \times 1/2 \times 1/2 = 1/8 = 0.125$, which is our value of β. To make $A\beta$ at least 1, A must then be at least 8 and that is controlled by the ratio of $R_f$ to $R_i$. $R_f$ is made variable to allow for adjustment in gain to account for component variations and other effects, as we shall see.

## Working with a Phase-Shift Oscillator

For this circuit, you will need a power supply that can provide both positive and negative dc voltages of 6 to 12 V. Since current draw is low, you can use batteries to provide power.

- Start by building the circuit of Figure 12.58. The extra 10 μF capacitors prevent feedback through the op-amp power supply pins. Set the potentiometer for the highest resistance between its connections.
- Connect power and you should see something that looks like a square wave at the output of the op-amp. This shows the op-amp output swinging back and forth between the power supply voltages as it unsuccessfully tries to balance the current in $R_f$ with that coming from the feedback network.
- Reduce the potentiometer resistance to obtain an undistorted sine wave that peaks a volt or so below the power supply voltages as seen in **Figure 12.59**. (This may be a touchy adjustment.) If you have a dual-channel oscilloscope, observe the input and output voltages of each RC section and verify that each contributes approximately 60°.
- Measure the period of the output waveform (one complete cycle) and calculate the frequency of the oscillator (f=1/period). Measure the resistance of the potentiometer

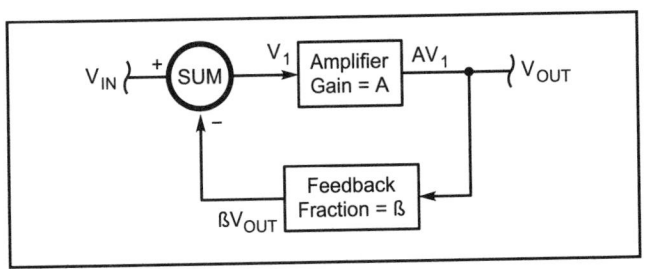

**Figure 12.57—This fundamental block diagram describes an oscillator as a pair of circuits, one providing gain and the other feeding back a fraction of the output signal into the input.**

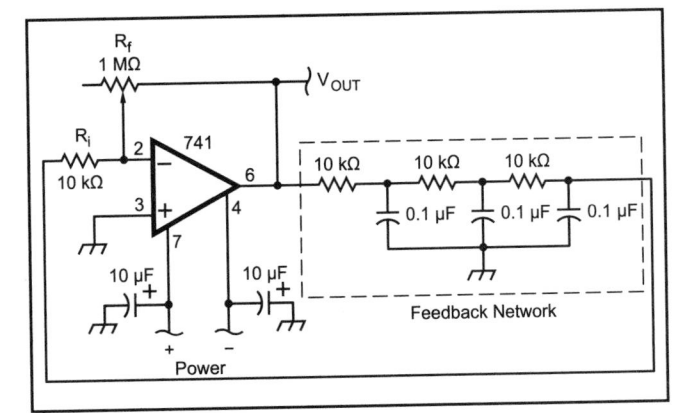

**Figure 12.58—The phase shift oscillator circuit. Each pair of 10 kΩ resistors and 0.1 μF capacitors in the feedback network adds 60° of phase shift at the frequency of oscillation.**

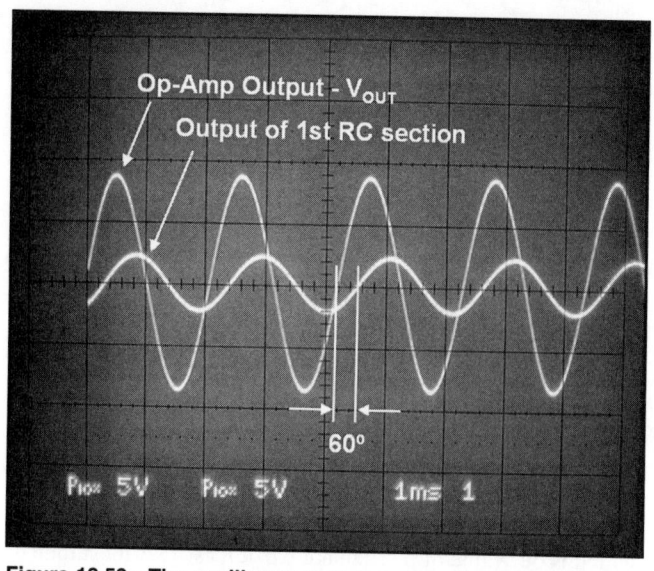

**Figure 12.59—The oscilloscope traces show the output signal from the op-amp and the smaller, phase-shifted signal at the output of the first RC filter section.**

$(R_f)$ after removing it from the circuit. Compute the amplifier's gain (A=resistance / 10 kΩ).

## Design Assumptions

You probably observed that the frequency was a lot different than the initial calculation of 275 Hz—my oscillator's frequency was 476 Hz. The voltage drop across each RC filter section was probably greater than $1/2$—my sections reduced the output to about 0.27 of the input. The gain of the amplifier will also be greater than 8 to compensate for that extra reduction. My potentiometer's resistance was 603 kΩ, for a gain of 60.3—approximately equal to $1 / (0.27 \times 0.27 \times 0.27)$.

These discrepancies result primarily from assumptions we made in the design process. Each RC section does not contribute exactly 60° because it is loaded by the next section in the network. That causes extra voltage drop and phase shift. The op-amp also contributes its own small amount of phase shift, meaning that the total feedback phase shift does not have to be exactly 180°. These two errors will result in a higher frequency at which $A\beta = -1$.

To see the effects of op-amp limitations, change the feedback capacitors from 0.1 μF to 0.001 μF. At this frequency, a 741 op-amp can't cause its output to change rapidly enough

to keep up and the output waveform will change to something that looks more like a triangle wave instead, no matter how you adjust amplifier gain.

## Buffered Oscillator

The phase-shift and voltage drop errors caused by the loading effects of each RC section can be eliminated by adding a *buffer* between each section. Replace the single op-amp with a quad op-amp such as the LM324. One op-amp section will replace the existing LM741. Add a *voltage follower* between each RC section by connecting an op-amp's output directly to its inverting input and connecting the input signal to the noninverting input. (This circuit is shown in the on-line reference listed below.)

Because the voltage follower presents a very high input impedance to the preceding circuit, each RC section can act more like the ideal filter we envisioned during the design process. The resulting frequency of oscillation and the gain required to achieve oscillation should be within 20% of the calculated values.

## Suggested Reading and a Donated Tool

*The ARRL Handbook* has an extensive chapter on oscillators, although not much on phase-shift oscillators. The section "How Oscillators Work" is highly recommended. A good application note, "The Design of Op-Amp Sine Wave Oscillators" is available on-line from Texas Instruments at **www.ti.com/sc/docs/apps/msp/journal/aug2000/aug_07.pdf**.

Another reader has graciously donated a software tool for Hands-On readers. Bill, N3TR, created a dandy spreadsheet to calculate resistor values for Pi and T attenuators. Enter input power, impedance and attenuation to get resistor values. The spreadsheet is available on the Hands-On Web site: **www.arrl.org/tis/info/html/hands-on-radio**.

## Shopping List

- LM741 (RadioShack 276-007) op-amp and (optional) LM324 quad op-amp (RadioShack 276-1711)
- 1 MΩ potentiometer
- 4—10 kΩ, $1/4$ W resistors
- 3 each—0.1 μF and 0.001 μF ceramic capacitors
- 2—10 μF, 16 V (or greater) electrolytic capacitors

## Next Month

Our next experiment will move from the workbench over to the blackboard as we discuss frequency response and decibels (dB). Understanding the mechanics and terminology of these important concepts is key to being a successful electronic experimenter.

# Experiment #18: Frequency Response

When the behavior of a circuit is dependent on frequency—and that's the case with just about any ac circuit—it's important to understand just how that circuit changes with frequency. That behavior description is called the circuit's *frequency response*. In mathematical terms it can be quite complex, but luckily there are some easy-to-understand methods of measuring and displaying frequency response. That's the topic this month and, along the way, we'll review what makes a dB a dB.

## Terms to Learn

- *Cutoff or Half-Power Frequency*—the frequency at which a circuit's output is one-half of some specified reference value (usually a maximum value of gain or response).
- *Magnitude Response*—a graph of a circuit's effect on the amplitude of a signal passing from that circuit's input to its output.
- *Phase Response*—a graph of a circuit's effect on the phase shift of a signal passing from that circuit's input to its output.

## Background

Technically, frequency response is an equation that describes how a circuit modifies a sine wave signal at any frequency. To most hams and experimenters, frequency response is usually represented as a pair of graphs. One graph, the magnitude response, shows how the circuit affects the signal's amplitude. The other, the phase response, describes the circuit's effect on the signal's phase.

Let's start with the most commonly seen response—magnitude. **Figure 12.60** shows an example: the magnitude response of a band-pass filter. The ratio of output to input amplitude in dB is shown on the Y axis with frequency on the X axis. (If you're not familiar with the decibel, take a detour to the sidebar, Decibels and Ratios.) The curve shows that the input signal is passed to the output with no loss (or 0 dB) between the frequency range of 200 Hz to 5 kHz. Above and below those frequencies the filter removes more and more of the signal until, at 1 Hz, only 1/200th (–23 dB) and, at 500 kHz, only 1/1000th (–30 dB) of the signal remains. At 20 Hz and 20 kHz, we see that the filter passes half of the input signal because the output is 3 dB lower than it is in the *passband*.

Many different types of magnitude measurements can be plotted compared to frequency—voltage, power, brightness, loudness and so on. The object is to show how a quantity or a ratio of quantities varies with frequency.

The phase response (more accurately, phase shift) graph shows how the phase of the circuit's output relates to that of the input for a sine wave signal. Phase is always measured from the input to the output. A negative value, such as –45°, means that the output is lagging the input. Leading phase does not mean that the output signal somehow appears before the input signal. It means only that once the input has been applied for a while, the phase of the output signal is a little ahead of the input.

**Figure 12.61** shows the phase response of a simple low-pass filter. At low frequencies, there is little effect on the phase. As the signal frequency rises, however, there is more and more phase shift until, at the cutoff frequency, there is 45° of lagging phase shift, plotted as a negative number. The phase shift then gradually approaches 90°.

## Obtaining a Frequency Response

With computer tools such as spreadsheets, it's easy to do the calculations and make a graph. If you don't have a spreadsheet, then graph paper (use semi-log paper if you can get it, with a linear axis for dB or phase and a logarithmic axis for frequency)[1] and a pencil will do just fine! A Microsoft *Excel* spreadsheet that you can use to make graphs is available on the Hands-On Radio Web site (**www.arrl.org/tis/info/HTML/Hands-On-Radio**).

There are some simple rules to follow whether using a spreadsheet or graph paper:

- Measure input and output in the same units, such as volts, and use the same measurement convention, such as RMS or peak-to-peak.
- Measure phase from the input to the output.
- Use 10 × log [ratio] for power and 20 × log [ratio] for voltage or current.

Measure the frequency response of the RC circuit shown in Figure 12.61. Set your function generator to output a sine wave of several volts. Connect it to $V_{in}$ and monitor it with one oscilloscope channel. Connect the other 'scope channel to $V_{out}$.

- You can measure the magnitude response with a voltmeter on its ac voltage setting if it will read RMS voltage accurately

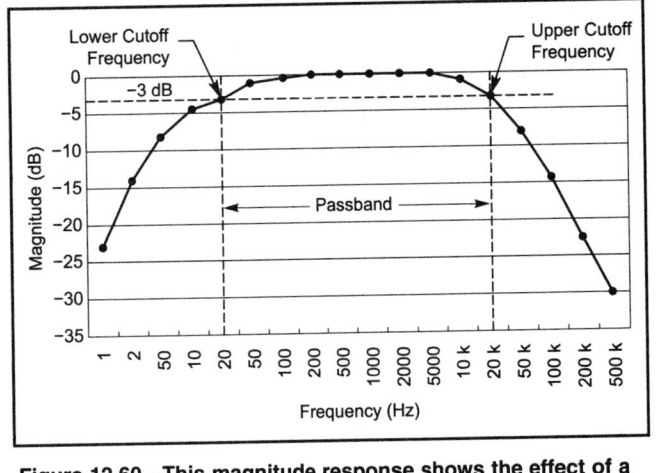

Figure 12.60—This magnitude response shows the effect of a band-pass circuit on a signal's amplitude as the frequency is varied. The upper and lower cutoff frequencies occur where only ½ of the input power is delivered to the output.

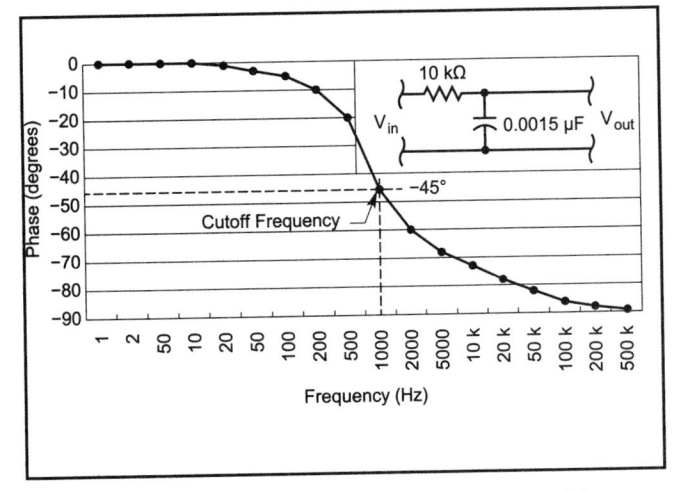

Figure 12.61—This is the phase response of simple RC low-pass filter. Note that the phase shift at the cutoff frequency is 45°, a trademark of single-pole filters.

## Decibels and Ratios

Why use dB? The decibel, or dB, is a mathematically convenient way of "compressing" wide variations in ratio by using logarithms. Since so many electrical phenomena are best viewed as ratios, using dB makes ratio relationships appear as straight lines on graphs.

A ratio between two power levels, $P_1$ and $P_2$, is calculated in dB as:

$$dB = 10 \log (P_1/P_2)$$

[Eq 1]

A power ratio of 10:1 is 10 dB, while 1000:1 is 30 dB and 10000 is 40 dB.

To compute dB using voltage (or current) ratios, the constant 10 in equation 1 must be changed to 20. This leads to the mistaken notion that there is "power dB" and "voltage dB"—not true! Where does the "20" come from? Recall that power is equal to $V^2/R$. Substituting that formula into equation 1 gives:

$$dB = 10 \log [ (V_1^2/R) / (V_2^2/R) ] = 10 \log [ (V_1 / V_2)^2 ] = 10 \times 2 \log (V_1 / V_2)$$

[Eq 2]

This assumes that the measurement of voltages occurs across the same value of resistance, which is usually the case. You can see that there is only one type of dB. The confusion usually occurs when we are measuring a change in power by a factor of 2, which is always 3 dB. If voltage changes by a factor of 2, that translates to 6 dB and a power ratio of 4. To change power by a factor of 2 requires a voltage change of $\sqrt{2}$ or 1.414. Don't be confused!

Another common ratio rule-of-thumb is the "1-2-5 rule." Have you've ever wondered why meter scales and frequency ranges seem to be calibrated in this sequence? It's because dividing a range this way, for example 1-2-5-10-20-50-100-200-500 Hz, makes the steps in approximately equal ratios which appear equally spaced on a logarithmic axis. This is another way to help ratio relationships appear as easy to grasp straight lines on graphs.

---

to frequencies higher than 10 kHz (check your meter's manual). You won't be able to measure phase, however.

• If you have a single channel 'scope, switch the probe back and forth between input and output for each measurement to be sure that the input voltage remains constant.

Follow the 1-2-5 rule for frequency, starting at 1 Hz, measuring input and output voltage and phase. Enter the values into the spreadsheet or make a table.

To measure phase, adjust the trace position so that the zero voltage value of each channel falls directly on the center calibration line of the oscilloscope graticule. Measure the time between the input and output signal zero-crossings. Convert the time to degrees of phase by multiplying by 360f (f is the frequency of the signal). As the output signal voltage becomes smaller, you will have to increase the sensitivity (fewer volts/division) of the display to measure voltage and phase, so use the proper scale for the voltage reading.

You will have a magnitude response graph that begins with approximately 0 dB at 1 Hz, reaches the cutoff frequency somewhere near 1 kHz, and steadily declines as frequency increases. The phase response should look a lot like Figure 12.61.

Swap the resistor and capacitor, with the resistor across the output, forming a high-pass filter. Measure the frequency response of this circuit. The magnitude response will increase with frequency to the very same cutoff frequency, gradually

approaching 0 dB. Phase response will start at approximately 90° at 1 Hz, reach 45° at the cutoff frequency, and then gradually drop to 0°. You may find it easier to start at high frequencies and work your way down to 1 Hz.

### Advanced Techniques

For actual measurements, you'll want to measure response at more frequencies than are covered by the 1-2-5 rule. For example, to plot a tuned circuit's response, you'll want to measure at several points close to resonance including the cutoff frequencies (where the magnitude is –3 dB exactly), whether or not they are on a 1-2-5 frequency. To use *Excel* for these graphs, use an "X-Y Scatter Plot" chart type and set the X-axis scale to be logarithmic. Enter all frequencies in exact numeric form (not as "200 k," for instance).

### Suggested Reading

The 2004 *ARRL Handbook* devotes several pages in Chapter 4 to logarithms and decibel relationships. As an example of how ratio relationships can be plotted as straight lines using logarithmic axes, check out the inductive and capacitive reactance versus frequency graph in Chapter 6.

### Shopping List

• 10 kΩ, ¼ W resistor
• 0.0015 μF capacitor, any type

### Next Month

Let's get back to the bench next month and learn about a neat circuit—the current source. We'll cover a couple of ways to generate constant current, including one of my favorites, the current mirror.

---

[1]Free software for printing graph paper directly to your printer is available at **www.farm.kuleuven.ac.be/pharbio/gpaper.htm**. This will handle many graphing requirements, including log and semi-log plots at up to 6 cycles per axis.—*Ed.*

# Experiment #19: Current Sources

You may be familiar with the voltage source—a power source that maintains a constant voltage regardless of the current drawn —but its cousin, the current source, is nearly unknown. The current source is a mighty handy tool to have in your designer's toolbox and can be constructed in a number of different ways.

## Terms to Learn

- *Compliance*—the range of output voltages over which a current source can maintain constant current.
- *Current-voltage characteristics*—a graph showing all of the combinations of voltage and current a power source can produce.
- *Internal impedance*—the power consuming elements inside a power source, usually shown as a single, equivalent resistance.

## Background

Voltage and current sources are the twin power sources of electronics. Batteries and power supplies do a credible imitation of an ideal voltage source. They deliver nearly constant voltage over a wide range of load currents. The current source that delivers a constant current independent of output voltage isn't used to power equipment but is, nevertheless, quite common. Current sources are found in battery chargers, transistor bias and load circuits, and resistance meters, to name just three uses. We'll learn how to make a current source with a transistor, an op-amp or a voltage regulator, and I'll explain one of my favorite circuits, the current mirror.

## Current-Voltage Characteristics

Practical power sources have limits: They can only supply so many watts, volts or amps. **Figure 12.62** shows the *current-voltage characteristics* of ideal (dashed line) and real (red line) voltage (VS) and current sources (CS). An *ideal* voltage source's output voltage, $V_S$, is the same at any current, whereas a real source's internal impedance, $Z_{INT}$, causes a voltage drop that gets bigger with current ($V_O = V_S - I_O \times Z_{INT}$). The sloping red line, shown in Figure 12.62, gets farther from $V_S$ as current increases. Power supplies usually also have a maximum current, $I_{LIMIT}$, at which they either shut down or blow up!

The ideal current source's internal impedance is infinite—it pumps out the same current no matter what the resulting output voltage has to be. For a real current source, as output voltage rises, more and more current flows through $Z_{INT}$, as shown by the sloping red line of Figure 12.62 labeled $CS_{REAL}$, leaving less for the load until the voltage limit is reached.

You'll never see the most common use for current sources—biasing transistors in analog ICs. This is an important function, as we saw in Experiments #1 and #2. You might use a current source every time you sit down at your workbench. Voltmeters send a known current through an unknown resistance and measure the resulting voltage, using Ohm's Law to calculate the resistance. Current sources are also used for battery charging where a constant current is required for trickle charging. Current sources—they're everywhere!

## A Single Transistor Current Source

**Figure 12.63A** shows how a single PNP transistor can be wired to provide a relatively constant current. Because collector current (the load current) equals $I_B \times \beta$, the load current can be set with a single resistor, R. Base voltage equals $V_{CC} - V_{EB}$ (assumed to be 0.7 V), so $I_B = (V_{CC} - 0.7) / R$. Load current is also dependent on $V_{CC}$, so a well-regulated supply must be used for this circuit.

Measure your transistor's beta if you can; otherwise, assume a value of 200 and we'll recalculate it. Let's design for a load current of 5 mA using a 12 V power supply. From the equation for $I_B$,

$$R = \beta (V_{CC} - 0.7) / 5 \text{ mA} = 452 \text{ k}\Omega \text{ (for } \beta = 200)$$

Use a value of 470 kΩ and build the circuit with a 1 kΩ load resistor. Measure current through the load resistor by either connecting your meter in series with it (remember to switch the leads to the current terminals) or by measuring voltage across it and using Ohm's Law.

If you assumed a value of 200 for β, load current is probably not exactly 5 mA. The actual value of beta can be calculated, using your measured base resistance and load current:

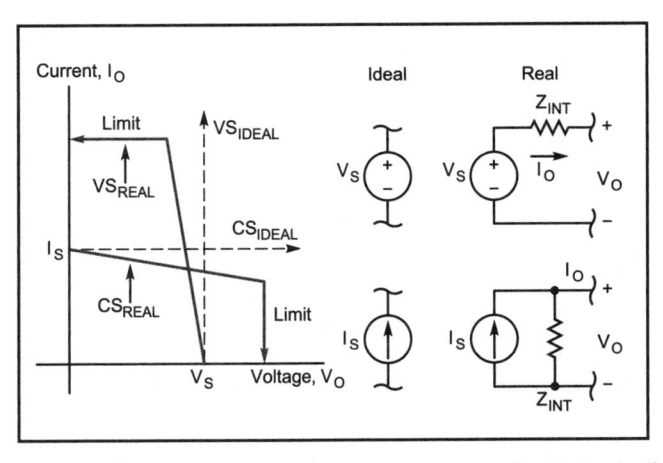

Figure 12.62—The current-voltage characteristics of ideal (dashed) and practical (red) voltage and current sources. The symbols and equivalent circuits for the sources are shown to the right.

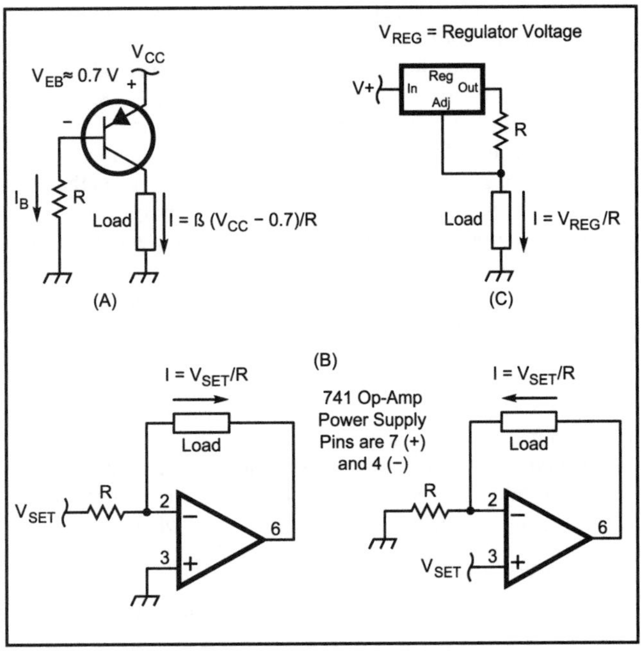

Figure 12.63—Three current source circuits. A single resistor sets the current for all three circuits. The circuit in A is quite dependent on $V_{cc}$, but those in B and C offer excellent current regulation.

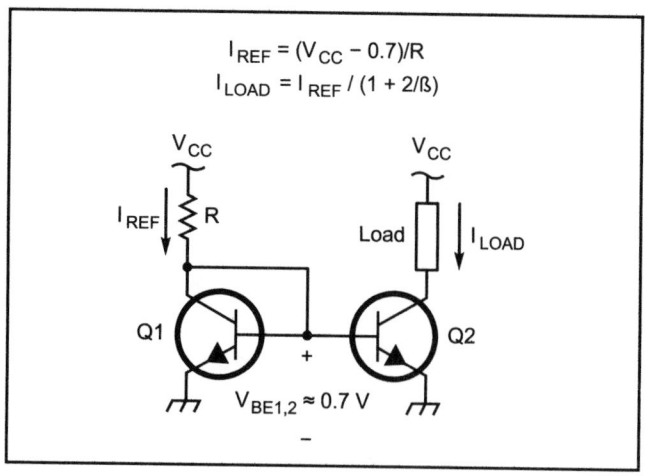

$$I_{REF} = (V_{CC} - 0.7)/R$$
$$I_{LOAD} = I_{REF} / (1 + 2/\beta)$$

$$V_{BE1,2} \approx 0.7 \text{ V}$$

**Figure 12.64—The current mirror's collector currents are matched by making $V_{BE}$ the same value in both transistors.**

$$\beta = I_{LOAD} R / (V_{CC} - 0.7)$$

Vary the load resistance and make a graph of load current and voltage. Raise the load resistance until the voltage across it limits near $V_{CC}$. You can even short-circuit the load and the transistor will still put out only 5 mA!

### Building a Floating Current Source

Sometimes, the load may not be grounded and that's when a *floating* current source is required, such as for a voltmeter. Figure 12.63B shows how to make such a current source by using an op-amp. The key is to remember that the high-gain of the op-amp forces the voltage at both the non-inverting (+) and inverting (−) terminals to be almost exactly the same, while allowing very little current to flow into its input pins.

In the right-hand circuit, the op-amp forces the voltage at pin 2 to $V_{SET}$. By Ohm's Law, the current through R must be $V_{SET}$ / R. Because no current flows into the op-amp's inverting input, the same current must flow in the load. The op-amp raises its output voltage until load current just balances the current through R. Both terminals of the load are thus above ground potential.

In the left-hand circuit, current is balanced through the load in the other direction. The input current is $V_{SET}$ / R. The op-amp lowers its output voltage until the load current balances the input current. This leaves one terminal of the load at ground potential (not grounded, just kept equal to ground) and the other at a negative voltage, requiring a ±12 V supply for this circuit.

When you build these circuits, $V_{SET}$ can be generated by a second power supply (be sure to connect the power supply common connections together) or by a battery. Aim, once again, for 5 mA of load current. Measure $V_{SET}$ and divide by 5 mA to get R, using the closest standard value. Confirm that both op-amp inputs are at the same voltage. Measure load current with a meter in series with the load or by measuring the load voltage and using Ohm's Law. If you can vary $V_{SET}$ or R, observe the effect on load current. Don't reduce R so much that it or the load dissipate too much power: $P = V_{SET}^2 / R$. Vary the load resistance, including an open and a short circuit, to see what happens.

### Using a Voltage Regulator

A common three-terminal regulator can be tricked into put-

ting out constant current instead of constant voltage! The regulator does its best to maintain a fixed voltage between its output and ground terminals. When a fixed-value resistor is connected between them, the current through the resistor is constant, as shown in Figure 12.63C. The regulator's ground terminal draws little current, so the current flows through the load, regardless of what the load voltage is.

The 7805 is a good choice for regulator-based current sources; it handles high current and is easy to attach to a heat sink. The only caveat is that the current set resistor, R, must be able to dissipate ($I_{LOAD}^2 R$) W. If 5 mA is the desired load current, R must be 5 V / 5 mA = 1 kΩ. The regulator will dissipate power equal to the load current times the voltage between its input and output pins. If you are using a 12 V supply, at 5 mA load current, the regulator dissipates (12 − 5) × 5 mA = 35 mW. Try various values of R and load resistance, again trying the open and short circuits.

### The Current Mirror

The circuit in **Figure 12.64** can throw you for a loop with Q1's base and collector shorted together. This is the current mirror, so named because the collector current of Q2 mirrors that in Q1. The current mirror is used when the reference current must be kept separate from the load current or when more than one load current must be controlled by a single reference current.

Current mirrors work because of the bipolar transistor's property that matched transistors with the same base-to-emitter voltage will have the same collector currents. Since the bases and emitters are connected together, $V_{BE}$ must be the same. Matching two transistors means that they usually are made of the same materials, have equal current gains (β) and operate at the same temperature. This is the usual case inside an IC or in a multiple-transistor package such as the MPQ2222—four 2N2222 transistors in a 16 pin DIP package.

Build the current mirror by using a pair of 2N3904 transistors (or an MPQ2222). If you can measure β, pick a pair of transistors with β within a few percent of each other. Set $I_{REF}$ to 5 mA by calculating the value for R = ($V_{CC}$ − 0.7) / 5 mA. With a 1 kΩ load, verify that $I_{LOAD}$ is close to 5 mA. Vary R to change $I_{REF}$ while observing load current, and vary the load resistance while monitoring $I_{LOAD}$.

### Suggested Reading

*The Art of Electronics*, by Horowitz and Hill, includes extensive material on current sources and current mirrors, including a number of variations on the mirror. A good on-line discussion can be found at **www.4qdtec.com/csm.html**.

### Shopping List

- MPS2907 or 2N3906 PNP transistor (RadioShack 276-2023 or 276-1604).
- 2N3904 NPN transistor (RadioShack 276-2016).
- 741 operational amplifier (RadioShack 276-007).
- 7805 voltage regulator (RadioShack 276-1770).
- Various values of 1/4 W resistors.

### Next Month

In September, we're going to meet the DA. Not the district attorney—the differential amplifier—a key element of the op-amp. You'll also learn about common-mode signals and the DA's ability to reject them. See you next month!

# Experiment #20: The Differential Amplifier

In all of our operational amplifier experiments, a *differential amplifier* (DA) was lurking behind the op-amp's input terminals. Sporting high gain and high input impedance, the DA applied its gain to only the *difference* in voltage at its inputs; ignoring any voltage that those inputs had in common. All this from just a pair of transistors and four resistors!

## Terms to Learn

*Common-mode*—a signal that appears equally at both inputs of a differential amplifier or on both connections to a signal source.

*Common-mode rejection ratio (CMRR)*—the ratio of differential-mode gain to common-mode gain, usually expressed in dB.

*Differential-mode*—a signal that appears as a difference in voltage between the inputs of a differential amplifier or between connections to a signal source, also called *normal mode*.

## Background

In many applications, it's useful to measure or amplify just the difference in voltage between two points, ignoring any voltage that is present at both points. For example, a low-level microphone signal with a dc offset or carrying ac hum needs to be amplified, while the offset or hum is ignored. For this job, a difference or differential amplifier is used. The ideal DA has high-gain, infinite input impedance, and only amplifies the difference in voltage at its inputs. This can be approximated with the simple circuit of **Figure 12.65**. This is an emitter-coupled DA, a pair of common-emitter (CE) amplifiers that share a path for their emitter currents. The output of the DA can remain differential (taken between the transistor collectors) or be converted to *single-ended* (referenced to ground) by only using one collector output.

Let's refresh our understanding of the CE amplifier circuit before proceeding. From our first experiment, the gain of the CE amplifier is $A_V \approx R_C/R_E$ and the transistor collector current is $I_C = \beta I_B$. This is true for each of the amplifiers, even if they share most of their emitter resistance in $R_1$. The sharing of $R_1$ is important.

Returning to Figure 12.65, consider what happens when the voltage at the base of transistor 1 goes up slightly and drops the same amount at the base of transistor 2. This is just what happens when a small differential signal is applied. $I_{C1}$ goes up and $I_{C2}$ goes down—the same amount. This leaves the voltage at point A (where the two currents combine) unchanged. That means we can treat point A as an ac ground, as long as both transistors aren't driven into cutoff or saturation and remain in their active regions. Thus $R_1$ doesn't affect gain, only collector current. The only difference in the CE amplifier's gain is that the input signal is actually twice the input at either transistor, so the differential gain, $A_{DM}$ is:

$$A_{DM} \approx R_C/2R_e \qquad [1]$$

How do we calculate transistor collector current? The quiescent current (with no signal applied) can be determined by using Kirchhoff's Voltage Law (KVL)—the sum of voltages around any current path is zero. Let's do a KVL from the transistor base, through $R_E$ and $R_1$, through the negative supply $V_{EE}$, and back to the base.

$$V_B + V_{BE} + R_E I_E + 2(R_1 I_E) - V_{EE} = 0$$

The base is at zero volts, so $V_B = 0$. If the transistor is in its active region, $V_{BE} \approx 0.7$ V. The voltage drop across $R_E$ from the emitter current follows. The next term accounts for the

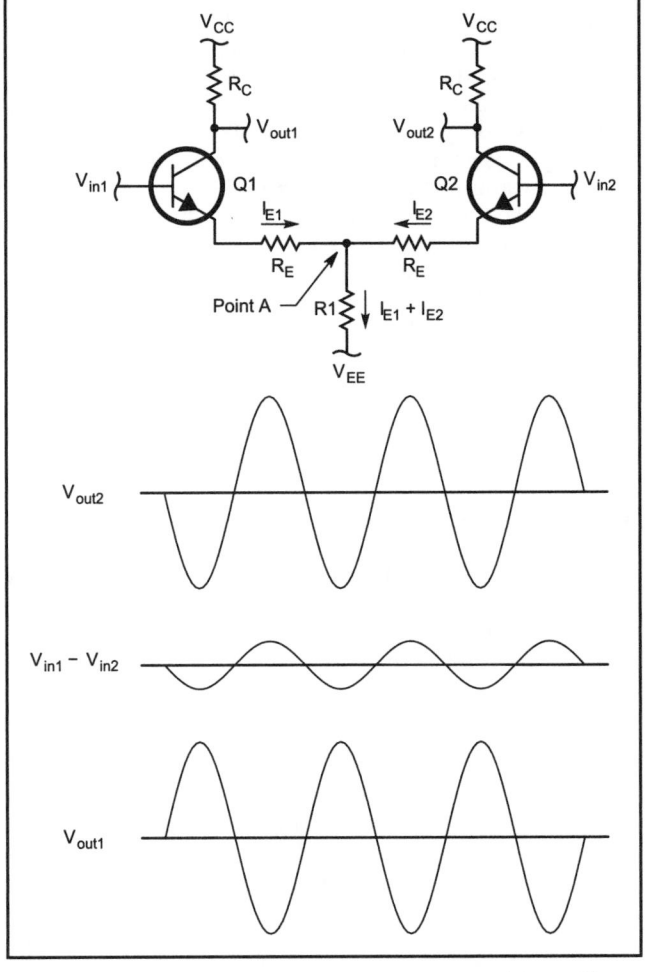

**Figure 12.65—The basic emitter-coupled differential amplifier circuit. The outputs from the collectors are equal and out of phase for an input signal appearing between the transistor bases.**

sharing of $R_1$, in which emitter current from both transistors flows. If the transistors and resistors are matched, the current will be the same in each transistor and so each contributes half of the voltage across $R_1$. Making these substitutions and solving:

$$I_E = (V_{EE} - 0.7) / (R_E + 2R_1) \qquad [2]$$

If the $\beta$ of the transistors is large (>100), we can make the simplifying assumption that $I_C = I_E$. Because we want high gain, equation 1 says that $R_E$ must be small, so a further simplification results in:

$$I_C = (V_{EE} - 0.7) / (2R_1) \qquad [3]$$

We can now design a DA with a specific gain and collector current.

## Design and Build a Differential Amplifier

- Start by selecting the power supply voltages. This experiment requires both positive and negative voltages. The usual case is that the voltages are balanced—I used ±12 V, but that's not required. If you are using a +12 V supply, you can create a negative supply with batteries. Make $V_{EE}$ at least −6 V to keep the resistor values reasonable.
- Choose a collector current—2 mA is a reasonable value.

Find $R_1$ by using Equation 3. 2 mA = (12 – 0.7) / (2$R_1$) so $R_1$ = 2.98 kΩ. Use a standard value from 2.7 to 3.3 kΩ. I used a value of 3 kΩ.

- Choose a gain—let's try for 30. We assumed that $R_E$ is small compared to $R_1$, so use 100 Ω (or 0.1 kΩ). Using Equation 1, $R_C$=2(0.1)30 = 6 kΩ. Use a standard value from 5.6 to 6.8 kΩ. I used a 6.2 kΩ resistor.

- Check your circuit's dc performance to be sure your calculations are okay. Ground the base of each transistor so that no signal is applied. Be sure $V_{BE}$ is close to 0.7 V. Check $I_C$ by measuring the voltage across $R_C$: $I_C$=$V_{RC}$/$R_C$. In my case $I_C$=11.2/6.2=1.8 mA. Also, measure the voltage at point A. Don't proceed unless your collector current and base current are close to your expected values.

- Apply a small 1 kHz signal of 100 mV or less to one transistor input as shown in **Figure 12.66A**. Observe the output voltage at each transistor collector with an oscilloscope. You should observe that the collectors have identical waveforms, 180° out of phase. Be sure that the output waveforms are undistorted, reducing the input signal if necessary. Measure the input voltage, $V_{IN}$. Check point A to observe that the dc voltage is unchanged.

- Even though we aren't applying a true differential signal (one transistor base is still grounded), we can still measure differential gain, $A_{DM}$, by measuring the output between the two collector outputs. Use a voltmeter to measure the ac voltage between the two collectors or use the ADD function of your oscilloscope. I measured $A_{DM}$ = ($V_{C1}$–$V_{C2}$)/$V_{IN}$ = 32.

- Measure the ac voltage at point A. It will be very small, confirming that point A is effectively an ac ground due to the balancing act of the two transistors.

## Common Mode Rejection

Gain is one thing, but rejecting unwanted signals is another. A common-mode signal is one that is present at both inputs in the same amount. Good examples of common-mode signals include 60 Hz ac hum, dc offset, or noise picked up by a long input cable. In any case, it's important to keep those signals from contaminating the amplifier output.

Let's return to the description of how the DA amplifies differential input signals a few paragraphs ago. Remember that it was important that the symmetry of the emitter current changes kept point A at a fixed voltage. For common-mode signals, both emitter currents change in the *same* direction and point A changes, too. This means that the circuit's common-mode gain formula must include $R_1$.

$$A_{CM} = R_C / (2R_1+R_E)$$

If we ignore $R_E$ because it is small compared to $R_1$,

$$A_{CM} » R_C / (2R_1) \qquad [4]$$

For the circuit we constructed, $A_{CM}$ should be about 6/(2×3)=1—much smaller than the differential gain of 30.

The ratio of differential to common-mode gain is called the *common-mode rejection ratio* or CMRR and is typically measured in dB. Larger values are better.

$$CMRR = 20 \log (A_{DM} /A_{CM}) \qquad [5]$$

## Measuring CMRR

- IConnect your input signal to the bases of *both* transistors as shown in Figure 12.66B.
- Increase the input voltage to 0.5 V (check to be sure the collector voltage of each transistor is undistorted).
- Measure the voltage between the collectors using a voltmeter or the oscilloscope's ADD feature. Calculate $A_{CM}$. My measured common mode gain was 0.6.
- Calculate CMRR in dB. My CMRR was 20 log (32/0.6)= 34.5 dB. This is pretty good for a simple circuit with un-

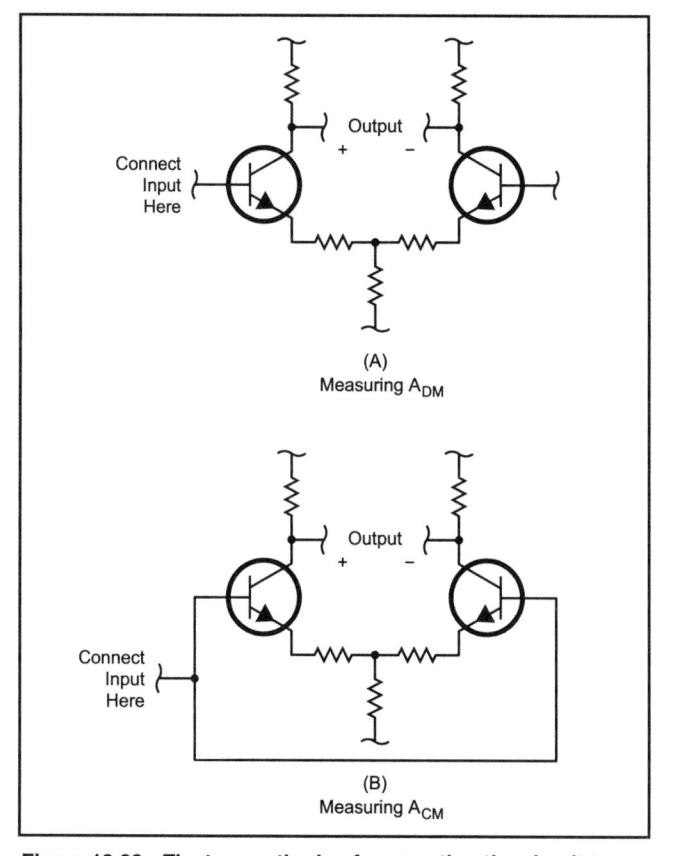

Figure 12.66—The two methods of connecting the circuit to measure differential gain (A) and common-mode gain (B).

matched resistors and transistors! It says that common mode signals are rejected by a factor of 50.

A circuit with better selection of transistor gains and resistor matching can have even better performance. Experiment with different transistors or match the pairs of resistors for $R_C$ and $R_E$ to see what effect this has on $A_{CM}$.

## Improving CMRR

Last month, we created a current source and I mentioned that they were used in op-amps. In fact, they are often used in place of $R_1$, creating a very high effective resistance due to their very low compliance. That means the common-mode gain of the circuit will be very low, as shown by Equation 4.

## Suggested Reading

Chapter 2 of *The Art of Electronics*, by Horowitz and Hill, has a very good discussion of differential amplifiers, including the use of current sources. Section 2.5 of *Experimental Methods in RF Design*, by Hayward, Campbell and Larkin also illustrates the differential amplifier.

## Shopping List

- Two 2N3904 NPN transistors (RadioShack 276-2016).
- Miscellaneous 1/4 W resistors.

## Next Month

Now it's time to extend our experiments beyond low-frequency signals to RF and the simplest impedance matching method—the L network. For this experiment, you'll need to have access to an antenna analyzer, such as the MFJ-259, that can display SWR in the 10 meter band.

# Experiment #21: The L-Network

This month's experiment moves away from the world of transistors and ICs to visit one of radio's most fundamental designs, the L-network. This building block is the foundation of numerous common impedance matching circuits; the Pi-network—found in amplifiers and the T-network—popular in transmatches. Are its inner workings the black magic of mystical RF designers? Hardly. Read on and find out for yourself!

## Terms to Learn

*Equivalent series (parallel) circuits*—a circuit whose series (parallel) components provide the same impedance at its terminals as the original circuit.

*Transformation ratio*—the ratio between the input and output impedances of a matching network.

## Background

Although radio designers have long used 50 Ω as the standard "system impedance" for antennas and equipment, it seems that hardly any circuits offer 50 Ω impedances without coaxing. Many antennas have a natural impedance far from 50 Ω. What's a ham to do? If you look at the impedance matching equipment and circuits, nearly all have the L-network as part of their pedigree.

The L-network is based on a technique known as *series-parallel transformations*. For any series combination of resistance, $R_S$, and reactance, $X_S$, there is a parallel combination of $R_P$ and $X_P$ that looks exactly the same to the voltage applied across the series combination. The same can be said in reverse.

Converting from the series form to the parallel form is governed by the following set of simple equations:

$$Q = X_S/R_S = R_P/X_P = \sqrt{(R_P/R_S) - 1} \qquad [1]$$

$$R_P = R_S (Q^2 + 1) \text{ and } R_S = R_P / (Q^2 + 1) \qquad [2]$$

$$X_S = QR_S \text{ and } X_P = R_P / Q \qquad [3]$$

Depending on which of the variables Q, $X_S$, $R_S$, $X_S$, and $R_P$ that you know, you can solve for the rest. $R_P$ must be greater than $R_S$. Note that the larger the *transformation ratio* between $R_P$ and $R_S$, the larger Q becomes. As Q becomes larger, the values of $X_S$ and $X_P$ become more extreme.

The general process of designing an L-network takes four steps:

1) Assign the larger impedance to be transformed to $R_P$.

2) Determine Q and calculate $X_P$. $X_P$ is a physical component in parallel with $R_P$.

3) $R_S$ is already known, so calculate $X_S$ to determine the series equivalent circuit.

4) Add a physical component with $-X_S$ in series with the parallel combination of $R_P$ and $X_P$.

The orientation of the network—whether the parallel component is at the input or output—depends on whether the input or output impedance is greater. Remember that since reactance is frequency dependent, the L-network will match the two impedances only at one frequency.

The "big trick" is to realize that you can treat a circuit as its electrical equivalent with no change in the electrical outcome. After $X_P$ has been added in parallel with $R_P$, the impedance of the combination has the correct resistive component, but also has reactance that must be cancelled. It is much easier to figure out what the necessary canceling reactance is if the parallel combination is treated as its series equivalent. The canceling reactance is just equal and opposite the equivalent series reactance.

This is much easier to understand as an example. Let's transform the 50 Ω resistive impedance of matched coaxial cable so that it looks like 10 Ω of resistance to match the collector impedance of a transistor amplifier as shown in **Figure 12.67**. Assign the coax impedance to $R_P$ and the collector impedance to $R_S$. From equation 1, Q = √ (50/10) – 1= 2 and from equation 3, $X_P$ = 50/2 = 25 Ω. Now use Eq [3] to find $X_S$ = 2×10 = 20 Ω. Since we want just the 10 Ω of resistance, we must cancel the remaining reactance by adding 20 Ω of the opposite type of reactance in series. This leaves us with only the effective resistance of 10 Ω.

We never did say whether the parallel reactance was inductive or capacitive. The problem is solved either way. However, depending on frequency, the reactance values may be more practical as inductance or capacitance. If the frequency is 28 MHz, for example, the parallel reactance could be either a 0.14 µH inductor or a 227 pF capacitor. Clearly, the capacitor would be a more practical choice to connect between an amplifier output and ground. Thus, the canceling inductance would be 0.32 µH.

What if we were matching the "other" way, from 50 Ω to a higher impedance? In that case, $R_P$ is assigned to the higher

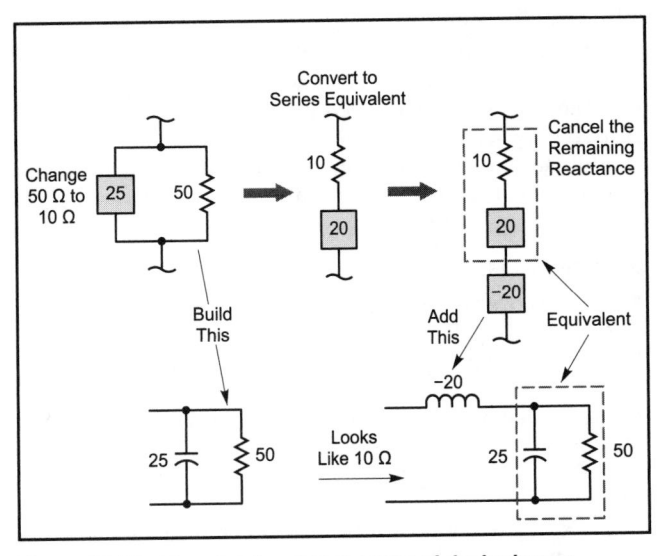

**Figure 12.67—The step-by-step process of designing an L-network by using parallel-series transformations and equivalent circuits.**

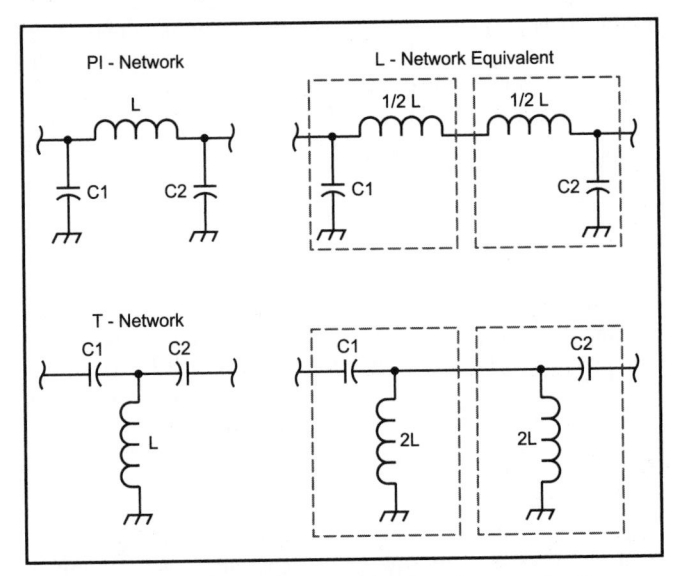

**Figure 12.68—The T-network and Pi-network are easier to understand as a pair of back-to-back L-networks.**

Figure 12.69—An SO-239 acts as a good prototyping platform for working with L-networks. An RF analyzer is shown and is convenient, although a low power transmitter and an SWR bridge will work.

impedance and the problem is worked out by the same procedure. The component added in parallel is always next to the higher impedance.

Now that you recognize what the L-network can do, look closely at the Pi and T-networks in **Figure 12.68**. Each is just a pair of L-networks back to back. Why are those circuits used rather than just L-networks? The T-network can match a wider range of impedances than an L-network, including impedances that are both higher and lower than the input impedance. The Pi-network uses the two-step transformation of back-to-back networks to provide low-pass filtering for harmonics and to manage the overall Q of the network. Yet both are based on the simple L-network.

### Design and Build an L-Network

This experiment assumes that you have an SWR analyzer, such as the MFJ-259, or a similar instrument. You can also use a low power (QRP) transmitter and an SWR bridge. Don't try this with more than a few watts unless you use heavy-duty components that can handle the power level. Use silver-mica, ceramic or air variable capacitors to avoid the parasitic effects of the inductance in other types of capacitors.

*Experiment #1*

A quarter-wave vertical over a good ground plane has an impedance of about 30 Ω at its resonant frequency. Construct an L-network to match the vertical's impedance (simulated by a 27 Ω resistor) to 50 Ω.

*Experiment #2*

A loop antenna has an impedance of around 150 Ω. Construct an L-network to match the loop's impedance to 50 Ω.
- Construct a load that simulates the impedance you're trying to match to 50 Ω. If you are using an SWR analyzer, a single resistor will suffice. If you are using a small transmitter, be sure the load is rated to take full transmitter power continuously. For example, 5-150 Ω, 1 W resistors will make a 30 Ω, 5 W load. Use non-inductive carbon composition or metal oxide resistors.
- Using a frequency of 28 MHz, determine the physical component values that have the calculated reactances. Remember that you can start with either a capacitor or an inductor. Use the one easiest to fabricate or obtain.
- Use the closest fixed-value capacitors to your calculated values, add capacitors in parallel (or series), use an air-variable or place an air-variable in parallel with a fixed value capacitor. The air variables allow you to tune for best match.
- Use fixed-value inductors only if you are using the low-power analyzer. Wind the inductors from hookup wire according to the following formula or Figure 6.40 in *The 2004 ARRL Handbook* for ½ inch or ¾ inch diameter coils. The on-line calculator at **hawkins.pair.com/radiocalcs.shtml** is also useful.

$$N = \sqrt{L(18\, d + 40\, l)} / d \qquad [4]$$

An SO-239 connector makes a good prototyping board for this experiment. Your regular prototype plug-in board won't work well at this frequency.

Follow the four-step procedure presented earlier to calculate your component values. Start by connecting your load resistor directly across the SO-239 to confirm that it is really presenting the expected load to the analyzer: an SWR of 1.7:1 for the 27 Ω load and 3:1 for the 150 Ω load. As shown in **Figure 12.69**, connect the SO-239 directly at the analyzer or bridge to avoid the effects of a transmission line on the impedance. Add the L-network between the load and the analyzer.

If you used an adjustable capacitor, tweak the network for optimum SWR. For a perfect match, the resistance will be 50 Ω and the reactance will be 0 Ω. You can stretch (raise) or compress (lower) the coil inductance for the same effect. I had to stretch my coil by about 10 percent. If you don't get a match and you are sure of your connections, double-check your calculations or try an on-line calculator such as **home.sandiego.edu/~ekim/e194rfs01/jwmatcher/matcher2.html**.

### Suggested Reading

*The ARRL Antenna Book*, 20th Edition, covers the use of L-networks in chapter 25, along with Pi and T-networks. Another good reference that covers impedance matching networks in detail is Walt Maxwell's *Reflections II*, published by Worldradio, although this edition is currently out of print. This is an excellent text that explains transmission line concepts in an easy-to-read style.

### Shopping List

- 27 Ω and 150 Ω non-inductive resistors.
- 20 or 22 gauge hookup wire.
- An SO-239 connector and a UHF double-male PL-259/PL-259 adapter.
- Fixed-value or air-variable capacitors in the 50 to 200 pF range.

### Next Month

Let's stay in impedance land next month and learn how to make a harmonic filter out of one of those mysterious transmission line stubs. Hang onto that SWR analyzer!

# Experiment #22—Stubs

Most hams know about transmission line matching and VSWR, but the mechanics of stubs and using them for filtering is often considered mysterious. Like most mysteries, stubs are not hard to design and use if you know the secret. This month, not only will you learn the secret, but you'll build a useful gadget in the bargain.

## Terms to Learn

- *Electrical length*—the length of a transmission line in terms of the wavelength ($\lambda$) of the energy traveling through it.
- *Termination*—a load attached to a transmission line.

## Background

So what is a stub and how does it work? A stub is just a length of transmission line terminated in a fixed impedance, usually a short or open-circuit, in parallel with another transmission line to create a tuning or canceling effect. The tuning and canceling are the result of interference between the RF energy in the two transmission lines. That was simple, wasn't it? Take a deep breath and read on.

Before proceeding, we'll need to review some fundamentals of transmission lines.

Because energy in a transmission line travels slower than in free space, the *physical* length of the transmission line is always *shorter* than its *electrical* length. For example, if a piece of RG-58 is 1 $\lambda$ long to energy traveling through it, the physical length of the cable will be about two-thirds as long as the wavelength of the same energy traveling in free space.

Impedances in a transmission line repeat every $1/2$ $\lambda$ along the line. (If terminated in its characteristic impedance, $Z_0$, however, impedance is the same everywhere along the line.) If I terminate any transmission line with a load whose impedance is 100 $\Omega$ at some frequency, f, then every $1/2$ electrical wavelength away from that load, the transmission line will again present a 100 $\Omega$ impedance. If the line is perfectly lossless, I can't tell how many half wavelengths I am from the load.

Open and short circuits reflect 100% of the energy in a transmission line. For an open-circuit, the incoming (or *incident*) and reflected voltages are in phase and add together. The incident and reflected currents are out-of-phase and cancel so that there is zero current at the open-circuit. For a short circuit, voltages cancel and currents add.

Stub design is based on these three key elements.

**Figure 12.70** illustrates how a $1/4$ $\lambda$ open stub (stubs are referred to by their electrical length and terminating impedance) creates an apparent short circuit. Imagine a single packet of RF energy just a few cycles long—a very short CW dit. The energy travels in the line from the transmitter, encountering the junction of the stub and the rest of the line. The energy divides between the line and stub. The wave traveling down the stub is phase shifted by 90° because the stub is an electrical $1/4$ $\lambda$ long. At the open-circuit, all of the energy is reflected with the voltages in phase (no additional phase shift). The reflected wave gets another 90° of phase shift going back along the stub for a total phase shift of 180°. At the junction, the out-of-phase voltages cancel or *null*, creating an apparent short circuit. The quarter-wave open stub presents a short circuit at its free end!

Complete reverse only occurs if the stub is completely lossless and exactly $1/4$ $\lambda$ long. Loss reduces the returning voltage, preventing a complete cancellation. Being off-frequency means that the net phase shift won't be precisely 180°. Nevertheless, the range of frequencies over which most of the voltages cancel is sufficient to be useful across a ham band.

What happens if the stub is shorted, instead of open? At the termination, the wave is reflected with voltage phase shifted 180° instead of zero, making the total phase shift 360° in the stub. The voltages now add back together, as if no stub was connected at all. The quarter-wave shorted stub acts like an open-circuit at its free end.

Longer stubs take advantage of the $1/2$ $\lambda$ repetition of impedance. If the quarter-wave stub is doubled in physical length, to become $1/2$ $\lambda$ long, its terminating impedance repeats at the free end. Leaving the physical length alone and doubling the frequency (halving the wavelength) has exactly the same effect so that the terminating impedance appears again at the free end. A stub any number of $1/2$ wavelengths long acts as if it were just $1/2$ $\lambda$ long, although with a little more loss.

## Harmonic Filtering

By far the most common application of stub is to act as a filter for transmitter harmonics. The free end of a $1/4$ $\lambda$ shorted stub presents an open-circuit at its *fundamental frequency*, but a short circuit at the second harmonic where it is $1/2$ $\lambda$ long. The free end also presents a short circuit at the fourth, sixth, eighth, and so on, harmonics where it is an integral number of $1/2$ wavelengths long. While passing energy at the fundamental frequency untouched, all even harmonics are canceled!

Half-wavelength stubs also filter harmonics, but in a slightly different manner. The free end of a shorted $1/2$ $\lambda$ stub presents an open-circuit at one-half its fundamental frequency because there it is a $1/4$ $\lambda$ stub. The stub acts like a short circuit at the fundamental and all harmonics.

**Table 12.4** lists the filtering effect of $1/4$ and $1/2$ $\lambda$ stubs cut for different ham bands.[1] The possibilities are endless!

The 60, 30, 17 and 12 meter bands are absent from the table because stubs cut to pass or null these bands don't have a similar response in any of the other HF bands. These bands are not *harmonically-related* to other bands.

## Design and Build a Multi-Band, Switchable Stub

Taking a look at rows four and five of Table 12.4, you can see that if a $1/4$-$\lambda$ 40-meter stub could be changed from short to open, it would pass or null signals from any of the four highest harmonically related HF bands, 40 through 10 meters. By attaching a switch to the end of an appropriate length of cable, you can do just that, as shown in **Figure 12.71**.

Cut 24 feet of coax with a solid polyethylene center insu-

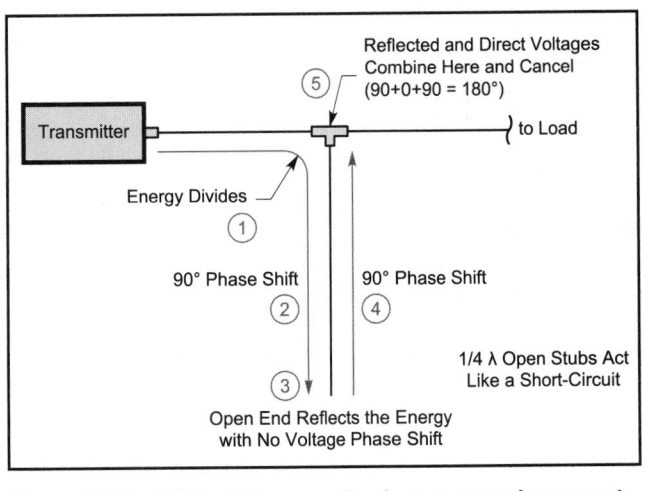

**Figure 12.70—A $1/4$ $\lambda$ stub uses reflections to cancel energy at its free end.**

## Table 12.4
### Useful ¼ and ½ λ Stubs for Filtering

| Stub Type | Passes | Nulls |
|---|---|---|
| ¼-λ 160-m shorted | 160 | 80,40,20,15,10 |
| ¼-λ 80-m shorted | 80 | 40,20,15,10 |
| ¼-λ 80-m open | 40,20 | 80 |
| ¼-λ 40-m shorted | 40,15 | 20,10 |
| ¼-λ 40-m open | 20,10 | 40,15 |
| ¼-λ 20-m shorted | 20 | 10 |
| ¼-λ 20-m open | 10 | 20 |

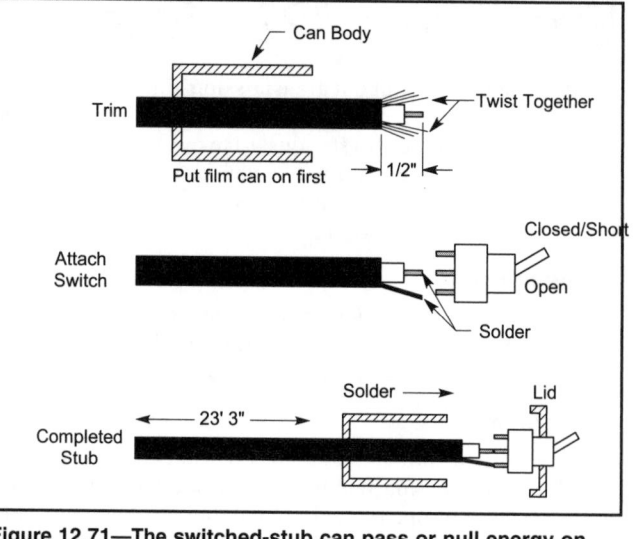

Figure 12.71—The switched-stub can pass or null energy on 40, 20, 15 and 10 meters.

lator, such as RG-58 or RG-213. (You can use foam-insulated coax if you adjust for the different velocity of propagation.) Install a coax connector on one end.

Trim about a half inch of jacket and center insulator from the cable. Twist the shield and center conductor together and attach the stub to your SWR analyzer as shown in **Figure 12.72**. Any type analyzer that displays reactance can be used.

Tune for the *lowest* frequency at which the reactance "X" goes to a minimum. Don't watch the SWR value—it will remain high—or the R value. At this frequency the stub is acting like a ½ λ shorted stub, so the frequency should be *twice* the 40 meter design frequency. Measure stubs at a short-circuit frequency because the SWR analyzers give a much sharper and clearer response than for high impedances.

Since you're starting with the stub too long, trim 1 inch at a time and repeat the measurement until the short occurs at twice the desired 40 meter frequency, that is, 14.200 MHz for a 7.100 MHz stub.

When you've reached the desired frequency, replace the short with a toggle switch as shown in Figure 12.71, cover it with the plastic container and attach the stub to your radio's output with a T connector.

Attach an antenna and listen to signals as you switch the stub from open to shorted on the different bands. You should hear a difference of around 3 S units as you change the stub between "pass" and "null."

### Tips on Stubs

I hope you'll try your hand at other types and uses of stubs. If you do, here are some helpful hints:
- Keep the shorting leads *short!*
- Trim open stub shields back from the end of the center insulator by ⅛ inch to prevent arcing from the extra voltage.
- Insulate and waterproof stub ends with shrink wrap or tape to prevent arcing or degrading the cable.
- Use low-loss cable to get the deepest null. RG-213 is good; surplus hardline is even better!
- Remember that the stub's electrical length must include all adapters, connectors and switches. If possible, trim to length with all such extra items attached.

### Suggested Reading

The best book available today on the subject of stubs is

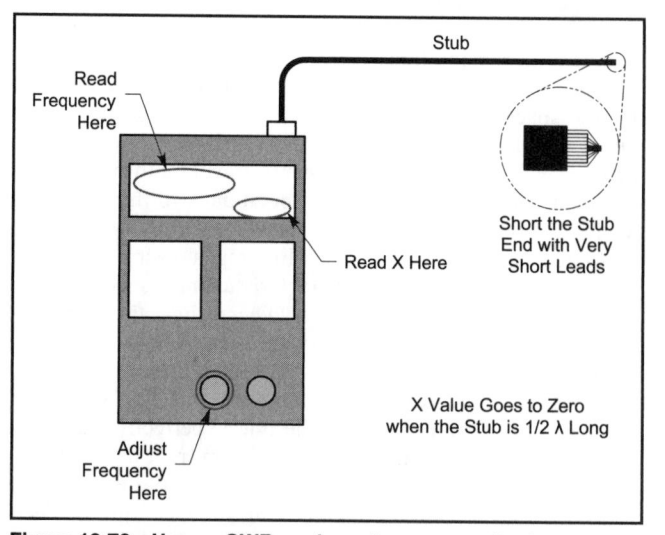

Figure 12.72—Use an SWR analyzer to measure the frequency at which the stub is ½ λ long.

W2VJN's *Managing Interstation Interference*[2] with lots of information about all kinds of interesting stubs and applications. The May 2001 *QST* article, "Making a Stub," by Dean Straw, N6BV, may also be helpful.

### Shopping List

- Plastic film can or pill bottle
- SPST or SPDT toggle switch
- 25 feet of RG-58 coaxial cable (any solid polyethylene 50 Ω cable will do)

### Next Month

It's time for a holiday open house at NØAX's workbench and ham shack! I'll show off my tool box and gadgets to encourage all the Hands-On Radio homebrewers and experimenters. I'd better get started on the clean-up right away!

[1]G. Cutsogeorge, *Managing Interstation Interference*, Table 11, International Radio (**www.qth.com/inrad**), 2003.
[2]See Note 1.

# Experiment #23: Open House in the NØAX Lab

What better way to celebrate the holiday season than with an open house for friends? In the case of Hands-On Radio, it will be "open lab." I'm delighted to wrap up the second year of the column by inviting you to take a look behind the word processor to see where the experiments come from.

## The Lab

You may think I must have a big, industrial-sized facility with the latest in technical gadgetry and instrumentation. Not so! While my little shop is fairly well equipped, what makes it play is having the right tools and parts conveniently located. **Figure 12.73** shows that my workbench is "co-located" with my ham shack and office. Having everything within arm's length or a step away has turned out to be a real boon after having had them in separate rooms before.

Even if you have a very small shack, it's a great idea to have a bit of room to do troubleshooting on the spot. You need to have access to antennas and power supplies to really check out the radio equipment. A piece of plywood, fiberboard, or even cardboard, will protect a desktop while you work on the electronics.

**Figure 12.74** shows the equipment layout on the workbench. The bench surface is plywood, which tolerates the various mechanical insults I throw at it. When the plywood gets too grungy, I turn it over or get a new piece. For sensitive electronics work, I unroll a static dissipating mat that stays clean between uses. Heavy-duty tasks get done in the garage where I can really make a mess!

Lighting is very important to being able to work with small parts and dig into equipment. All of the lights are movable—there are two clamp fixtures that can slide horizontally, and one swing-arm lamp that can move in close. I also have some small photoflood bulbs that I can use for photography or when lots of light is needed. A pocket flashlight and a mini-gooseneck lamp illuminate those tight spots. A head-mounted magnifier comes in handier with each passing year.

The flooring is linoleum, not carpet. If possible, the floor in your lab should be a smooth surface. Carpeting in a lab environment traps dirt, shavings, metal bits, small parts and solder blobs melt it. If you're stuck with carpet, pick up some of the office rug protectors for rolling chairs and trim them to fit around your workbench. You won't regret it!

The room I use for all three jobs—shack, bench, and office—is just 10×16 feet, so I have to make the most of available space with drawers, shelves and carts. Tools are kept in a rolling set of drawers or in a toolbox. Even the radio equipment is on movable carts or cabinets so that I can easily work in back of the gear.

You can never have too many cables—dc, ac line cords, RF, data—they're all used in today's ham shack. Keeping them straight is another thing. You can see two cable racks in Figure 12.73, at the left. I also installed a piece of pegboard with long hooks to hold coils of coax and data cables. Avoid throwing your cables in a box. You'll waste a lot of time untangling them and you'll never find the one you want.

## My Friends, the Test Instruments

Surveying the workbench shown in Figure 12.74, you'll see the equipment that I use most often. There are two power supplies; one is a dual 0-20 V dc lab supply and the other a high-current supply designed for powering radios. A Variac is to the left of the supplies—good for testing line-powered equipment.

The function generator and voltmeter are used for almost every experiment and building job. Don't scrimp on a voltmeter. A flexible function generator can substitute for several single-purpose generators and many can be found on the surplus market.

Other favorite instruments include the reliable Bird wattmeter and an assortment of common "slugs" or sensing elements and dummy loads. An MFJ Antenna Analyzer is never far from my bench, either. I picked up a small gel-cell battery to run the analyzer; it's paid for itself several times over.

While I've certainly used a lot of oscilloscopes, I'm happy with my 15-year-old Hitachi 4-channel model. With a bandwidth of 100 MHz, it handles everything I'd use a 'scope for in ham radio. Above that frequency, a spectrum analyzer is more likely to do the job. There are lots of scopes like it as surplus. The Hands-On Radio Web site (**www.arrl.org/tis/info/ HTML/Hands-On-Radio/**) has numerous links to sources of

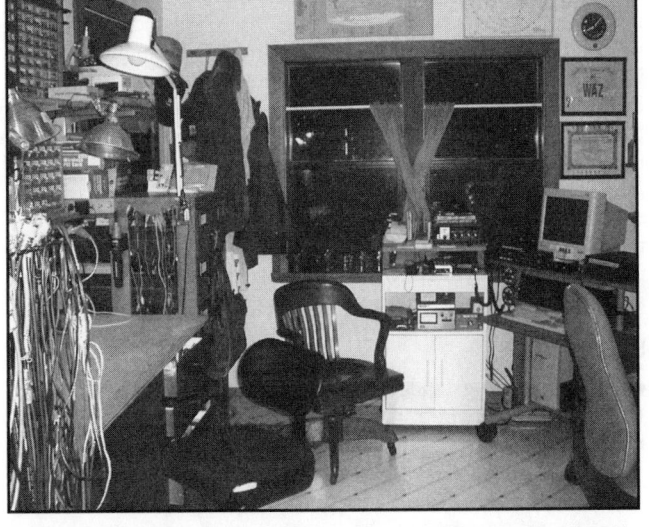

Figure 12.73—The workbench is surrounded by parts and tools and the shack just a few feet away. Having what I need close by is a big help!

Figure 12.74—On the bench, you can see the instruments that I use most frequently. Parts bins hold bulk parts and small junk boxes. The oscilloscope is on a rolling cart.

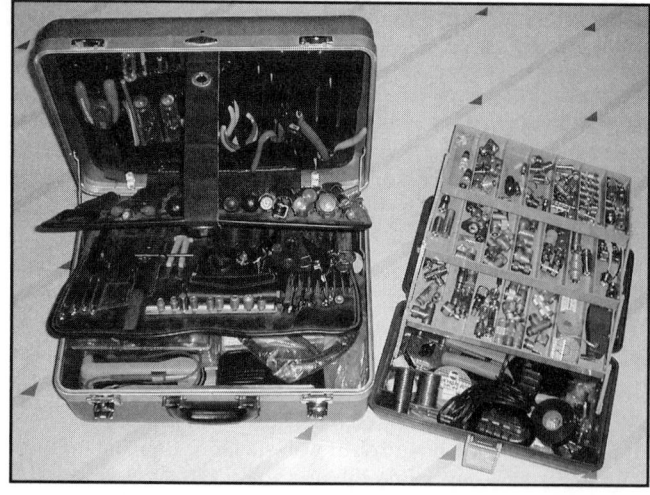

Figure 12.75—Keeping tools and parts in a toolbox means they're always in the same place and ready to go when you are.

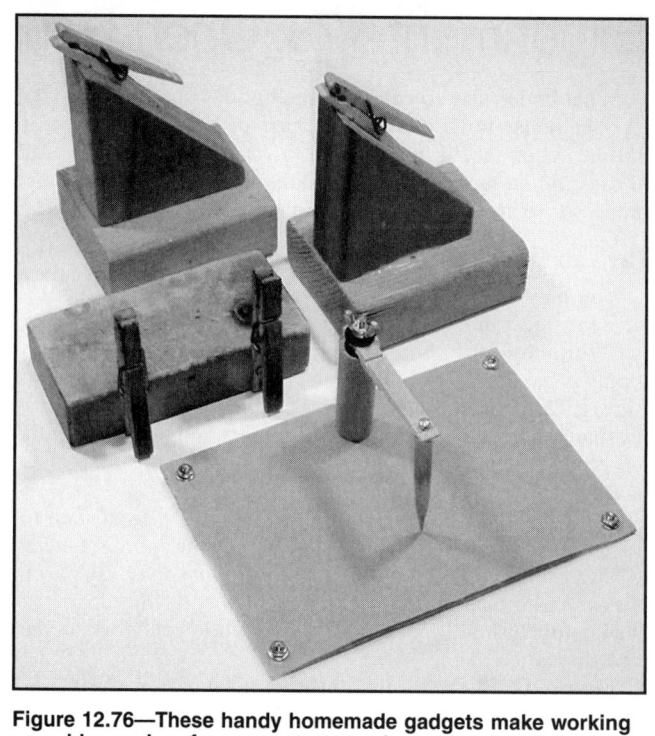

Figure 12.76—These handy homemade gadgets make working on cables and surface-mount parts a lot easier. Wooden materials won't melt or gouge. And, if charred or damaged, they're easy to replace.

test equipment. I found the 'scope cart at a hamfest for $15 where it did double duty as a shopping cart for the day!

## The Trusty Toolboxes

My faithful, go-everywhere, hold-everything, toolboxes are shown in **Figure 12.75**. I splurged on the pallet case from Jensen (**www.jensentools.com**) years ago and I've never regretted it. The case is big enough to hold a spare voltmeter, soldering gear, spare parts and cables.

The tackle box has turned out to be a great way to store coax connectors and adapters. It contains everything I need to build or repair cables. All of my adapters are kept sorted and handy. Tackle boxes are inexpensive and great for all sorts of similar uses.

Along with tools and instruments, I find myself keeping a rather large collection of electronic parts and hardware. You can keep them in individual drawers or in cardboard parts bins. I like both, and I keep a few junk boxes going for parts and components, as well.

Buying parts one or two at a time is the most expensive way, so I try to buy extra. Hamfests are a great source of spare parts, too. Sometimes, entire parts cabinets are sold with parts inside. You can keep your lab well stocked by keeping a list of needed stuff in a notebook. When you see a sale or bargain, you'll know exactly what you need.

## Gadgets

No shack and lab tour is complete without mentioning a special gadget or two. **Figure 12.76** shows some of my all-time favorites—gadgets that I have used year-in and year-out. Just clothespins and wood? Yes! The three pin-and-block gadgets on the left make working with cables and connectors a lot easier. They hold wires and metal securely without biting into hot plastic. The clothespin jaws are rounded for a firm grip and spring-loaded for easy adjustment. All it takes is wood screws and/or glue to make a set of these.

The odd-looking apparatus in the front is the latest incarnation of my surface-mount "third hand." The printed-circuit board is placed on the cardboard and maneuvered under the point of the dowel (which swivels and can be raised or lowered). The tiny SMT parts are held on the board by the point

of the dowel for me to solder. When the cardboard or dowel wear out, I replace them. I encourage you to make a set for yourself and improvise!

## Organization and Cost

The best part about my lab (to me) is that I can put my hands on any tool, part, or instrument in seconds. The biggest barrier to accomplishment is the wasting of time or having your train of thought derailed as you go on a "tool hunt" or root around for parts. Keep your workbench reasonably organized and free of junk (well, mostly free) and you will reap benefits in fun and efficiency. There's nothing like getting an idea and being able to sit right down and build it!

You may be totaling costs in your head and thinking: "I can't afford to buy all of that!" Remember, this is my collection of more than 35 years of electronic-ing. My workbench is a work-in-progress—I am continually trading or upgrading. I always buy the highest quality materials I can afford, especially avoiding cheap tools. Start with the basics (**www.arrl.org/tis/info/homebrew.html**) and keep going. The holiday season is the time for big tool sales, as well (hint, hint)!

Thanks for taking part in my open house. I hope it will encourage you to build and repair your own circuits and equipment. I started a long time ago with modest capabilities and improved, step-by-step, with the help of friends and uncounted articles in *QST* and other magazines and books. Good luck!

## Shopping List
- Wooden, spring-loaded clothespins
- Scraps of 2×4 wood, thick cardboard and $1/4$ inch dowel
- Glue, wood screws and machine screws/nuts/washers

# Abbreviations List

**A**

a—atto (prefix for $10^{-18}$)
A—ampere (unit of electrical current)
ac—alternating current
ACC—Affiliated Club Coordinator
ACSSB—amplitude-compandored single sideband
A/D—analog-to-digital
ADC—analog-to-digital converter
AF—audio frequency
AFC—automatic frequency control
AFSK—audio frequency-shift keying
AGC—automatic gain control
Ah—ampere hour
ALC—automatic level control
AM—amplitude modulation
AMRAD—Amateur Radio Research and Development Corporation
AMSAT—Radio Amateur Satellite Corporation
AMTOR—Amateur Teleprinting Over Radio
ANT—antenna
ARA—Amateur Radio Association
ARC—Amateur Radio Club
ARES—Amateur Radio Emergency Service
ARQ—Automatic repeat request
ARRL—American Radio Relay League
ARS—Amateur Radio Society (station)
ASCII—American National Standard Code for Information Interchange
ATV—amateur television
AVC—automatic volume control
AWG—American wire gauge
az-el—azimuth-elevation

**B**

B—bel; blower; susceptance; flux density, (inductors)
balun—balanced to unbalanced (transformer)
BC—broadcast
BCD—binary coded decimal
BCI—broadcast interference
Bd—baud (bids in single-channel binary data transmission)
BER—bit error rate
BFO—beat-frequency oscillator
bit—binary digit
bit/s—bits per second
BM—Bulletin Manager
BPF—band-pass filter
BPL—Brass Pounders League
BPL—Broadband over Power Line
BT—battery
BW—bandwidth
Bytes—Bytes

**C**

c—centi (prefix for $10^{-2}$)
C—coulomb (quantity of electric charge); capacitor
CAC—Contest Advisory Committee
CATVI—cable television interference
CB—Citizens Band (radio)
CBBS—computer bulletin-board service
CBMS—computer-based message system
CCITT—International Telegraph and Telephone Consultative Committee
CCTV—closed-circuit television
CCW—coherent CW
ccw—counterclockwise
CD—civil defense
cm—centimeter
CMOS—complementary-symmetry metal-oxide semiconductor
coax—coaxial cable
COR—carrier-operated relay
CP—code proficiency (award)
CPU—central processing unit
CRT—cathode ray tube
CT—center tap
CTCSS—continuous tone-coded squelch system
cw—clockwise
CW—continuous wave

**D**

d—deci (prefix for $10^{-1}$)
D—diode
da—deca (prefix for 10)
D/A—digital-to-analog
DAC—digital-to-analog converter
dB—decibel (0.1 bel)
dBi—decibels above (or below) isotropic antenna
dBm—decibels above (or below) 1 milliwatt
DBM—double balanced mixer
dBV—decibels above/below 1 V (in video, relative to 1 V P-P)
dBW—decibels above/below 1 W
dc—direct current
D-C—direct conversion
DDS—direct digital synthesis
DEC—District Emergency Coordinator
deg—degree
DET—detector
DF—direction finding; direction finder
DIP—dual in-line package
DMM—digital multimeter
DPDT—double-pole double-throw (switch)
DPSK—differential phase-shift keying
DPST—double-pole single-throw (switch)
DS—direct sequence (spread spectrum); display
DSB—double sideband
DSP—digital signal processing
DTMF—dual-tone multifrequency
DVM—digital voltmeter
DX—long distance; duplex
DXAC—DX Advisory Committee
DXCC—DX Century Club

**E**

e—base of natural logarithms (2.71828)
E—voltage
EA—ARRL Educational Advisor
EC—Emergency Coordinator
ECL—emitter-coupled logic
EHF—extremely high frequency (30-300 GHz)
EIA—Electronic Industries Alliance
EIRP—effective isotropic radiated power
ELF—extremely low frequency
ELT—emergency locator transmitter
EMC—electromagnetic compatibility
EME—earth-moon-earth (moonbounce)
EMF—electromotive force
EMI—electromagnetic interference
EMP—electromagnetic pulse
EOC—emergency operations center
EPROM—erasable programmable read only memory

**F**

f—femto (prefix for $10^{-15}$); frequency
F—farad (capacitance unit); fuse
fax—facsimile
FCC—Federal Communications Commission
FD—Field Day
FEMA—Federal Emergency Management Agency
FET—field-effect transistor
FFT—fast Fourier transform
FL—filter
FM—frequency modulation
FMTV—frequency-modulated television
FSK—frequency-shift keying
FSTV—fast-scan (real-time) television
ft—foot (unit of length)

**G**

g—gram (unit of mass)
G—giga (prefix for $10^9$); conductance
GaAs—gallium arsenide
GB—gigabytes
GDO—grid- or gate-dip oscillator
GHz—gigahertz ($10^9$ Hz)
GND—ground

**H**

h—hecto (prefix for $10^2$)
H—henry (unit of inductance)
HF—high frequency (3-30 MHz)
HFO—high-frequency oscillator; heterodyne frequency oscillator
HPF—highest probable frequency; high-pass filter
Hz—hertz (unit of frequency, 1 cycle/s)

**I**

I—current, indicating lamp
IARU—International Amateur Radio Union
IC—integrated circuit
ID—identification; inside diameter
IEEE—Institute of Electrical and Electronics Engineers
IF—intermediate frequency
IMD—intermodulation distortion
in.—inch (unit of length)
in./s—inch per second (unit of velocity)
I/O—input/output

IRC—international reply coupon
ISB—independent sideband
ITF—Interference Task Force
ITU—International Telecommunication Union
ITU-T—ITU Telecommunication Standardization Bureau

**J-K**

j—operator for complex notation, as for reactive component of an impedance ($+j$ inductive; $-j$ capacitive)
J—joule (kg m$^2$/s$^2$) (energy or work unit); jack
JFET—junction field-effect transistor
k—kilo (prefix for $10^3$); Boltzmann's constant ($1.38 \times 10^{-23}$ J/K)
K—kelvin (used without degree symbol) absolute temperature scale; relay
kB—kilobytes
kBd—1000 bauds
kbit—1024 bits
kbit/s—1024 bits per second
kbyte—1024 bytes
kg—kilogram
kHz—kilohertz
km—kilometer
kV—kilovolt
kW—kilowatt
kΩ—kilohm

**L**

l—liter (liquid volume)
L—lambert; inductor
lb—pound (force unit)
LC—inductance-capacitance
LCD—liquid crystal display
LED—light-emitting diode
LF—low frequency (30-300 kHz)
LHC—left-hand circular (polarization)
LO—local oscillator; Leadership Official
LP—log periodic
LS—loudspeaker
lsb—least significant bit
LSB—lower sideband
LSI—large-scale integration
LUF—lowest usable frequency

**M**

m—meter (length); milli (prefix for $10^{-3}$)
M—mega (prefix for $10^6$); meter (instrument)
mA—milliampere
mAh—milliampere hour
MB—megabytes
MCP—multimode communications processor
MDS—Multipoint Distribution Service; minimum discernible (or detectable) signal
MF—medium frequency (300-3000 kHz)
mH—millihenry
MHz—megahertz
mi—mile, statute (unit of length)
mi/h (MPH)—mile per hour
mi/s—mile per second
mic—microphone
min—minute (time)
MIX—mixer
mm—millimeter
MOD—modulator

modem—modulator/demodulator
MOS—metal-oxide semiconductor
MOSFET—metal-oxide semiconductor field-effect transistor
MS—meteor scatter
ms—millisecond
m/s—meters per second
msb—most-significant bit
MSI—medium-scale integration
MSK—minimum-shift keying
MSO—message storage operation
MUF—maximum usable frequency
mV—millivolt
mW—milliwatt
MΩ—megohm

**N**

n—nano (prefix for $10^{-9}$); number of turns (inductors)
NBFM—narrow-band frequency modulation
NC—no connection; normally closed
NCS—net-control station; National Communications System
nF—nanofarad
NF—noise figure
nH—nanohenry
NiCd—nickel cadmium
NM—Net Manager
NMOS—N-channel metal-oxide silicon
NO—normally open
NPN—negative-positive-negative (transistor)
NPRM—Notice of Proposed Rule Making (FCC)
ns—nanosecond
NTIA—National Telecommunications and Information Administration
NTS—National Traffic System

**O**

OBS—Official Bulletin Station
OD—outside diameter
OES—Official Emergency Station
OO—Official Observer
op amp—operational amplifier
ORS—Official Relay Station
OSC—oscillator
OSCAR—Orbiting Satellite Carrying Amateur Radio
oz—ounce ($^1/_{16}$ pound)

**P**

p—pico (prefix for $10^{-12}$)
P—power; plug
PA—power amplifier
PACTOR—digital mode combining aspects of packet and AMTOR
PAM—pulse-amplitude modulation
PBS—packet bulletin-board system
PC—printed circuit
PD—power dissipation
PEP—peak envelope power
PEV—peak envelope voltage
pF—picofarad
pH—picohenry
PIC—Public Information Coordinator
PIN—positive-intrinsic-negative (semiconductor)
PIO—Public Information Officer
PIV—peak inverse voltage

PLC—Power Line Carrier
PLL—phase-locked loop
PM—phase modulation
PMOS—P-channel (metal-oxide semiconductor)
PNP—positive negative positive (transistor)
pot—potentiometer
P-P—peak to peak
ppd—postpaid
PROM—programmable read-only memory
PSAC—Public Service Advisory Committee
PSHR—Public Service Honor Roll
PTO—permeability-tuned oscillator
PTT—push to talk

**Q-R**

Q—figure of merit (tuned circuit); transistor
QRP—low power (less than 5-W output)
R—resistor
RACES—Radio Amateur Civil Emergency Service
RAM—random-access memory
RC—resistance-capacitance
R/C—radio control
RDF—radio direction finding
RF—radio frequency
RFC—radio-frequency choke
RFI—radio-frequency interference
RHC—right-hand circular (polarization)
RIT—receiver incremental tuning
RLC—resistance-inductance-capacitance
RM—rule making (number assigned to petition)
r/min (RPM)—revolutions per minute
rms—root mean square
ROM—read-only memory
r/s—revolutions per second
RS—Radio Sputnik (Russian ham satellite)
RST—readability-strength-tone (CW signal report)
RTTY—radioteletype
RX—receiver, receiving

**S**

s—second (time)
S—siemens (unit of conductance); switch
SASE—self-addressed stamped envelope
SCF—switched capacitor filter
SCR—silicon controlled rectifier
SEC—Section Emergency Coordinator
SET—Simulated Emergency Test
SGL—State Government Liaison
SHF—super-high frequency (3-30 GHz)
SM—Section Manager; silver mica (capacitor)
S/N—signal-to-noise ratio
SPDT—single-pole double-throw (switch)
SPST—single-pole single-throw (switch)
SS—ARRL Sweepstakes; spread spectrum
SSB—single sideband
SSC—Special Service Club
SSI—small-scale integration
SSTV—slow-scan television
STM—Section Traffic Manager

SX—simplex
sync—synchronous, synchronizing
SWL—shortwave listener
SWR—standing-wave ratio

**T**

T—tera (prefix for $10^{12}$); transformer
TA—ARRL Technical Advisor
TC—Technical Coordinator
TCC—Transcontinental Corps (NTS)
TCP/IP—Transmission Control Protocol/ Internet Protocol
tfc—traffic
TNC—terminal node controller (packet radio)
TR—transmit/receive
TS—Technical Specialist
TTL—transistor-transistor logic
TTY—teletypewriter
TU—terminal unit
TV—television
TVI—television interference
TX—transmitter, transmitting

**U**

U—integrated circuit
UHF—ultra-high frequency (300 MHz to 3 GHz)
USB—upper sideband
UTC—Coordinated Universal Time (also abbreviated Z)
UV—ultraviolet

**V**

V—volt; vacuum tube
VCO—voltage-controlled oscillator
VCR—video cassette recorder
VDT—video-display terminal
VE—Volunteer Examiner
VEC—Volunteer Examiner Coordinator
VFO—variable-frequency oscillator
VHF—very-high frequency (30-300 MHz)
VLF—very-low frequency (3-30 kHz)
VLSI—very-large-scale integration
VMOS—V-topology metal-oxide-semiconductor
VOM—volt-ohmmeter
VOX—voice-operated switch
VR—voltage regulator
VSWR—voltage standing-wave ratio
VTVM—vacuum-tube voltmeter
VUCC—VHF/UHF Century Club
VXO—variable-frequency crystal oscillator

**W**

W—watt ($kg\ m^2s^{-3}$), unit of power
WAC—Worked All Continents
WAS—Worked All States
WBFM—wide-band frequency modulation
WEFAX—weather facsimile
Wh—watthour
WPM—words per minute
WRC—World Radiocommunication Conference
WVDC—working voltage, direct current

**X**

X—reactance
XCVR—transceiver
XFMR—transformer
XIT—transmitter incremental tuning
XO—crystal oscillator

XTAL—crystal
XVTR—transverter

**Y-Z**

Y—crystal; admittance
YIG—yttrium iron garnet
Z—impedance; also see UTC

*Numbers/Symbols*

5BDXCC—Five-Band DXCC
5BWAC—Five-Band WAC
5BWAS—Five-Band WAS
6BWAC—Six-Band WAC
°—degree (plane angle)
°C—degree Celsius (temperature)
°F—degree Fahrenheit (temperature)
α—(alpha) angles; coefficients, attenuation constant, absorption factor, area, common-base forward current-transfer ratio of a bipolar transistor
β—(beta) angles; coefficients, phase constant current gain of common-emitter transistor amplifiers
γ—(gamma) specific gravity, angles, electrical conductivity, propagation constant
Γ—(gamma) complex propagation constant
δ—(delta) increment or decrement; density; angles
Δ—(delta) increment or decrement determinant, permittivity
ε—(epsilon) dielectric constant; permittivity; electric intensity
ζ—(zeta) coordinates; coefficients
η—(eta) intrinsic impedance; efficiency; surface charge density; hysteresis; coordinate
θ—(theta) angular phase displacement; time constant; reluctance; angles
ι—(iota) unit vector
K—(kappa) susceptibility; coupling coefficient
λ—(lambda) wavelength; attenuation constant
Λ—(lambda) permeance
μ—(mu) permeability; amplification factor; micro (prefix for $10^{-6}$)
μF—microfarad
μH—microhenry
μP—microprocessor
ξ—(xi) coordinates
π—(pi) ≈3.14159
ρ—(rho) resistivity; volume charge density; coordinates; reflection coefficient
σ—(sigma) surface charge density; complex propagation constant; electrical conductivity; leakage coefficient; deviation
Σ—(sigma) summation
τ—(tau) time constant; volume resistivity; time-phase displacement; transmission factor; density
φ—(phi) magnetic flux angles
Φ—(phi) summation
χ—(chi) electric susceptibility; angles
Ψ—(psi) dielectric flux; phase difference; coordinates; angles
ω—(omega) angular velocity $2\pi F$
Ω—(omega) resistance in ohms; solid angle

# FEEDBACK

Please use this form to give us your comments on this book and what you'd like to see in future editions, or e-mail us at **pubsfdbk@arrl.org** (publications feedback). If you use e-mail, please include your name, call, e-mail address and the book title, edition and printing in the body of your message. Also indicate whether or not you are an ARRL member.

Where did you purchase this book?
☐ From ARRL directly ☐ From an ARRL dealer

Is there a dealer who carries ARRL publications within:
☐ 5 miles ☐ 15 miles ☐ 30 miles of your location? ☐ Not sure.

License class:
☐ Novice ☐ Technician ☐ Technician Plus ☐ General ☐ Advanced ☐ Amateur Extra

Name _____

ARRL member? ☐ Yes ☐ No

Call Sign _____

Daytime Phone ( ) _____ Age _____

Address _____

City, State/Province, ZIP/Postal Code _____ E-mail: _____

If licensed, how long? _____

Other hobbies _____

| For ARRL use only | H&K |
|---|---|
| Edition | 17 18 19 20 |
| Printing | 1 2 3 4 5 6 7 8 9 10 11 12 |

Occupation _____

From _____

_____

_____

EDITOR, HINTS & KINKS
ARRL—THE NATIONAL ASSOCIATION FOR
 AMATEUR RADIO
225 MAIN STREET
NEWINGTON CT 06111-1494

— — — — — — — — — — — — — — — — please fold and tape — — — — — — — — — — — — — — — — —